Elements of Abstract Algebra

Elements of

Abstract Algebra

Richard A. Dean   California Institute of Technology

John Wiley and Sons, Inc., New York London Sydney

Library of Congress Catalog Card Number: 65-27661
Printed in the United States of America
ISBN 0 471 20451 X

To the memory of HARVEY

Harvey Lewis Williams (1873–1946)
taught mathematics for 41 years at
Granville High School, Granville, Ohio.
His counsel: "Commune with mathematics."

Preface

This book is an outgrowth of the introductory algebra course given at the California Institute of Technology. The course, and more generally this textbook, is intended as an introduction to the topics and techniques of abstract algebra that are finding ever wider applications in mathematics and the applied sciences. This book also serves to introduce the student to a kind of mathematics that, in its abstraction and generality, in its application of the axiomatic method, and in its study of a proof as a means of understanding mathematics, resembles honest mathematical research more closely than does the typical course in the calculus. However, the formal prerequisites are only the equivalent of a modern high school mathematics program. Of course, the additional experience provided by any sound course in mathematics is invaluable.

In writing this book I simply wished to set down my plan for an introductory treatment of algebra and to enjoy the luxury, not always afforded in a course, of including some topics treated infrequently at this level, and excluding other topics that have been treated extensively.

In this spirit the book contains no development of linear algebra and determinants, nor is there a development of the integers from Peano postulates, nor of the real numbers from the rationals, nor of transfinite arithmetic. While these are, of course, important topics, they are not required for the material in this book.

If this book has a theme, it is the group concept. The group concept is the most central of all algebraic concepts; indeed, the techniques employed in group theory have long served as a pattern for other topics in algebra. If this book has a goal, it is the Galois theory for fields of characteristic zero and a complete proof of the criterion that the zeros of a polynomial be expressible in radicals.

Chapter 1 is an introduction to groups. This chapter is the longest of the book for it includes a number of examples, notably cyclic groups, permutation groups, and dihedral groups. It develops the key notions of subgroup, homomorphism and factor group, and direct product. I have found that in the classroom it is worth the time to treat this material in a fair amount of detail and to expect the class to be reasonably proficient in manipulating group concepts. The facility with abstraction gained here pays handsome dividends during the remainder of the course. Thus Chapter 2, Rings, follows easily because many of the theorems appear as natural analogues of group-theoretic ones. In this treatment the first theorems about systems with two binary operations become routine.

I have rejected the thesis that an introduction to algebra must begin with a study of the integers. While an informal discussion of number theory is interesting and useful it does not prepare a student for the subsequent abstraction of an axiomatic treatment of groups, rings, and vector spaces. On the other hand, a development from the Peano postulates is a tedious tour de force which usually produces little useful number theory.

Chapter 3, The Integers, constitutes a middle-ground approach to number theory. The integers are presented as an ordered integral domain in which the ordering accomplishes a well-ordering of the positive elements. The fact that this axiom system is categorical is too important a result to ignore and too significant to pass off with a "make-believe" proof. The crucial subtlety is a theorem giving sufficient conditions for an inductive scheme to define a function. This section and this rather technical result may, of course, be omitted without impairing the continuity of the whole book. Indeed, except for the results on the arithmetic of the integers (Section 3.6), the whole chapter may be omitted, provided the reader is willing to grant the very elementary properties of ordered integral domains and well-ordered sets. Even the arithmetic is essentially repeated in the more general context of a euclidean domain in Chapter 5.

The succeeding chapters on fields, euclidean domains, polynomials, and vector spaces follow in a straightforward manner. In Chapter 8, Field Extensions, the existence and uniqueness of a splitting field for a polynomial is the principal result. The side trips through finite fields and the Wedderburn theorem on finite division rings may be included or excluded, depending on the reader's interest. The material of Chapter 9, Finite Groups, may also be selected in this way. All of it is essential for a real command of group theory, and in particular the sections on solvable groups are indispensable for Galois theory. I have not yielded to the blandishments of a "slick" treatment of the classical basis theorem for finitely generated abelian groups. The proof appearing in Chapter 9 is completely constructive for finitely presented abelian groups. Throughout the book I have tried to make all proofs constructive and to give problems utilizing the constructions. The pedagogical bias of this textbook is that theory becomes meaningful when concrete problems are solved. For the uniqueness part of the basis theorem I have given P. Cohn's proof of the cancellation law for cyclic direct factors of an abelian group. With this theorem a very natural proof for the uniqueness follows simply.

Finally, the book ends with a chapter on Galois theory. Galois theory serves not only as an example of beautiful mathematical theory, but also as a significant pedagogical tool; by linking group theory and field theory the understanding of each topic is strengthened. As beautiful as the theorem on the Galois correspondence is when it stands alone, it is probably a mistake to begin this chapter unless the reader is prepared to fight through the surprisingly complicated details of the theorems on the solution of equations by radicals. I believe in, and for the most part follow, the admonition attributed to Chekhov: "Do not bring a cannon on stage unless you are prepared to fire it."

A word about Chapter 0. It should be gone over very hurriedly to point out what it contains. It is not intended to be a real part of the book and for that reason Chapter 0 contains no exercises. Proceed to Chapter 1 as quickly as possible! Chapter 0 should be used as an appendix and a glossary of notation and terminology. However, because it does provide a vocabulary and does include some indispensable results, it must precede. There will be times when it is necessary to return to Chapter 0 for clarification. At such times you will find it useful to give a more careful reading to the pertinent sections, perhaps even to construct some additional examples and concoct some problems.

As always, the exercises play a key role in the understanding of text material. More than 350 problems have been included. Unashamedly, the results of some of the problems will be needed subsequently in the book. On these occasions I shall give a brief outline of a solution. Some problems are unreasonable; they have been starred. Such problems may serve best as class discussion problems.

The numbering scheme for theorems and lemmas is standard. Within a chapter the theorems are numbered consecutively from 1 to n. Lemmas are numbered independently from 1 to m. If, for example, in Chapter 5 we quote Theorem 8 of Chapter 2 we shall refer to it simply as Theorem 2.8. At the top of alternate pages are the titles of the current section and the numbers of theorems and lemmas in their full decimal form. Definitions have not been numbered in an attempt to encourage the student to learn definitions as they occur and to avoid the sea of numerals that would result. All definitions are clearly annotated in the index; the page on which the definition occurs is in bold-faced type.

I am indebted most heavily to my colleagues and students at the California Institute of Technology. Over the four years of evolution and preparation of this manuscript their comments and incisive criticisms have resulted in a vast number of improvements and modifications. The nicest proofs are theirs. I should like particularly to acknowledge the help of the late Morgan Ward whose handywork abounds in many of the proofs and exercises. I am also grateful to Professors Peter Hilton, Robert Stoll, and J. Dean Swift who read most carefully a final draft of the manuscript and whose criticisms have removed a large number of inaccuracies and inelegancies. Mention of their names does not constitute an endorsement and, of course, the errors and misjudgments that remain are mine.

I also thank John Wiley and Sons for their patience and skill in reproducing the 85 figures, some of which appear in two colors.

Pasadena, California   Richard A. Dean

January, 1966

Contents

Chapter 0   1

    0.1.   Arithmetic, 1
    0.2.   Sets, 4
    0.3.   Relations, 7
    0.4.   Functions and Mappings, 10
    0.5.   Operations and Operators, 14
    0.6.   Combinatorics, 16

Prologue   20

Chapter 1   Groups   24

    1.1.   Introduction, 24
    1.2.   Group Axioms, 24
    1.3.   Examples, 25
            Exercise 1, 28
    1.4.   Basic Lemmas 29
            Exercise 2, 34
    1.5.   Isomorphism, 35
            Exercise 3, 37
    1.6.   Permutation Groups, 37
            Exercise 4, 40
    1.7.   Cyclic Groups, 42
    1.8.   Dihedral Groups, 44
    1.9.   Subgroups, 48
            Exercise 5, 57
    1.10.   Homomorphisms, 59
            Exercise 6, 67
    1.11.   Direct Products, 68
            Exercise 7, 72

Chapter 2 Rings **73**

2.1. Definitions, 73
2.2. Basic Lemmas, 77
2.3. Subrings, 78
    Exercise 1, 79
2.4. Homomorphisms, 80
    Exercise 2, 88
2.5. Integral Domains, 89
    Exercise 3, 92

Chapter 3 The Integers **93**

3.1. Introduction, 93
3.2. Order, 94
3.3. Order in Integral Domains, 94
    Exercise 1, 97
3.4. Well-Ordered Sets, 98
    Exercise 2, 99
3.5. The Integers, 100
    Exercise 3, 105
3.6. Arithmetic in the Integers, 106
    Exercise 4, 110

Chapter 4 Fields **112**

4.1. Introduction, 112
4.2. Field of Quotients, 112
    Exercise 1, 116
4.3. Subfields, 116
4.4. Homomorphisms of Fields, 118
    Exercise 2, 119
4.5. The Real Numbers, 120
    Exercise 3, 124
4.6. The Complex Numbers, 125
    Exercise 4, 130

Chapter 5 Euclidean Domains **132**

5.1. Introduction, 132
5.2. The Euclidean Algorithm, 134
    Exercise 1, 137
5.3. Arithmetic in Euclidean Domains, 138
    Exercise 2, 142
5.4. Application to Groups, 143
    Exercise 3, 146

Chapter 6 Polynomials **147**

6.1. Introduction, 147

6.2. Polynomial Rings, 149
Exercise 1, 154

6.3. Polynomials Over a Field, 154
Exercise 2, 158

6.4. The Complex Numbers, 159
Exercise 3, 161

6.5. Special Properties of $F[x]$, 161
Exercise 4, 166

6.6. Factorization in $R[x]$, 166
Exercise 5, 172

6.7. Field of Quotients of $R[x]$, 173

6.8. Polynomials in Several Variables, 173
Exercise 6, 175

Chapter 7 Vector Spaces **176**

7.1. Introduction, 176

7.2. Definitions and Examples, 177
Exercise 1, 179

7.3. Subspaces, 180
Exercise 2, 182

7.4. Dependence and Basis, 182
Exercise 3, 188

7.5. Linear Transformations, 189
Exercise 4, 194

7.6. Solutions of Systems of Linear Equations, 194
Exercise 5, 198

7.7. Algebras, 199
Exercise 6, 205

Chapter 8 Field Extensions and Finite Fields **206**

8.1. Construction of Field Extensions, 206
Exercise 1, 213

8.2. Classification of Extensions, 213

8.3. Transcendental Extensions, 216

8.4. Algebraic Extensions, 218
Exercise 2, 221

8.5. Finite Fields, 222
Exercise 3, 227

8.6.   Simple Extensions, 228
8.7.   Roots of Unity, 229
8.8.   Wedderburn's Theorem, 233
         Exercise 4, 236

Chapter 9   Finite Groups   237

9.1.   Cauchy's Theorem, 237
9.2.   *p*-Groups, 239
         Exercise 1, 242
9.3.   The Sylow Theorems, 242
         Exercise 2, 247
9.4.   Solvable Groups, 248
         Exercise 3, 254
9.5.   Abelian Groups, 255
         Exercise 4, 267

Chapter 10   Galois Theory   269

10.1.   Fundamental Theorem of Galois Theory, 269
          Exercise 1, 279
10.2.   Cyclotomic Fields and Cyclic Extensions, 280
10.3.   Solution of Equations by Radicals, 283
10.4.   Equations of 2nd and 3rd Degree, 290
          Exercise 2, 296
10.5.   The General Polynomial of *n*th Degree, 297
10.6.   The Discriminant, 300
10.7.   Symmetric Polynomials, 302
          Exercise 3, 303

         Answers to Exercises, 305

         Symbols and Notations, 313

         Index, 317

Elements of Abstract Algebra

Elements of Abstract Algebra

Chapter 0

In this introductory chapter we shall review some facts about arithmetic and collect a few basic concepts about sets, relations, and functions. Most of these notions will be familiar, and this chapter merely serves to introduce the notations and conventions used throughout the book and to select from all the many mathematical facts we already know those which have a special significance to this book. For now we adopt the point of view that we can use these well-accepted facts from arithmetic and set theory without proof. Occasionally in this chapter we do give a short supporting argument for a theorem in the hope that it will make the theorem more meaningful. This chapter should be given a quick but careful reading before going on to the Prologue and the beginning of the text proper. It will probably be wise to return to Chapter 0 from time to time to recall definitions and notations as the need arises.

0.1. ARITHMETIC

In this chapter and in the two succeeding chapters we shall make use of the integers as a source of examples. We shall use them to prove theorems and to state definitions. The properties we shall need will be familiar, and not until Chapter 3 will we attempt a careful treatment of the integers as an axiomatic theory. We take for granted that integers can be added, subtracted, multiplied, and that they are ordered by "greater than" and "less than." We shall denote the set of integers by I.

Theorem 1. If a and b are positive integers and if a divides b then $a \leq b$.

We adopt the usual notation which employs a vertical bar to denote division. We write $a \mid b$ if and only if a divides b. If a does not divide b we write $a \nmid b$. Thus $2 \mid 4$, $3 \mid 12$, while $2 \nmid 5$.

Theorem 2. If a is a positive integer and b is any integer, then there are integers q and r such that

$$b = a \cdot q + r \quad \text{where} \quad 0 \leq r < a.$$

If $0 \leq b < a$ we may take $q = 0$ and $r = b$. If $b \geq a$ then Theorem 2 says, in the language of elementary arithmetic, that either a divides b (this is the case $r = 0$) or that if we divide a into b we get a remainder which is less than a.

Definition. An integer which is neither 0 nor ± 1 is called a *prime* if, for all integers a and b, whenever $p \mid ab$ then $p \mid a$ or $p \mid b$. An integer which is neither 0, ± 1 nor a prime is called *composite*.

Theorem 3. Let p be an integer such that $p \neq 0$, ± 1. p is a prime if and only if, for all integers a and b, whenever $p = ab$ then $p = \pm a$ or $p = \pm b$.

It is common practice to interchange the roles of the definition of a prime and Theorem 3. Our usage coincides with the generally accepted definition we give in Chapter 2 of a prime element in the more general context of an arbitrary integral domain. In Chapter 2 an element that satisfies the conclusion of Theorem 3 will be called an irreducible element.

Theorem 4. (*Induction principle*). A statement concerning an integer m may be proved for all integers m greater than or equal to a particular one, say a_0, by the following two steps:

A. Give a proof or a verification that the statement holds for the integer a_0.

B. Prove the following lemma: Let k be any integer such that $k \geq a_0$. *If* the statement is true for k *then* the statement is true for the integer $(k + 1)$.

Step (*B*) is called the "inductive step," and the hypothesis of the lemma is called the "induction hypothesis." We say that the statement has been proved by "induction on m."

Here is another way to view this principle. Suppose we have a statement which we assert is true for all integers greater than or equal to a_0. If a critic says this is not so, then there must be a smallest integer h such that $h \geq a_0$ for which our statement fails. Now clearly $h \neq a_0$ because we have proved in (*A*) that our result holds for a_0. Thus $h > a_0$ and $(h - 1) \geq a_0$. Moreover, since h was chosen to be the smallest integer for which our statement failed, it must be that our statement is true for $(h - 1)$. But then if we put $k = (h - 1)$ in lemma *B*, which we have proved, and to which our critic does not object, we conclude that the statement is true for the integer $(k + 1)$, that is, for h. Thus our critic must be mistaken.

A similar scheme may also be used to define a concept involving integers.

A^*. Define explicitly the concept for an initial integer a_0. (In practice a_0 is usually 0, 1, or 2.)

B^*. Let k be any integer such that $k \geq a_0$. The concept is defined for $(k + 1)$ in terms of the concept for the integers m such that $a_0 \leq m \leq k$. (In this step it is appropriate to treat the concept as fully defined for integers between a_0 and k.)

Example 1. We shall define exponentiation to nonnegative integral powers by induction. Let r be a real number.

A^*. $r^0 = 1$.

B^*.   If k is a nonnegative integer then $r^{(k+1)} = r^k \cdot r$.

We often see r^k "defined" by some notational device as $r^k = \underbrace{r \cdots \cdot r}_{k \text{ factors}}.$

While this is at best inelegant and at worst nonsense, it may best convey the notion! The advantage of using induction to make definitions of mathematical concepts is that a proof may then be formulated by induction, which is precise, elegant, and complete. As an example let us prove by induction the addition and multiplication laws for exponentiation using the definition above.

I. If r is a real number, then for all nonnegative integers n and m,

$$r^n \cdot r^m = r^{n+m}.$$

We prove this by induction on m. The statement is true when $m = 0$ since, by definition A^*, $r^0 = 1$ and $r^n \cdot 1 = r^n = r^{n+0}$. Now for lemma B. The special assumptions of this lemma are that k is a positive integer and that $r^n \cdot r^k = r^{n+k}$. Then $r^n \cdot r^{(k+1)} = r^n \cdot (r^k r)$ by definition B^*, whereas, by associativity, $r^n \cdot (r^k r) = (r^n \cdot r^k) \cdot r$. But we have assumed $r^n \cdot r^k = r^{n+k}$ so that we have $r^n \cdot r^{(k+1)} = r^{n+k} \cdot r$, which, by definition, is $r^{(n+k)+1} = r^{n+(k+1)}$. Thus lemma B, the inductive step, has been established.

II. If r is a real number, then for all nonnegative integers n and m,

$$(r^n)^m = r^{nm}.$$

We prove this by induction on m. The statement holds when $m = 0$ as $(r^n)^0 = 1 = r^0$. The inductive hypotheses assumes that $k \geq 0$ and that $(r^n)^k = r^{nk}$. Now $(r^n)^{(k+1)} = (r^n)^k \cdot r^n$ by definition B^* and from the inductive hypothesis, $(r^n)^k = r^{nk}$. Hence $(r^n)^{(k+1)} = r^{nk} \cdot r^n$. From (I) and the distributive law for integers we have $r^{nk} \cdot r^n = r^{nk+n} = r^{n(k+1)}$ and thus the inductive step has been established.

0.2. SETS

We shall adopt an informal attitude toward set theory. We shall be talking about sets and their elements; we shall be operating with sets, considering relations on sets, functions from one set to another, and forming new sets by various constructions. Nowhere in this text shall we attempt to provide a proper foundation for set theory. Our development assumes this as a framework for mathematics and uses it informally as a language to express mathematical ideas. It is, however, our intention, to be careful with set theoretic operations in the sense that every theorem could, in a rather straightforward way, be incorporated into a formal set theory. We shall try to point out those occasions when this is not possible by routine methods.

We take as primitive notions those of "set" and "membership". Membership is a statement about two sets; if A and B are sets, either A is a member of B or A is not a member of B. Membership is denoted by the symbol $\in$ and we use the usual symbolic shorthand

$$A \in B$$

for any of the following synonymous statements:

The set A is a member of the set B.
The set A belongs to the set B.
A is in B.

The notation $A \notin B$ means that A is not a member of B.
If $A \in B$ we say that A is an *element* of B.

We conceive a set as being a separate entity which is a collection of its elements. In our view elements are just other sets. "Set" is a collective noun just as are "flock" and "theory." A "flock" is a collection of "geese," a "theory" is a collection of "theorems," and a "set" is a collection of "elements." We often use a notation to make the relative distinction between a set and its elements by using lower case letters for the elements of a set and an upper case letter for the set. Thus "$a \in A$" will be a typical notation in this book.

The equality symbol $(=)$ is used between two symbols denoting sets as a symbolic shorthand to assert that the two symbols are names for the same set. Thus $2 = 1 + 1$ asserts that 2 and $1 + 1$ are names for the same integer; they denote the same set.

But, what do we mean when we say that two sets are the "same"? Intuitively, it would be natural to agree that two sets are the same if they have the same elements. Indeed, we adopt, as an axiom, the following criteria for deciding when two sets are the same. The axiom is stated in terms of the primitive concepts.

Axiom of Extensionality

$A = B$ if and only if, for all sets x, whenever $x \in A$ then $x \in B$ and whenever $x \in B$ then $x \in A$.

This axiom states that a set is determined by its members. When it is convenient we often list the elements that are members of a set A and show that this list is intended to constitute the set by surrounding the list with braces. For example, $\{0, 1\}$ denotes the set whose elements are 0 and 1. Note that $\{0, 1\} = \{1, 0\}$ and $\{0, 0\} = \{0\}$.

A set S which has only one member, $S = \{a\}$, is called a *singleton* set. The set which contains no members shall be referred to as the *empty set* or the *null set* and shall be denoted by $\varnothing$.

A listing is impossible for infinite sets and inconvenient for others. In those cases we often employ the so-called set-builder notation. An example will give the idea. Suppose we wish to denote the set R of real numbers between 0 and 1. We choose a symbol for an element, say r. If r is a member of R then r is a real number and $0 \leq r \leq 1$. The set R is denoted in the set-builder notation in the following way:

$$\{r : r \text{ is a real number and } 0 \leq r \leq 1\}.$$

This is read, "the set of all r such that r is a real number and 0 is less than or equal to r and r is less than or equal to 1."

More generally, a set is often determined by the conditions its elements must satisfy. If for brevity we call these conditions C then we denote the set determined by these conditions by

$$\{x : x \text{ satisfies the conditions } C\}.$$

We are taking the view that a set is determined by a condition or property. The set consists of precisely those elements satisfying a specific condition or conditions. The conditions may be quite complex and indeed it may not always be possible to decide whether an element satisfies the given conditions.

The empty set is a set such that $x \notin \varnothing$ for all sets x. We also have $\varnothing = \{x : x \neq x\}$.

We also employ one other notational convenience in denoting sets. If we are listing a set of elements we may give a few typical members and follow them with three dots $(\ldots)$ to indicate that the set may have more elements which we do not care to describe further. Thus we might denote the positive integers as $\{1, 2, 3, \ldots\}$. This is rather unsatisfactory since the elements of the set must really be determined from the context of the situation; in particular, we must decide whether the set is infinite or finite.

Here are a number of special abbreviations: $|A|$ denotes the cardinal number of the elements in A. We write $A \subseteq B$ if and only if $x \in B$ whenever $x \in A$. Thus $A \subseteq B$ means that every element of A is an element of B. $A \subseteq B$ is often read "A is contained in B" or "A is included in B" and we say that A is a *subset* of B. Clearly $A = B$ if and only if $A \subseteq B$ and $B \subseteq A$. Note that for all sets A it is true that $\varnothing \subseteq A$ and $A \subseteq A$. A and $\varnothing$ are called *improper* subsets of A; all other subsets of A are called *proper* subsets. We write $A \subset B$ if $A \subseteq B$ and $A \neq B$.

$$A - B = \{x : x \in A \text{ and } x \notin B\}.$$
$$A \cup B = \{x : x \in A \text{ or } x \in B\}.$$

The word "or," here, is used in the inclusive sense of "and/or." An example is $\{0, 1, 2\} \cup \{0, 3\} = \{0, 1, 2, 3\}$.

$$A \cap B = \{x : x \in A \text{ and } x \in B\}.$$

If A is a set we shall write $\bigcup A$ for the set $\{x :$ there exists an $a \in A$ such that $x \in a\}$. $\bigcup A$ is called the set union of the sets in A. Similarly we write $\bigcap A$ for the set $\{x : x \in a$ for all $a \in A\}$. $\bigcap A$ is called the set intersection of the sets in A. Note that if $A = \{a_1, a_2\}$ then $\bigcup A = a_1 \cup a_2$.

We shall employ two kinds of diagrams to show various relations between sets. One type is the familiar Venn diagram with regions denoting sets. Let us take for example,

$$A = \{\text{all integers}\},$$
$$B = \{\text{all integral multiples of 6}\},$$
$$C = \{\text{all integral multiples of 15}\},$$
$$B \cap C = \{\text{all integral multiples of 30}\},$$

Figure 1 illustrates this technique.

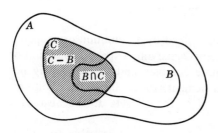

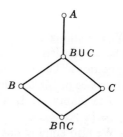

Figure 1   Figure 2

Another type of diagram uses a point to denote a set. If a set B is a subset of a set A, then the point for A is drawn higher than the point for B and a line is drawn from one point to the other. Figure 2 illustrates this technique for the above example. Our convention does not draw a distinct line from B to A since the line segments from B to $B \cup C$ and from $B \cup C$ to A provide an indication that B is a subset of A. Another line would only be superfluous. In the language of the next section the inclusion relation ($\subseteq$) is a transitive relation on the subsets of a set and we exploit this in the diagram.

We say that the members of a set A are *mutually disjoint* if for any two distinct sets a and b in A, $a \cap b = \varnothing$.

Example 2. Let a be the set of odd integers and b be the set of even integers. Then $A = \{a, b\}$ has mutually disjoint members. If c is the set of multiples of 3 and $B = \{a, b, c\}$ then the elements of B are not mutually disjoint. Note that $\bigcup A = \bigcup B$.

We have a constant need to use the concept of an "ordered pair" of elements. For example, in analytic geometry a point in the plane is given by two numbers—its coordinates. By agreement we write first the x-coordinate of the point and then its y-coordinate. In this way the point with coordinates (1, 2) is distinguished from the point (2, 1). Our notational scheme makes the distinction for us; the x-coordinate appears as the number on the left. We can get away from the dependence on the notational scheme of "left" and "right" by a definition introduced by Norbert Wiener and C. Kuratowski:

$$(a, b) = \{\{a\}, \{a, b\}\}.$$

Thus the ordered pair (a, b) is a set consisting of at most two elements, the singleton set $\{a\}$ and the set $\{a, b\}$. Clearly, if $a \neq b$ then $(a, b) \neq (b, a)$. Indeed, $(a, b) = (b, a)$ if and only if $a = b$. Note that $(a, a) = \{\{a\}\}$, the singleton set whose only element is the singleton set $\{a\}$. More generally, $(a, b) = (c, d)$ if and *only if* $a = c$ and $b = d$. $A \times B$ denotes the set $\{(a, b) : a \in A \text{ and } b \in B\}$. $A \times B$ is called the *Cartesian product* of A and B.

0.3. RELATIONS

Let A and B be sets. If there is a reason to associate certain elements in A with certain elements in B, the English language uses the word "relation" and says that the associated elements are related. Thus if A is the set of living men in the world and B is the set of living women in the world we might say that man a is related to woman b if a has at one time been married to b. This relationship may of course be quite complex! The important notion is that we are selecting certain ordered pairs (a, b) from $A \times B$ and saying that for the ordered pairs selected, a and b are related. This is, of course, a matter of definition for whatever purpose is desired, and is the essence of the formal mathematical definition of relation.

Definition. A *binary relation* between sets A and B is a subset T of the cartesian product $A \times B$.

As an example consider A to be the set of positive integers and B to be the set of negative integers. Let $T = \{(a, b) : a + b = 0\}$. Thus T contains the pairs $(1, -1)$, $(2, -2)$, and so forth. Often we employ a special symbol, say τ, and write $a \, \tau \, b$ if and only if $(a, b) \in R$. Similarly we write $a \, \tau \, b$ if and only if $(a, b) \notin R$. If $A = B$ then we speak of a *binary relation on A*.

Example 3. Let A be the set of nonnegative integers. Let $T = \{(a, b) : a$ divides $b\}$. Here the relational symbol is a vertical line as we have already mentioned.

A special subset of A of importance in discussing a relation T is the domain $\mathscr{D}_T$ of the relation T:

$$\mathscr{D}_T = \{a : \text{There exists } b \in B \text{ such that } (a, b) \in T\}.$$

Similarly the range $\mathscr{R}_T$ of T is a subset of B:

$$\mathscr{R}_T = \{b : \text{There exists } a \in A \text{ such that } (a, b) \in T\}.$$

Example 4. Let $A = B$ be the set of all real numbers. Let

$$T = \{(x, y) : x^2 + (y - 1)^2 = 1\}.$$

We have

$$\mathscr{D}_T = \{x : -1 \leq x \leq 1\} \quad \text{and} \quad \mathscr{R}_T = \{y : 0 \leq y \leq 2\}.$$

The points in the plane whose cartesian coordinates correspond to this relation constitute a circle of radius 1 with center $(0, 1)$.

A special class of relations on a set A that play a fundamental role in mathematics consists of those relations called equivalence relations.

Definition. A binary relation E on a set A is called an *equivalence relation* on A provided the following three properties hold:

1. For all $a \in A$, $(a, a) \in E$.
2. For all a and b in A, if $(a, b) \in E$ then $(b, a) \in E$.
3. For all a, b, and c in A, if $(a, b) \in E$ and $(b, c) \in E$ then $(a, c) \in E$.

A relation which satisfies (1) is called *reflexive*.
A relation which satisfies (2) is called *symmetric*.
A relation which satisfies (3) is called *transitive*.

If we introduce the special symbol $(\sim)$ for an equivalence relation E, we may restate the properties as follows:

1*. For all $a \in A$, $a \sim a$.
2*. For all a and b in A, if $a \sim b$ then $b \sim a$.
3*. For all a, b, and c in A, if $a \sim b$ and $b \sim c$ then $a \sim c$.

It is often thought that symmetry and transitivity imply reflexivity by arguing that (2*) gives $a \sim b$ and $b \sim a$ so that (3*) gives $a \sim a$. However, the following example shows that this is not the case.

Example 5. Let $A = \{x, y\}$ and $R = \{(y, y)\}$.

Thus $y \sim y$ is the only relation! (1*) does not hold as $x \nsim x$; however, (2*) and (3*) do hold. The trouble with the fallacious argument above is that x may be related to no element, as is the case in Example 5. If x were related to some element, then this argument would be valid and would show that $x \sim x$.

Examples of Equivalence Relations

1. Let A be the set of plane geometric figures. Let $a \sim b$ if and only if a is congruent to b.

2. Let A be the set in (1). Let $a \sim b$ if and only if a is similar to b.

3. Let A be the set of automobiles existing in the world today. Let $a \sim b$ if and only if a and b are made by the same manufacturer.

4. Let A be the set of all integers. Let $a \sim b$ if and only if 2 divides $a - b$.

5. Let A be the set of all continuous functions on the closed interval $[0, 1] = \{x : 0 \leq x \leq 1\}$. Let $a(x) \sim b(x)$ if and only if $\int_0^1 a(x)\,dx = \int_0^1 b(x)\,dx$.

The most important property of an equivalence relation on a set is that it partitions the set into mutually disjoint subsets called equivalence classes. An equivalence class containing an element x consists precisely of the elements related to x. In the example (4) above there are two equivalence classes, the odd numbers and the even numbers. In (1) above there are many equivalence classes, one of them is the set of all squares of side one inch. The equivalence classes of (2) and (4) are illustrated in Figure 3. The general situation is stated in the next theorem.

Theorem 5. Let A be a nonempty set and let σ denote an equivalence relation on A. For all $x \in A$ let $S_x = \{y : y \, \sigma \, x\}$. A is the set sum of the set of mutually disjoint nonempty subsets S_x; $A = \bigcup \{S_x : x \in A\}$. S_x is called an *equivalence class* of A under σ. Conversely, if A is the set sum of a set T of mutually disjoint nonempty subsets of A, then an equivalence relation τ on A can be defined so that the elements of T become the equivalence classes of A under τ.

PROOF. *Part I.* Let σ denote an equivalence relation on the nonempty set A. For every $x \in A$, let S_x be the subset of A defined in the theorem. Since σ is

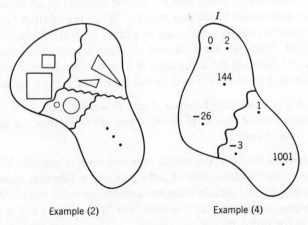

Example (2)   Example (4)

Figure 3

reflexive, $x \in S_x$ and so S_x is nonempty. It follows easily that $A = \bigcup \{S_x : x \in A\}$.

Now suppose that $S_x \cap S_y \neq \varnothing$ and let $z \in S_x \cap S_y$. By definition we have $z \sigma x$ and $z \sigma y$, hence $x \sigma y$ and $y \sigma x$ follow from the transitivity and the symmetry of σ. But now if $v \in S_x$ then $v \sigma x$ and as $x \sigma y$, by transitivity, again we have $v \sigma y$. Thus $S_x \subseteq S_y$. Similarly we conclude that $S_y \subseteq S_x$ and so we have $S_x = S_y$. Thus the equivalence classes of A under σ form a mutually disjoint set of nonempty subsets of A. We have in fact that $S_x = S_y$ if and only if $x \sigma y$.

Part II. Let $A = \bigcup T$ where T is a set of mutually disjoint nonempty subsets of A. Remember an element t of T is a subset of A. We define a relation E on A as follows: $(x, y) \in E$ if and only if x and y belong to the same subset $t \in T$. E is trivially reflexive and symmetric. E is also easily seen to be transitive, and hence E is an equivalence relation which we shall denote by τ. Now we must prove that if $t \in T$, then there exists an $x \in A$ such that $t = \{y : y \in A$ and $y \tau x\}$. By assumption, t is a nonempty subset of A, so let $x \in t$. Now, by definition, for all $y \in A$ we have $y \tau x$ if and only if y belongs to t. Hence $t = \{y : y \in A$ and $y \tau x\}$.

$$* \quad * \quad *$$

0.4. FUNCTIONS AND MAPPINGS

One of the most central concepts of all mathematics is that of *function*. In its pristine form a function is a special kind of relation.

Definition. A *function* f is a relation between sets A and B such that:

$$\text{If } (a, b) \in f \quad \text{and} \quad (a, c) \in f \quad \text{then} \quad b = c.$$

This definition simply states that the second member of an ordered pair in f is uniquely determined by the first member. When the relation f is a function we are accustomed to write the ordered pair as $(a, f(a))$. Note, too, that we have departed from our usual custom of using upper case letters for sets since the usual notation for a function is a lower case letter. Later we shall find it convenient to use lower case Greek letters for certain functions.

Definition. If f is a function between A and B such that $\mathcal{D}_f = A$ we say that f is a function *from A into B.* If $\mathcal{D}_f = A$ and $\mathcal{R}_f = B$, then we say that f is a function *from A onto B.*

The distinction between the words *into* and *onto* is crucial! We have, of course, that every function from A onto B is also a function from A into B and any function is a function from its domain onto its range. We use the standard jargon of saying that "f is into" (or "f is onto") if f is a function from A into (or onto) B.

In Examples 6–8 to follow let A be the set of all real numbers and let $A = B$.

Example 6. $f = \{(x, y) : y = x^2\}$ is a function. $\mathscr{D}_f = A$ and $\mathscr{R}_f = \{x : 0 \leq x\}$. f is into.

Example 7. $g = \{(x, y) : y^2 = x^2\}$ is not a function since, for example, $(1, 1)$ and $(1, -1)$ belong to g. $\mathscr{D}_g = \mathscr{R}_g = A$.

Example 8. $h = \{(x, y) : y = \sqrt{1 - x^2}\}$ is a function. $\mathscr{D}_h = \{x : |x| \leq 1\}$ and $\mathscr{R}_h = \{y : 0 \leq y \leq 1\}$.

Example 9. Let $A = \{a_1, a_2, a_3, a_4\}$ and $B = \{b_1, b_2, b_3, \ldots\}$. Let $k = \{(a_1, b_1), (a_2, b_1), (a_3, b_3)\}$. k is a function. $\mathscr{D}_k = \{a_1, a_2, a_3\}$ and $\mathscr{R}_k = \{b_1, b_3\}$.

Example 10. Let A be any set. The identity function ι from A onto A is $\{(x, x) : x \in A\}$; that is to say $\iota(x) = x$.

Example 11. Let A and B be any sets. Let b be a fixed element in B. The constant function f_b is $\{(x, b) : x \in A\}$; that is to say $f_b(x) = b$.

Example 12. Let A be any set. Let S be any subset of A. Let $B = \{0, 1\}$. The *characteristic function* c_S is the function $\{(x, 1) : x \in S\} \cup \{(x, 0) : x \notin S\}$; that is to say

$$c_S(x) = \begin{cases} 1 & \text{if} \quad x \in S \\ 0 & \text{if} \quad x \notin S \end{cases}$$

Example 13. A *sequence* is a special function. Let A be a subset of the nonnegative integers $\{0, 1, 2, \ldots\}$. Let B be any set. A sequence is a function s from A into B. We usually denote the second element of the ordered pair $(i, b) \in s$ by s_i and in this way write the sequence $\{s_i : i \in A\}$. If $A = \{0, 1, \ldots\}$, we usually write $\{s_0, s_1, \ldots\}$.

Definition. Let A be the finite set of positive integers $\{1, 2, \ldots, n\}$. Let B be any set. An *n-tuple* of elements from B is a sequence from A into B. An n-tuple shall be denoted $(b_1, \ldots, b_n)$.

An ordered pair (a, b) may be identified with a 2-tuple and $A \times B$ may be identified with the set of all 2-tuples (s_1, s_2) which are functions from $\{1, 2\}$ into $A \cup B$ such that $s_1 \in A$ and $s_2 \in B$. $A_1 \times \cdots \times A_n$ shall denote all n-tuples $(a_1, \ldots, a_n)$ from $A_1 \cup \cdots \cup A_n$ such that $a_i \in A_i$ for $i = 1, \ldots, n$.

In analytic geometry we learn to plot the points (x, y) satisfying a relation on the real numbers to make a graph. Examples 6, 7, and 8 are pictured in Figure 4.

We shall picture Example 9 in a different manner. We exploit the notion that a function associates with a particular element of a set A at most one element of a set B. The word "mapping" for this idea is a suggestive one and it is used as a synonym for function. If $(a, b) \in f$ then b is called the

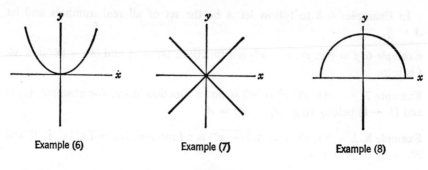

| Example (6) | Example (7) | Example (8) |

Figure 4

image of *a* under *f*, and *a* is called a preimage of *b* under *f*. Notice that an element of *B* may have many preimages or no preimage under *f*. Thus a function maps certain elements of *A* into elements of *B*. To picture this it is convenient to draw a symbolic set *A* and a symbolic set *B* and attach some arrows to indicate this mapping. Figure 5 is a picture of this kind for

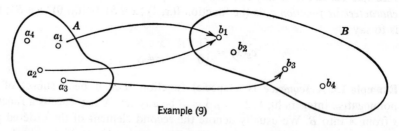

Example (9)

Figure 5

Example 11. More generally we draw a picture as shown in Figure 6. Symbolically we write $f: A \to B$ when f is a mapping from *A* into *B*.

Definition. Let $A \subseteq A_1$ and $B \subseteq B_1$. If $f: A \to B$ and $g: A_1 \to B_1$, we say g is an *extension* of f if $f \subseteq g$. If $f: A \to B$ and if $S \subseteq A$, we say $h: S \to B$ is the *restriction* of f to S if $\mathcal{D}_h = S \cap \mathcal{D}_f$ and $h \subseteq f$.

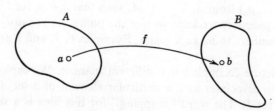

Figure 6

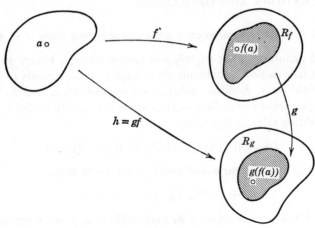

Figure 7

Example 14. Let $A = B = \{$rational numbers$\}$. Let $f: A \to B$ be the function $\{(r, r^2) : r \in A\}$. Let $A_1 = B_1 = \{$real numbers$\}$. Let $g = \{(r, r^2) : r \in A\} \cup \{(x, 0) : x \in A_1 - A\}$. Thus g is an extension of f. Let $S = \{x : x$ is a rational number and $0 \le x \le 1\}$. Let $h : S \to S$ be the function $\{(r, r^2) : r \in S\}$. Here, h is the restriction of f to S.

Definition. A mapping $f: A \to B$ is called *one-to-one*, if whenever (a, b) and (c, b) are in f then $a = c$.

We shall abbreviate "one-to-one" by "1–1". It is but an exercise of vocabulary to see that a function is 1–1 if and only if every element in its range has a unique preimage in A.

Definition. *Composition of mappings.* Let $f: A \to B$ be a mapping of A into B and let $g : B \to C$ be a mapping of B into C. The mapping $h : A \to C$ of A into C given by $h = \{(a, g(f(a))) : a \in A\}$ is called the composition of f and g. We write $h = gf$. Figure 7 illustrates this process.

It is important to realize that our notation applies the mappings from right to left. gf means to first apply the mapping f and then the mapping g. This is consistent with standard functional notation. Thus $\sin 2x$ represents the composition of the function f given by $f(x) = 2x$ and the function g given by $g(y) = \sin y$, while $2 \sin x$ represents fg.

> **Theorem 6.** If f is a 1–1 mapping from A into B, then there is a function $g : B \to A$ from B onto A such that gf is the identity function on A. The function g is uniquely determined if and only if $|A| = 1$ or f is 1–1 and maps A onto B.

0.5. OPERATIONS AND OPERATORS

Definition. A *binary operation* on a set A is a mapping from $A \times A$ into A.

In more picturesque, but slightly less precise terms, a binary operation is a rule that tells us how to combine an ordered pair of elements to obtain an element of the set A. Addition, subtraction, multiplication, and division provide examples from our earliest mathematical experiences. Indeed, we might list the addition table in this form:

$$+ = \{((1, 1), 2), ((1, 2), 3), ((2, 1), 3), \ldots\}$$

With the help of a circular use of notation we might write

$$+ = \{((a, b), c) : a + b = c\}!$$

If m is a binary operation on A we may, without any loss of precision, view m as a set of ordered triples (3-tuples) from A. We may consider m as the set $\{(a, b, c) : ((a, b), c) \in m\}$. For example, $(1, 2, 3) \in +$.

If m is a binary operation on A we shall often use a new symbol, say $(*)$, and write $a * b = c$ if $((a, b), c)$ belongs to m. Often we simply juxtapose a and b, writing $ab = c$. This is the usual practice for multiplication in algebra while $(\times)$ or $(\cdot)$ is usually used for multiplication of real numbers. Thus, we often see $2 \times 3 = 6$ or $2 \cdot 3 = 6$.

Example 15. Let S be a set. Let A consist of all mappings from S into S. Composition of mappings is a binary operation on A.

Definition. Let a binary operation on A be denoted by $(*)$. The operation is said to be *associative* provided for all a, b, and c in A, $(a * b) * c = a * (b * c)$. The operation is said to be *commutative* provided for all a and b in A, $a * b = b * a$.

If $(*)$ denotes a binary operation on A we have not yet defined what is meant by the symbol $a_1 * a_2 * \cdots * a_n$. For example if the binary operation is $(+)$ on the integers what does $6 + 4 + 1$ denote? 11, of course! However if the binary operation is subtraction $(-)$ on the set of integers then the symbol $6 - 4 - 1$ is ambiguous.

Definition. Let $m : A \times A \to A$ be a binary operation on a set A which shall be denoted by $(*)$. By $a_1 * a_2 * a_3$ we shall denote the image under m of the ordered pair $(a_1 * a_2, a_3)$. That is, $a_1 * a_2 * a_3$ is the element obtained by first determining $(a_1 * a_2)$ and then $(a_1 * a_2) * a_3$. Indeed it is customary to use parentheses to indicate that we are to first determine $a_1 * a_2 (= a_4)$ and then $a_4 * a_3$. By induction define $a_1 * a_2 * \cdots * a_{n-1} * a_n = (a_1 * \cdots * a_{n-1}) * a_n$.

This notational convention is referred to as association to the left. If the associative law holds for $(*)$ then it can be proved that every way of inserting parentheses in the symbol $a_1 * \cdots * a_n$ to reduce its calculation to a sequence of binary operations results in the same element of A.

To be precise, we are here defining, by induction, a function φ from the set of all n-tuples, $n = 2, 3, \ldots$, into A by induction as follows:

$$\varphi(a_1, a_2) = a_1 * a_2$$
$$\varphi(a_1, a_2, \ldots, a_n, a_{n+1}) = \varphi(a_1, a_2, \ldots, a_n) * a_{n+1}$$

A hiatus exists at this point because we do not know that a function, in the precise sense of our earlier definition, has been defined. Indeed, what is the set of ordered pairs that constitutes the function? We shall remove this hiatus in Chapter 3 when we establish a general scheme for defining a function by induction. For now, we rely on our intuition and the assumption in Section 0.1 that we may make a definition in this way.

Theorem 7. Let A consist of all the mappings from a set S into S. The binary operation of composition defined on A is associative.

PROOF. Let f, g, and h be mappings from S into S. We are to prove that $(hg)f = h(gf)$. There is no question that $(hg)f$ and $h(gf)$ are functions from S into S since we have observed that composition is a binary operation on A. We have only to prove that they are the same function, that is, that the sets of ordered pairs which constitute the two functions are equal. To do this it clearly suffices to show that the image of every $x \in S$ is the same under $(hg)f$ and $h(gf)$. We find that $(hg)f(x) = (hg)(f(x)) = h(g(f(x)))$, while $h(gf)(x) = h(gf(x)) = h(g(f(x)))$. Thus the image of x under each function is $h(g(f(x)))$. Figure 8 illustrates the situation.

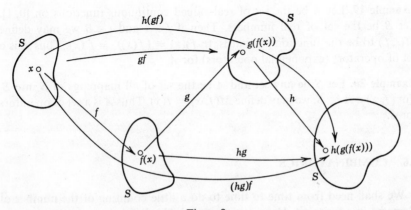

Figure 8

Definition. An *n-ary operation* on a set A is a mapping from the set of all *n*-tuples from A into A.

Example 16. Let A be the set of integers. A ternary (3-ary) operation on A is defined by mapping the 3-tuple (a, b, c) into $ab + c$.

As in the case of a binary operation we may think of an *n*-ary operation as a set of $(n + 1)$-tuples.

A unary (1-ary) operation on A is just a function from A into A. We shall have no occasion to consider operations other than unary and binary operations.

Definition. Let $(*)$ be a binary operation defined on a set S. A subset $T \subseteq S$ is said to be *closed under* $(*)$ if the restriction of $(*)$ to $T \times T$ is an operation on T.

Thus $T \subseteq S$ is closed under a binary operation $(*)$ if for all $(t_1, t_2) \in T \times T$, then $t_1 * t_2 \in T$.

Example 17. If I is the set of all integers and $I_+ = \{x : x \in I, x > 0\}$ then I_+ is closed under addition but not under subtraction.

The concept of a binary operation can be generalized usefully to the notion of a set of operators on a set.

Definition. A set B is said to be a set of *operators* for A by M if M is a mapping from $B \times A$ into A.

The effect of this definition is that there is a rule that tells us how to combine an element from B and an element from A to obtain an element in A.

Example 18. If M is a binary operation on A, then A is a set of operators for A. In this way, for example, we could view $2+$ not as an integer but as the operation ("effect") of adding 2 to every integer.

Example 19. Let A be the set of real-valued continuous functions on $[0, 1]$. Let B be the set of real numbers. Then if $f \in A$ and $r \in B$ we may define $M(r, f)$ to be the function f^r, that is, $(r \cdot f)(x) = (f(x))^r = f^r(x)$. Thus B is a set of operators (exponential operators) for A.

Example 20. Let S be any set and A be the set of all mappings of S into S. For $(f, x) \in A \times S$, we may define $M(f, x) = f(x)$. Thus A is a set of operators for S.

0.6. COMBINATORICS

We shall need from time to time to do a little counting of the number of elements in a finite set. Here are some of the basic results.

Theorem 8. If S is a set of n elements then
1. The total number of subsets of S is 2^n.
2. If $n \geq 1$, the number of subsets of S with an even number of elements is the same as the number of subsets with an odd number of elements. This number is 2^{n-1}.

3. If $\binom{n}{k}$ denotes the number of subsets with k elements then

$$\binom{n}{k} = \binom{n}{n-k} \text{ and for } n > k \geq 1, \quad \binom{n-1}{k-1} + \binom{n-1}{k} = \binom{n}{k}.$$

4. For $n \geq k \geq 0$, $\binom{n}{k} = n!/k!(n-k)!$ (We follow the convention that $0! = 1$.)

5. For numbers a, b we have the binomial formula: $(a + b)^n = \sum_{k=0}^{k=n} \binom{n}{k} a^k b^{n-k}$.

PROOF. Conclusions (1), (2), and (3) are easily proved simultaneously by induction on n. For $n = 0$ conclusion (1) is obvious and the other two conclusions hold vacuously. (It is also easy to verify these conclusions for $n = 1$ and $n = 2$.) Thus step A of our induction proof is complete. The inductive hypothesis for step B states that (1), (2), and (3) hold for all sets with $n - 1$ elements. We shall now prove, on the basis of this assumption the conclusions for a set with n elements. Let S be a set with n elements where we shall assume, to avoid trivialities, that $n \geq 2$. Let x be a particular element of S which we keep fixed throughout our discussion. Let $S' = S - \{x\}$. We note that S' has $n - 1$ elements and that if A is a subset of S then if $x \notin A$ then $A \subseteq S'$, whereas if $x \in A$ then there is a unique set $A' \subseteq S'$ such that $A = A' \cup \{x\}$; indeed, $A' = A - \{x\}$. Let K be the number of subsets of S' with an even number of elements (or an odd number of elements). We have that $2K = 2^{n-1}$. Now adjoin the element x to each subset of S'. Clearly if $E' \subseteq S'$ and E' has an even number of elements, then $E = E' \cup \{x\}$ has an odd number of elements, whereas if $O' \subseteq S'$ has an odd number of elements then $O = O' \cup \{x\}$ has an even number of elements. Thus to count the number of subsets of S, with an even number of elements we have K subsets that have an even number of elements and are subsets of S' and K more of the form $O' \cup \{x\}$. Since, as we have observed, each subset A of S has a unique expression of the form A' or $A' \cup \{x\}$ with $A' \subseteq S'$ it is now clear that there are exactly $2K$ subsets of S with an even number of elements. Similarly there are $2K$ subsets of S with an odd number of elements, a total of $4K = 2^n$ subsets of S. Thus (1) and (2) are established. To prove (3) we first note that $\binom{n}{k} = \binom{n}{n-k}$ by noting that the correspondence of every subset with its complement is a 1–1 correspondence and that if $A \subseteq S$ has k elements then its complement must have $n - k$ elements. The second part of (3) follows in a way analogous to (2). If $A \subseteq S$ has k elements and $k \geq 1$ then $A = A' \subseteq S'$ or $A = A' \cup \{x\}$ depending on whether $x \notin A$ or $x \in A$. Thus the number of subsets of S having k elements must be the sum of the number of subsets of S' having k elements and the number of subsets of S' having $k - 1$ elements (to which we adjoin x to get a set with k elements that contains x). That is, $\binom{n}{k} = \binom{n-1}{k} + \binom{n-1}{k-1}$.

Conclusion (4) follows by a very standard induction on n; we leave the details to the reader. (5) too has a standard induction proof, however more directly, it is the observation that a term $a^k b^{n-k}$ arises in the product $(a + b)^n$ by choosing the term a from k of the factors $(a + b)$ and b from the remaining $n - k$ factors. Thus the coefficient of $a^k b^{n-k}$ is simply the number of subsets of $\{1, \ldots, n\}$ having k elements. (1) can of course be proved from (3), (4), and (5): take $a = b = 1$. (2) also follows (3), (4), and (5); take $a = 1$ and $b = -1$. (3) is just the law governing the formation of Pascal's triangle.

$$* \quad * \quad *$$

A second combinatorial lemma is the classical "pigeonhole" principle attributed to P. G. L. Dirichlet (1805–1859).

Theorem 9. If a set of n distinct elements is partitioned into k subsets where $0 < k < n$, then some subset must contain at least two elements.

This theorem simply states that if n "letters" are to be placed into k "pigeonholes" where $n > k > 0$, then at least two letters must be placed into the same pigeonhole. More mathematically speaking, a finite set cannot be placed into a 1–1 correspondence with a proper subset of itself.

This principle is often used in parlor games; for example, if a drawer contains only black and white socks, how many socks must be pulled from the drawer to insure getting at least one matching pair? Dirichlet used this principle to show that if r is a positive real number and N is any positive integer then there are integers a and b with $0 < b \leq N$ such that $|br - a| \leq 1/N$. (The subtle part of this result is the bound on $b: 0 < b \leq N$.) We note that each positive number r has the form $r = r_0 + r_1$ where r_0 is a non-negative integer and $0 \leq r_1 < 1$. Let us call r_1 the fractional part of r and denote it by $\{r\}$. We also note that the unit interval $[0, 1]$ is neatly divided into N intervals of the form $[t/N, (t + 1)/N]$, $0 \leq t < N$; each interval of length $1/N$. These are the pigeonholes. Dirichlet now argues that $\{0\}, \{r\}, \{2r\}, \ldots, \{Nr\}$ are $N + 1$ numbers in the unit interval $[0, 1]$. These are the "letters." Thus at least two must fall into the same pigeonhole, that is, into the same interval. Thus for some pair of integers, $0 \leq p < q \leq N$, we must have that $|\{pr\} - \{qr\}| \leq 1/N$.

Now if $pr = u + \{pr\}$ and $qr = v + \{qr\}$ where u and v are integers we have that $|\{qr\} - \{pr\}| = |(q - p)r - (v - u)| \leq 1/N$ and indeed, $0 < q - p \leq N$.

SUPPLEMENTARY READING

P. R. Halmos, *Naive Set Theory*, Princeton, N.J.: Van Nostrand (1960).

L. Henkin, On mathematical induction, *American Mathematical Monthly*, **67** (1960), 323–338.

I. Niven and H. S. Zuckerman, *An Introduction to the Theory of Numbers*, New York: John Wiley and Sons (1960).

R. R. Stoll, *Set Theory and Logic*, San Francisco: W. H. Freeman (1963).

Prologue

To give some idea of what we shall attempt to do in this book we need an understanding of the term "abstract algebra." Probably the abstract algebra most familiar to you is that of the integers although you would not have called it "abstract" nor "algebra." First of all there is the set of integers and you probably feel you know what these elements are; you can even match them with points on a line. You have for years used the binary operations of addition, subtraction, and multiplication. You know what sort of laws these operations obey. Moreover, you can state some true theorems about the integers. As applied to the integers the term "abstract algebra" encompasses the set of integers, the binary operations of addition, subtraction, and multiplication defined on this set, a list of basic axioms these operations satisfy, a relation which orders the integers, a list of axioms which the order relation satisfies, and finally a whole host of theorems which describe the behavior of the integers under these operations and relations. Some of these theorems are easy consequences of the axioms, others are extremely difficult, requiring techniques and knowledge of other mathematical systems, and of course many questions remain unsolved. Traditionally the study of this mathematical system is called number theory.

The chief aim of such a study is to obtain a description of the structure of the integers. We could of course fill libraries with special facts about special integers. This would probably not only be dull, but to employ a picturesque metaphor, we would lose sight of the forest for the trees. How can we view the forest? We can state theorems valid for all integers, or even theorems valid for certain subsets of integers. We can look for subsets with special properties and we can discover relations on the integers which display key properties. We can study the functions from the integers into themselves. We shall, of course, have to select from all possible functions those which do tell us something of the integers as a whole. Just which relations and functions are fruitful for study is a matter of hindsight. We judge the effectiveness of the techniques by how much they tell us about particular questions.

More generally an abstract algebra is a set S of elements together with a number of operations and relations on S. It is well to recall that these operations and relations are just sets of n-tuples. To study an abstract algebra is to learn something of how the individual elements behave, to discover some theorems about the system and to find some properties which describe the system. We do this by isolating distinguished subsets of S, determining how these subsets of S interact under the operations and relations, and, most important, by studying functions on S.

If you think about it for a minute you will see that for the purpose of studying the structure of an abstract algebra, it is not so important to know all the ordered triples that constitute a binary operation on S as it is to know the properties the operation satisfies. For example, it is not as important to know the decimal expansion of the product of 84,927 and 101,110,112 as it is to know that multiplication and addition are associative, commutative, and that multiplication distributes over addition.

Therefore in describing an abstract algebra we usually do not attempt, indeed, if S is infinite we usually cannot give, a complete list of the $(n + 1)$-tuples corresponding to each n-ary operation. We may give a rule that will enable us to compute the operation if the elements of S are given in a certain form, or we may define an operation by induction. It is the usual custom to state that an n-ary operation exists on S which satisfies a prescribed list of properties—axioms. This procedure permits us a great economy. If S and T are different sets, the mathematical systems concerning S and T will, *a priori* be different, since the n-tuples corresponding to the operations will be different sets. However, it often happens that S and T share the same kinds of operations and relations in that the same axioms are assumed about an operation on S and a corresponding operation on T. If this is the case then our study of the two abstract algebras can be expedited if we select those operations common to S and T and study a system with operations which have these axioms. For then, every provable theorem in this general system will state a fact valid for all abstract algebras having operations and relations corresponding to these and satisfying these axioms. In particular they will be valid in S and T.

This procedure is more than an economy. In fixing our attention on a few properties we have a chance to discover why a certain theorem is true. We try to strip from a theorem and its proof all that is inessential. We try to recognize what minimal conditions are necessary for the validity of the theorem. For example consider the law of integral exponents $(ab)^n = a^n b^n$ for rational numbers. What properties of the rational numbers do we need to prove this law? We do not need to know, for example, that between every two rational numbers is another rational number; we did not need to know that if $ab = 0$ then $a = 0$ or $b = 0$. We need in fact only the associativity and commutativity of the multiplication operation. In realizing this we can see that $(ab)^n = a^n b^n$ and $n(a + b) = na + nb$ is the *same* law but written in different notations for the different operations. We can also see that $\sqrt{2}(a + b) = \sqrt{2}a + \sqrt{2}b$ must hold for quite a different reason.

This procedure is called the axiomatic method. If we wish to study a particular set S with specific operations and relations we first list the basic properties enjoyed by the operations and relations on S, which we wish to study. Then, in abstraction, we consider an arbitrary set with operations and relations assumed defined on it which are characterized by the axioms corresponding to the basic properties that were selected. This gives rise to a class of abstract algebras. An abstract algebra is a member of the class if the set of elements admits operations and relations which satisfy the axioms.

A class of abstract algebras will likely have many members if the number of operations and relations considered and the number of axioms are small. Of course if there are too few axioms, the class will be so large that only mild theorems of little interest can be proved. On the other hand, if a class of abstract algebras has too many operations, relations, and axioms, the class may have only a few members, or even no members.

Indeed, as we shall see in Chapter 3, an innocent enough appearing list of operations, relations, and axioms turns out to describe a class of abstract algebras in which any two members are essentially the same—indeed each is an exact copy of the integers.

We shall solve the problem, when we can, of deciding whether a class of abstract algebras has at least one member—that is, whether a set of axioms concerning certain operations and relations is consistent—by finding an example of such a system and explicitly verifying the axioms.

We consider, in turn, the broad classes of abstract algebras which are called groups, rings, fields, and vector spaces. These classes were selected because so many different and useful mathematical systems can be viewed as members of one or more of these classes. In each case we shall find some theorems that will help to describe the structure of any particular such mathematical system. The more theorems we can prove, the better we shall understand the system. Our *modus operandi* will be first to examine the immediate consequences of the axioms, next to find appropriate subsets and to see how these subsets help describe the system, and then to consider the properties of mappings from an algebra of one class onto another of the same class.

In mathematics the word "algebra" refers to a mathematical system in which all the operations on a set are finitary. It is possible that there are an infinite number of operations, but each operation is an n-ary operation for some positive integer n. In contrast the calculus studies an infinite operation—the limit. A limit can map an infinite sequence of real numbers into a real number, although for some sequences no limit exists. No such process occurs in an algebra, by definition. This is not to say that algebra does not mix with other mathematical disciplines for all branches of mathematics are concerned with some finitary operations, and when they are, algebraic methods are the appropriate tools for research. Conversely, some of the most difficult algebraic questions have been settled by results obtained by nonalgebraic methods. The strong interdependence between various branches of mathematics is one of the major characteristics of mathematics in this century. This book attempts to provide an introduction to some of the algebraic concepts that are significant in all mathematics.

I | Groups

1.1. INTRODUCTION

The first class of abstract algebras we shall study is the class of groups. We could introduce groups as a result of an abstraction process carried out on the integers. To do this we would select the addition operation and a few of the properties this operation satisfies as the axioms. Or we could consider a set S and the set of all 1–1 mappings from S onto S. To do this, we would select the composition of mappings as the operation to be studied and select as axioms some of the properties this operation satisfies. These two diverse examples give evidence of the universality of the group concept.

Historically, groups arose in another context. They were first used effectively by Augustin Louis Cauchy (1789–1857) and by Evariste Galois (1811–1832) in their studies of the theory of equations. Here groups were not taken from any system of numbers, but rather were used to describe the effect of mapping the roots of an equation onto themselves. The present abstract formulation represents a considerable degree of sophistication from these early treatments. The first axiomatic formulation for an abstract group was given in 1870 by Leopold Kronecker (1823–1891).

1.2. GROUP AXIOMS

Definition. A group is a nonempty set of elements S together with a binary operation defined on S, here denoted ($\circ$), which satisfies the following axioms:

G1. The operation ($\circ$) is associative: For every triple (a, b, c) of elements from S, $(a \circ b) \circ c = a \circ (b \circ c)$.

G2. Under ($\circ$), S possesses at least one right *identity* element: There exists an element $e \in S$ such that, for every $a \in S$, $a \circ e = a$.

G3. For some right identity element e there is for every $a \in S$ at least one right *inverse* element a^* such that $a \circ a^* = e$.

We write $\langle S, \circ \rangle$ to denote a set S with a binary operation defined on it. The symbol $(\circ)$ used here stands for the set of triples from S which constitute the binary operation.

Any element satisfying G2 shall be called a right identity for the group. Note that if e is a right identity, $e \circ e = e$. In the axiom G3, the element a^* depends on the particular right identity element in question as well as on the element a. The notation stresses the dependence on a since we shall prove in Lemma 2 that there is but one identity element. Moreover, in Lemma 5 we prove that for each a, the element a^* is unique.

Notice that a set of elements alone is not a group. A group is the mathematical system obtained by defining a binary operation on a set of elements. To give an example of a group we must specify the set of elements and the operation. We shall speak loosely of the group elements and the group operation.

1.3. EXAMPLES

Example 1. Let S be the set of integers: $\{0, 1, 2, 3, \ldots, -1, -2, -3, \ldots\}$. Let the operation be addition. G1 is well-known to be true! The right identity element is 0 and the right inverse of a is $(-a)$.

Example 2. Let S be the set of positive rational numbers. Let the operations be multiplication. G1 is well-known to be true! The identity element is 1 and the inverse of a is $1/a$.

Example 3. Let S be the set of positive integers and zero. Let the operation be addition. This system is not a group since G3 is not satisfied, although the other axioms do hold.

Example 4. Let S be the set of all integers. Let the operation be subtraction. This system is not a group because G1 does not hold although the other axioms do hold.

Example 5. Let S be the set of all vectors in the plane. Let the operation be vector addition. This is a group, with the zero vector as the identity.

Example 6. Let S be the set of all vectors in the plane. Consider the "operation" of "dot" or "scalar" product. This is not an operation on S because the dot product of two elements of S is not a member of S.

Example 7. Let S be the set of all strictly monotone increasing functions mapping $[0, 1]$ onto $[0, 1]$. Recall that a function is strictly monotone increasing if $x < y$ implies that $f(x) < f(y)$. The condition that $[0, 1]$ be mapped onto $[0, 1]$ implies that $f(0) = 0$ and $f(1) = 1$. The operation is composition: $(f \circ g)(x) = f(g(x))$. Since $0 \le g(x) \le 1$, it follows that $0 \le f(g(x)) \le 1$ and indeed that $f \circ g$ maps $[0, 1]$ onto $[0, 1]$. Since $x < y$ implies that $g(x) < g(y)$

and so in turn, $f(g(x)) < f(g(y))$. Thus $f \circ g$ is a strictly monotone increasing function from [0, 1] onto [0, 1]. G1 holds by Theorem 0.7. The identity element is the function ι such that $\iota(x) = x$. If f is a function in S, f^{-1} is the function defined by $f^{-1}(x) = y$ if and only if $f(y) = x$. It takes but a little work to verify that a function has been defined in the above way and that it satisfies the criterion for membership in S. Note that in general $f \circ g \neq g \circ f$. Figure 1 illustrates this point of the example.

Example 8. Let S be the set of rotations of the plane about the origin. An element of S is the mapping of the plane into itself obtained by rotating every point a certain number of degrees. The operation $a \circ b$ is defined as the composition of two rotations; first perform the rotation b and then the rotation a.

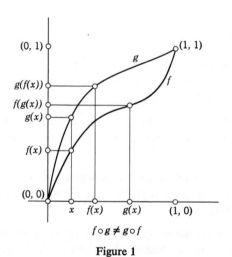

$$f \circ g \neq g \circ f$$

Figure 1

Example 9. Consider the equilateral triangle of Figure 2. A symmetry of the triangle is any mapping σ of it onto itself such that for any two of its points, the distance between x and y is the same as the distance between $\sigma(x)$ and $\sigma(y)$. We take it as intuitively obvious that a symmetry must send a vertex into a vertex. It is a theorem that any symmetry of the triangle may be accomplished by a rotation R about its center or by a reflection about one of the three bisectors A, B, or C. Clearly R must be a rotation of 0, 120, or 240 degrees. There are thus six distinct symmetries of the triangle. The symmetries of the triangle form a group under composition: Composition of symmetries yields a symmetry. By Theorem 0.7 this operation is associative, the identity is the identity mapping, a rotation of 0 degrees, and each symmetry has a natural inverse.

A symmetry is completely described by its effect on the vertices. Let us number the positions of the vertices (1, 2, 3) as shown in Figure 2. Consider the reflection about the bisector A. The vertex at (1) is fixed, the vertices at (2) and (3) are interchanged. We indicate this symmetry and its effect upon the triangle by writing the vertex *positions* (1, 2, 3) in a row and directly beneath the number (i) we write the *position* of the vertex, which is the image of the vertex at (i), under the symmetry. Thus

$$A = \begin{pmatrix} 1 & 2 & 3 \\ 1 & 3 & 2 \end{pmatrix}$$

Similarly $B = \begin{pmatrix} 1 & 2 & 3 \\ 3 & 2 & 1 \end{pmatrix}$, and $C = \begin{pmatrix} 1 & 2 & 3 \\ 2 & 1 & 3 \end{pmatrix}$. By identifying a vertex with

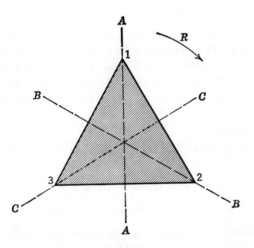

Figure 2

its position we may employ function notation to write $A(1) = 1$, $A(2) = 3$, $C(2) = 1$, and so on. Denote by R a rotation of 120 degrees, by S a rotation of 240 degrees, and by J a rotation of 0 degrees.

$$R = \begin{pmatrix} 1 & 2 & 3 \\ 2 & 3 & 1 \end{pmatrix}, \quad S = \begin{pmatrix} 1 & 2 & 3 \\ 3 & 1 & 2 \end{pmatrix}, \quad \text{and} \quad J = \begin{pmatrix} 1 & 2 & 3 \\ 1 & 2 & 3 \end{pmatrix}.$$

We have $R \circ A = \begin{pmatrix} 1 & 2 & 3 \\ 2 & 1 & 3 \end{pmatrix}$ because, for example, the vertex at position 2

gets mapped into position 3 by A and then into position 1 by R. The notational scheme does this mechanically for us since $(R \circ A)(2) = R(3) = 1$, or, schematically,

$$R \circ A = \begin{pmatrix} 1 & 2 & 3 \\ 2 & 3 & 1 \end{pmatrix} \circ \begin{pmatrix} 1 & 2 & 3 \\ 1 & 3 & 2 \end{pmatrix} = \begin{pmatrix} 1 & 2 & 3 \\ 2 & 1 & 3 \end{pmatrix}$$

Note that $R \circ A \neq A \circ R = \begin{pmatrix} 1 & 2 & 3 \\ 3 & 2 & 1 \end{pmatrix}$.

Example 10. Let S consist of a single element z. Let the operation be defined by $z \circ z = z$. $\langle S, \circ \rangle$ is a group.

Example 11. Let S consist of two elements, denoted a, b. Let the operation be defined by the table:

$$a \circ a = a \qquad b \circ a = b$$
$$a \circ b = b \qquad b \circ b = a$$

Note that the table gives the binary operation explicitly. We can see that a serves as an identity element, and with respect to it, each element serves as its own inverse. The verification of the associative law is more tedious. Theoretically we must check all possible ordered triples from $\{a, b\}$. There are eight of these. However some shortcuts can be made by observing for $x \in \{a, b\}$, $x \circ a = a \circ x = x$, while $x \circ b = b \circ x = x'$, where x' denotes the element other than x.

An important class of groups satisfies the additional axiom that the group operation is commutative:

G4. For every pair a, b of elements from S, $a \circ b = b \circ a$.

Definition. A group is called commutative or *abelian* if G4 holds.

The name *abelian* is in honor of the Norwegian mathematician, Niels Henrik Abel (1802–1829). Abel in 1824 showed the impossibility of solving, in general, equations of the fifth degree in terms of radicals. His further investigations concerned the solution of equations in terms of radicals for those equations that could be associated with a commutative group of permutations on the roots of the equations. Thus the name *abelian* is an appropriate one for these groups. The groups of examples 1, 2, 5, 8, 10, and 11 are abelian.

EXERCISE 1

1. Construct the symmetries of the square.
2. Show that the two functions on the nonzero rational numbers

$$f_1(x) = x \text{ and } f_2(x) = \frac{1}{x}$$

form a group under the operation of composition of functions.

3. Show that the three functions on $T = \{x : x$ is a rational number, $x \neq 0,$ $x \neq 1\}$

$$f_1(x) = x; \qquad g_2(x) = \frac{1}{1 - x}; \qquad g_3(x) = \frac{x - 1}{x}$$

under the operation of composition of functions satisfy G1, G2, G3, and G4.

4. Let T be the set defined in Exercise 3. Find the smallest group of functions on T containing f_2 and g_2 of Exercises 2 and 3.

5. Let A be a set and f a mapping from A into A. Here, f is said to have a *left* inverse if there is a function g such that the composite function gf is the identity function, that is, $gf(x) = g(f(x)) = x$. Similarly a *right* inverse is defined. Show that f has a left inverse if and only if f is 1–1. Show that f has a right inverse if and only if f is an *onto* function.

6. Let P be the set of points of the plane. For a and b in P, define $a \circ b$ to be the midpoint of the line segment from a to b. Which of G1, G2, G3, and G4 does ($\circ$) satisfy?

7. For each 4-tuple (a, b, c, d) of integers such that $ad - bc = 1$, let a function $\tau_{(a,b,c,d)}$ be defined on the set S which is the set union of the rational numbers and $\{\$\}$ as follows:

(i) If $c \neq 0$, then

$$\tau_{(a,b,c,d)}(x) = \begin{cases} \dfrac{ax + b}{cx + d} & \text{if } x \neq -\dfrac{d}{c} \text{ and } x \neq \$ \\[2mm] \dfrac{a}{c} & \text{if } x = \$ \\[2mm] \$ & \text{if } x = -\dfrac{d}{c} \end{cases}$$

(ii) If $c = 0$ then

$$\tau_{(a,b,c,d)}(x) = \begin{cases} \dfrac{ax + b}{d} & \text{if } x \neq \$ \\[2mm] \$ & \text{if } x = \$ \end{cases}$$

(Note that from $ad - bc \neq 0$ and $c = 0$ it follows that $d \neq 0$.)
Show that these mappings form a group under composition.

8. Let S be the set of numbers of the form $\sqrt[3]{a}$ where a is an integer:

$$S = \{\sqrt[3]{a} : a \text{ is an integer}\}.$$

Let $\sqrt[3]{a} \circ \sqrt[3]{b} = \sqrt[3]{a + b}$. Show that $\langle S, \circ \rangle$ is a group.

9. Let S be the set of integers. Let $a \circ b = a + b - 2$. Show that $\langle S, \circ \rangle$ is a group.

10. Let S be the set of nonzero rational numbers. Let $a \circ b = a/b$. Which group axioms hold for $\langle S, \circ \rangle$?

11. In Example 9, the symmetries of the triangle, find subsets of two and three elements which form groups under the same operation as the whole group.

1.4.   BASIC LEMMAS

In this section we shall give the elementary consequences of the group axioms. We could have assumed many of these properties as additional axioms, but aside from the esthetic appeal of a system of a few axioms, there is also less work involved in verifying that a particular system is a group.

Lemma 1. Let $\langle S, \circ \rangle$ be a group in which e is a right identity for which axiom G3 holds. If x is any element of S such that $x \circ x = x$ then $x = e$.

PROOF. Let x^* be an element such that $x \circ x^* = e$ as provided by G3. Then we have

$$
\begin{aligned}
e = x \circ x^* &= (x \circ x) \circ x^* && \text{as } x = x \circ x, \\
&= x \circ (x \circ x^*) && \text{by associativity,} \\
&= x \circ e && \text{as } x \circ x^* = e \text{ by assumption,} \\
&= x && \text{by axiom G2, as } e \text{ is a right} \\
& && \quad \text{identity by assumption.}
\end{aligned}
$$

* * *

We shall frequently use this lemma to establish that a certain element is a right identity. It is a convenient criteria for we have only to verify $x \circ x = x$; we do not have to verify that $s \circ x = s$ for all $s \in S$.

In passing we remark that in general if a set R has a binary operation ($\#$) defined on it and if $x \in R$ is an element such that $x \# x = x$ then x is called an *idempotent* of R. If R is the integers and ($\#$) is multiplication then 0 and 1 are the only idempotents. The next lemma states that in a group there is only one idempotent—the identity.

Lemma 2. If $\langle S, \circ \rangle$ is a group, there is only one element satisfying G2.

PROOF. There is at least one element satisfying G2. Call it e. If f is another, that is, if $a \circ f = a$ for all a in S, then in particular $f \circ f = f$. By Lemma 1, $f = e$.

* * *

Lemma 3. If $\langle S, \circ \rangle$ is a group in which e is the identity and if $a \circ a^* = e$, then $a^* \circ a = e$ also.

PROOF. We shall calculate $(a^* \circ a) \circ (a^* \circ a)$ and show that it equals $(a^* \circ a)$. From Lemma 1 it will then follow that $a^* \circ a = e$.

$$
\begin{aligned}
(a^* \circ a) \circ (a^* \circ a) &= [(a^* \circ a) \circ a^*] \circ a && \text{(associativity)} \\
&= [a^* \circ (a \circ a^*)] \circ a && \text{(associativity)} \\
&= (a^* \circ e) \circ a && (a \circ a^* = e \text{ was assumed)} \\
&= a^* \circ a && (e \text{ is a right identity).}
\end{aligned}
$$

* * *

Lemma 4. If $\langle S, \circ \rangle$ is a group in which e is the identity, then $e \circ a = a$ for all a in S.

PROOF. Let a^* be an element such that $a \circ a^* = e$. From Lemma 3 we now know that $a^* \circ a = e$ also. Then $a = a \circ e = a \circ (a^* \circ a) = (a \circ a^*) \circ a = e \circ a$.

$$* \quad * \quad *$$

Lemma 5. (*Uniqueness of the Inverse Element*). If $\langle S, \circ \rangle$ is a group in which e is the identity element, if $a \circ b = e$ and $a \circ a^* = e$, then $b = a^*$.

PROOF. From Lemma 3, $a^* \circ a = e$. Thus:

$$a^* = a^* \circ e = a^* \circ (a \circ b) = (a^* \circ a) \circ b = e \circ b = b.$$

Here the last equality holds by Lemma 4.

$$* \quad * \quad *$$

Lemma 2 proves that the identity element is unique and Lemma 4 shows that it is a left identity. Lemma 5 shows that for any a, the inverse a^* is unique and Lemma 3 shows it is a left inverse also. Symmetrical arguments show that replacing *right* by *left* in both G2 and G3 results in the same theory.

Notation Convention.

It is a common practice, which we shall usually follow hereafter, to adopt the multiplicative notation of juxtaposition to denote the group operation. We shall need to depart from this convention occasionally and in those cases the notation will be defined anew. In accordance with the multiplicative notation we shall denote the group identity by 1 and the inverse of a by a^{-1}. When this convention is used we shall simply say, for example, "Let S be a group . . ." rather than the more explicit "Let $\langle S, \circ \rangle$ be a group . . . ."

Theorem 1. If S is a group and a and b are any two elements, there is a unique element c such that $ac = b$, and there is a unique element d such that $da = b$.

Another way of stating this theorem is to say that in a group the equations $ax = b$ and $xa = b$ have unique solutions.

PROOF. Let $c = a^{-1}b$. Then $ac = a(a^{-1}b) = (aa^{-1})b = 1b = b$. This shows that at least one solution exists. On the other hand if $ac = b$ and $ac' = b$, then we have:

$$c = 1c = (a^{-1}a)c = a^{-1}(ac) = a^{-1}b = a^{-1}(ac') = (a^{-1}a)c' = 1c' = c'.$$

(Notice that we have essentially multiplied $ac = b$ and $ac' = b$ on the left by a^{-1}.) The details of the second half of this proof are left to the reader.

$$* \quad * \quad *$$

Corollary (*Cancellation Law*). If S is a group and if $ab = ac$ or $ba = ca$, then $b = c$.

PROOF. This is the uniqueness assertion of Theorem 1.

Theorem 2. (*Calculation Rule for Inverses*). If S is a group, then $(ab)^{-1} = b^{-1}a^{-1}$, and for any positive integer n,

$$(a_1a_2\ldots a_n)^{-1} = a_n^{-1}a_{n-1}^{-1}\ldots a_1^{-1}.$$

PROOF. We have $1 = (ab)(ab)^{-1}$ by definition, whereas

$$(ab)(b^{-1}a^{-1}) = a(bb^{-1})a^{-1} \quad \text{(associativity)}$$
$$= a1a^{-1} = aa^{-1} = 1.$$

The conclusion $(ab)^{-1} = b^{-1}a^{-1}$ follows by the unicity of the inverse.

The proof for general n proceeds by induction on n. When $n = 1$ there is nothing to prove, and we have just proved the formula for $n = 2$. Our induction really starts at $n = 2$. To establish the inductive step we assume for $k \geq 2$ that $(a_1a_2\ldots a_k)^{-1} = a_k^{-1}a_{k-1}^{-1}\ldots a_1^{-1}$. Then,

$$(a_1a_2\ldots a_k a_{k+1})^{-1} = ((a_1\ldots a_k)a_{k+1})^{-1} = a_{k+1}^{-1}(a_1\ldots a_k)^{-1}$$
$$= a_{k+1}^{-1}a_k^{-1}\ldots a_1^{-1}.$$

Thus the inductive step has been verified and our theorem holds.

* * *

Notation

Let S be a group, $x \in S$, and n a nonnegative integer. In accord with our multiplicative notation we define x^n as we did in Chapter 0 and prove in the same fashion the familiar laws on exponents. We define $x^{-n} = (x^{-1})^n$, and it follows easily that the laws on exponents hold for all integers. As we show in the subsequent sections, the set $\{x^n : n \text{ an integer}\}$ plays an important role in the study of a group. The set is a group itself which we shall later call a cyclic subgroup of G.

For abelian groups $(xy)^2 = x^2y^2$ but if the group is not abelian it may happen that $(xy)^2 \neq x^2y^2$. In Example 9 we have that $(R \circ A)^2 \neq R^2 \circ A^2$. A general and more precise statement is given in Problem 6 of Exercise 2.

Theorem 3. Let G be a group and let $g \in G$. If $g^r = g^s$ for two distinct integers r and s then there is a positive integer m such that

(1) $g^m = 1$ and if $0 \leq i < j < m$ then $g^i \neq g^j$.
(2) If $g^t = 1$ then m divides t.
(3) $\{g^n : n \text{ an integer}\} = \{1, g, g^2, \ldots, g^{m-1}\}$.

PROOF. We may suppose that $r > s$, and from $g^r = g^s$ we conclude that $g^{r-s} = 1$. Thus there is a positive integer t such that $g^t = 1$. We choose for m the smallest positive integer such that $g^m = 1$. Now if $0 \leq i < j < m$ and if $g^i = g^j$, then $g^{j-i} = 1$ and $0 < j - i < m$, contrary to the choice of m. Thus (1) holds. Next suppose $g^t = 1$. From Theorem 0.2 we may write $t = mq + v$ where $0 \leq v < m$. Then $1 = g^t = g^{mq+v} = g^{mq}g^v = (g^m)^q g^v = 1g^v = g^v$.

From the choice of m it cannot be that $0 < v < m$, so it must be that $v = 0$. Thus $m \mid t$ and (2) holds. Now consider g^n. Just as before we have $n = mp + w$ where $0 \le w < m$ and so $g^n = g^w$. This proves (3).

$*$ $*$ $*$

Definition. The number of elements in a group shall be called its *order*. We shall write $|G|$ for the order of the group G. G is called finite or infinite as its order is finite or infinite.

A device first introduced by Arthur Cayley (1821–1895) gives a handy way of considering a group. A table displaying the group operation, now referred to as a Cayley table, is constructed by indexing the rows and the columns of the table by the group elements. See Figure 3. The element appearing in the yth row and the xth column is the element yx.

	a	b	c	$\dots$	x	$\dots$
a						
b						
c						
$\vdots$						
y					z	Here $z = yx$
$\vdots$						

Figure 3

Such a table has many interesting features. One is that it is a latin square— each element appears exactly once in each row and column. This is a direct consequence of Theorem 1. If the same ordering is used for the columns as for the rows, the sequence along the main diagonal from upper left-hand corner to lower right-hand corner are the squares a^2. By Lemma 1, and Lemma 2 for one such diagonal entry, $a^2 = a$. This is the identity, and it is customary to make it the index of the first row and column. If $ab = ba$, for all a and b in S, then the table will be symmetric about the main diagonal, and conversely.

These properties can be used to write down the group tables for groups of low order. Let us use this to investigate the possibilities for a group of order 3. If such a group exists we call the elements e, a, and b, letting e be the identity. Since a appears in the ath row, there are two possibilities for aa and ab. Either

$aa = b$ or $aa = e$. In the latter case as Figure 4a shows, b would appear twice in the bth column, hence the ath row must be a, b, e. Then the bth row is determined by the latin square property to be b, e, a. Thus, if there is a group with three elements it must look like Figure 4b.

	e	a	b
e	e	a	b
a	a		
b	b		

Figure 4a

	e	a	b
e	e	a	b
a	a	b	e
b	b	e	a

Figure 4b

It is easy to see that axioms G2 and G3 hold. It is not so easy to verify associativity. Formally we must verify that $(xy)z = x(yz)$ for all choices of x, y, and z from e, a, and b. Thus 27 equations must be checked. It is easy to see that if any of x, y, or z are e, then the associative law does hold. Hence there are only 8 critical equations to be checked. However, the table is symmetric about the main diagonal. Thus if we have verified $x(yz) = (xy)z$, we have also $(zy)x = z(yx)$. Hence only six crucial tests remain:

$$a(aa) = (aa)a, \qquad b(bb) = (bb)b$$
$$a(ba) = (ab)a, \qquad b(ab) = (ba)b$$
$$a(bb) = (ab)b, \qquad a(ab) = (aa)b.$$

As a consequence of these arguments, there is one and only one possibility for a Cayley table of a group of three elements. Different sets of three elements will constitute different groups, however, the Cayley table shows that the two groups will behave alike.

EXERCISE 2

1. Write out the Cayley tables for the group of symmetries of the triangle and the square.

2. Let $\langle G, \circ \rangle$ be a group with identity e. Show that if $x^2 = x \circ x = e$ for all x in G, then the group is abelian.

3. Let S be a nonempty set on which an associative binary operation $(\circ)$ has been defined. Show that if, for all pairs c, d in S there are elements a and b such that

$$a \circ c = d \quad \text{and} \quad c \circ b = d,$$

then $\langle S, \circ \rangle$ is a group.

4. Let S be the set of ordered pairs of integers. Let a binary operation $(\circ)$ be defined on S as follows:

$$(a, b) \circ (c, d) = (a + d, b + d)$$

Show that $(\circ)$ is associative. Find an ordered pair ε which is a right identity and such that for all $\alpha \in S$, there is an α^* such that $\alpha^* \circ \alpha = \varepsilon$. Prove that $\langle S, \circ \rangle$ is not a group. This exercise shows that the assumption of a right identity and a left inverse for an associative binary operation is not equivalent to the group axioms.

5. Are the following group tables?

	e	a	b	c	d
e	e	a	b	c	d
a	a	e	c	d	b
b	b	d	e	a	c
c	c	b	d	e	a
d	d	c	a	b	e

	e	a	b	c	d	f
e	e	a	b	c	d	f
a	a	b	c	d	f	e
b	b	c	e	f	a	d
c	c	d	f	e	b	a
d	d	f	a	b	e	c
f	f	e	d	a	c	b

6. Let S be a set on which an associative binary operation $(\circ)$ has been defined which satisfies the following cancellation law: Whenever $x \circ a = x \circ b$ or $a \circ x = b \circ x$ then $a = b$. Show for all (ordered) pairs of elements a, b in S

$$a \circ b = b \circ a \quad \text{if and only if} \quad (a \circ b)^2 = a^2 \circ b^2.$$

7. Give an example of a set S and an operation $(\circ)$ which satisfies the hypothesis of Problem 6 but is not a group.

8. In a group $\langle G, \circ \rangle$, for elements x and y, show that $(x^{-1} \circ y \circ x)^k = x^{-1} \circ y \circ x$ if and only if $y^k = y$.

1.5. ISOMORPHISM

Let us review the argument about the Cayley table for a group of three elements. It began by supposing that a group consisting of exactly three elements existed whose elements, without loss of generality, were called e, a, b. Again without loss of generality the identity was denoted by e. Now there are many distinct groups of three elements, depending on the set of elements considered. However, in the above discussion all examples were treated simultaneously by giving the names e, a, b to the elements of the group. We found that only one possibility existed for the multiplication table and that in fact it was a group. We really established that the behavior of all groups of three elements is identical. In general, we shall call such groups *isomorphic*. This now becomes a technical term which is made precise by the following definition:

Definition. Let $\langle S, \circ \rangle$ and $\langle T, * \rangle$ be two groups. These groups are isomorphic if

   (1) A one-to-one mapping φ from S onto T can be defined so that
   (2) $\varphi(g \circ h) = \varphi(g) * \varphi(h)$, for all $g, h \in S$.

We write $S \cong T$ if S and T are isomorphic groups. We call a mapping $\varphi : S \to T$ an isomorphism if (1) and (2) hold.

Requirement (1) assures that S and T have the same order. This is surely necessary if S and T are to behave alike as groups. Requirement (2) states that if we look at the two tables, matching the elements according to φ, then the tables are exactly alike. In short, if we were to change the table for the group S by relabeling the elements according to φ, then we would obtain the table for the group T. If (2) holds for a function φ, we say that φ *preserves* the group operation.

Example 12. Let S be the group of positive real numbers in which the group operation is ordinary multiplication. Let T be the group of all real numbers in which the group operation is addition. Then $\varphi(x) = \log x$ is a 1–1 correspondence and indeed if $\varphi(y) = \log y$, then $\varphi(xy) = \log xy = \log x + \log y$. Thus φ is an isomorphism.

Example 13. Let G be the group of all integers under addition. Let H be the group of all even integers under addition. Then $\varphi(x) = 2x$ is a 1–1 correspondence and $\varphi(x + y) = 2(x + y) = 2x + 2y$.

Example 14. Let S be the group of all real numbers under addition. Let T be the group of positive real numbers under multiplication. The correspondence $\varphi(x) = 2^{x-1}$ is a 1–1 correspondence of S onto T, but it does not yield an isomorphism because $\varphi(1) = 1$ and $\varphi(2) = 2$, yet $\varphi(1 + 2) = \varphi(3) = 4$, while $\varphi(1) \cdot \varphi(2) = 1 \cdot 2 = 2 \neq 4$.

Example 15. Let three groups be given by their Cayley tables:

1.

	e	a	b	c
e	e	a	b	c
a	a	e	c	b
b	b	c	a	e
c	c	b	e	a

2.

	e	a	b	c
e	e	a	b	c
a	a	e	c	b
b	b	c	e	a
c	c	b	a	e

3.

	e	a	b	c
e	e	a	b	c
a	a	c	e	b
b	b	e	c	a
c	c	b	a	e

Each of these tables does represent a group and in each e is the identity. Tables 1 and 2 are not isomorphic because in Table 2, $x^2 = e$ for all x, while in Table 1 $b^2 \neq e$. On the other hand Tables 1 and 3 are isomorphic under $\varphi(e) = e$, $\varphi(a) = c$, $\varphi(b) = b$, and $\varphi(c) = a$.

We shall see in Problem 6 of Exercise 3 that any group with exactly 4 elements is isomorphic with either the group with Table 1 or the group with Table 2. The first is called a cyclic group since its elements may be written e, b, $b^2(=a)$, $b^3(=c)$. The second is called simply the "four-group." Every element satisfies the relation $x^2 = e$. Both groups are abelian.

Theorem 4. If φ is an isomorphism from the group $\langle G, \circ \rangle$ onto the group $\langle H, * \rangle$ then φ maps the identity of G onto the identity of H and $\varphi(a^{-1}) = \varphi(a)^{-1}$ for all $a \in G$.

PROOF. Let $\varphi(e) = f$. Since $e \circ e = e$, it follows that $\varphi(e \circ e) = \varphi(e) = \varphi(e) * \varphi(e)$, or that $f * f = f$. By Lemma 1 it follows that f is the identity of $\langle H, * \rangle$. Next, suppose that $\varphi(g) = h$ and that $\varphi(g^{-1}) = k$. As $\varphi(g \circ g^{-1}) = \varphi(e) = f$, it follows that $h * k = f$. Since inverses are unique in $\langle H, * \rangle$, it must be that $k = h^{-1}$.

In Example 12, the multiplicative identity of S is 1 and it corresponds to the additive identity 0 of T, and $1/x$ corresponds to the additive inverse $-\log x$ in T. On the other hand in Example 14, $\varphi(0) = \frac{1}{2} \neq 1$.

EXERCISE 3

1. Groups arise in many different situations. Find two different mathematical situations in which a group of order 3 is found.

2. Describe an infinite class of distinct groups each of which is isomorphic to the integers under addition.

3. Is the additive group of integers isomorphic with the additive group of all rational numbers?

4. Let $\langle S, \circ \rangle$ be a group. Let T be a set on which a binary $(*)$ has been defined. Suppose that S can be mapped onto T in a 1–1 fashion by φ so that $\varphi(a \circ b) = \varphi(a) * \varphi(b)$. Show that $\langle T, * \rangle$ is a group.

5. Let S be the set of integers. Prove that $\langle S, \circ \rangle$ is a group where $(\circ)$ is defined,

$$a \circ b = a + b - 1,$$

by finding a set of rational numbers T such that $\langle T, + \rangle$ is a group isomorphic to $\langle S, \circ \rangle$.

6. Show that there are at most two nonisomorphic groups of order 4 by constructing the possible Cayley tables.

1.6. PERMUTATION GROUPS

We have seen that the group of symmetries of the equilateral triangle can be described by listing the effect of each group element on the vertices of the triangle. An element of this group effects a permutation of the vertices. We shall now consider groups of permutations.

✳***Definition.*** Let S be a set of elements. A permutation π on the set S is a 1–1 mapping from S onto itself.

A permutation is a function; the terminology is historical and once was usually reserved for finite sets. We shall often denote the permutation π by the scheme of listing the elements of S on two rows. Immediately below an element of the top row we write its image under π:

$$\pi = \begin{pmatrix} \ldots \ldots a \ldots \\ \ldots \pi(a) \ldots \end{pmatrix}$$

Example 16. If S is the set of all integers, then the mapping $\pi(x) = 2 + x$ is a permutation.

Example 17. If S is the set of positive integers, then the mapping described by $\pi(2x - 1) = 2x$ and $\pi(2x) = 2x - 1$ is a permutation.

$$\pi : \begin{pmatrix} 1 & 2 & 3 & 4 & 5 & 6 & \ldots \\ 2 & 1 & 4 & 3 & 6 & 5 & \ldots \end{pmatrix}.$$

Example 18. Let G be a group. Let $a \in G$. The mapping $\pi_a : G \to G$ defined by

$$\pi_a(x) = ax$$

is a permutation. To prove this we first note that π_a is a function, and if $ax = ay$, then $x = y$ by the Corollary to Theorem 1. Hence the mapping is 1–1. Furthermore, the mapping is onto, since by Theorem 1, the equation $ax = b$ has a solution c and so $\pi_a(c) = b$.

> **Theorem 5.** The set of all permutations on a set S forms a group under the operation of composition.

PROOF. We know from Chapter 0 that the composition of two permutations ρ and π of S is a mapping from S into S. $\rho\pi$ is a 1–1 mapping since if $\rho(\pi(x)) = \rho(\pi(y))$, then $\pi(x) = \pi(y)$ as ρ is a 1–1 mapping. But then $x = y$ as π is a 1–1 mapping. Furthermore the mapping is onto, for if $b \in S$, then for some $c \in S$, $\rho(c) = b$. But then for some $d \in S$, $\pi(d) = c$. Hence $\rho\pi(d) = \rho(c) = b$ and so $\rho\pi$ is a permutation. By Theorem 0.7, the group operation is associative.

The permutation ι, where $\iota(x) = x$ for all $x \in S$, is the identity. To obtain the inverse of a permutation π, let π^{-1} be the mapping defined as follows: $\pi^{-1}(x) = y$ if and only if $\pi(y) = x$. We have only to verify that this gives a mapping which is a permutation. Since π is a 1–1 mapping from S onto S, the definition yields a bona fide mapping. If $\pi^{-1}(x) = \pi^{-1}(y) = z$, then $\pi(z) = x$ and $\pi(z) = y$, by definition; and since π is a mapping, $x = y$. Hence π^{-1} is 1–1. Because π is onto, π^{-1} is onto also, for if $b \in S$, let $\pi(b) = c$. Then it follows that $\pi^{-1}(c) = b$. Clearly $\pi(\pi^{-1})$ is the identity permutation. Thus all the group axioms have been verified and the proof is complete.

*   *   *

This group is called the full symmetric group on S. It should be easy to see that if S and T are sets which can be put into 1–1 correspondence, then the full symmetric groups on S and T are isomorphic. If S has n elements, the full symmetric group on S is denoted S_n.

Definition. A permutation π on a set S is said to *fix* x $(x \in S)$ if $\pi(x) = x$ and to *move* x if $\pi(x) \neq x$.

Example 19. The full symmetric group S_3 on the three symbols 1, 2, 3 consists of the six permutations:

$$J = \begin{pmatrix} 1 & 2 & 3 \\ 1 & 2 & 3 \end{pmatrix} \qquad C = \begin{pmatrix} 1 & 2 & 3 \\ 2 & 1 & 3 \end{pmatrix}$$

$$A = \begin{pmatrix} 1 & 2 & 3 \\ 1 & 3 & 2 \end{pmatrix} \qquad R = \begin{pmatrix} 1 & 2 & 3 \\ 2 & 3 & 1 \end{pmatrix}$$

$$B = \begin{pmatrix} 1 & 2 & 3 \\ 3 & 2 & 1 \end{pmatrix} \qquad S = \begin{pmatrix} 1 & 2 & 3 \\ 3 & 1 & 2 \end{pmatrix}$$

This group is isomorphic to the group of symmetries of the equilateral triangle.

The order of S_n is $n!$ This is easy to see as follows: Let the elements of S be denoted by the numerals $1, 2, \ldots, n$. Consider a permutation π of the elements of S. Here, $\pi(1)$ can be chosen from among n symbols; $\pi(2)$ can then be chosen as any of the $(n - 1)$ remaining symbols; $\pi(3)$ can be chosen from among any of the $(n - 2)$ remaining symbols, and so on. For $\pi(n)$ there is no choice, for by now all but one symbol have been assigned. Hence there are a total of $n \cdot (n - 1) \cdot (n - 2) \cdot \; \cdots \; \cdot 1 = n!$ possible permutations.

The next theorem, which was first proved by Cayley, states that every group is isomorphic to a group of permutations on some set. In general this group of permutations will not be the full symmetric group. The motivation for the proof of the theorem is the observation made in Example 18—that the mapping $\pi(x) = ax$ is a permutation of the group elements.

> **Theorem 6** (*Representation Theorem for Groups*). If G is a group then G is isomorphic to a group of permutations.

PROOF. We must find a set S and on it define suitable permutations so that the theorem holds. This is a "bootstraps" operation; we must construct the set S from what we are given, and all we are given is the group G. We have seen in Example 18 that the mapping π_a, $\pi_a(x) = ax$ is a permutation of the group elements. Moreover it is clear that the permutation π_b is different from π_a if and only if $a \neq b$ since π_a sends the identity of G into a while π_b sends it into b. Let $H = \{\pi_a : a \in G\}$. We shall show that H is a group under the natural product of permutations, and the mapping $\Phi : G \to H$ defined by $\Phi(a) = \pi_a$ is a group isomorphism. As we have just observed, Φ is a 1–1 mapping. We shall now show that Φ preserves the group operation.

Now let a and b be elements of G. Under Φ they correspond to permutations π_a and π_b. We must show that the permutation to which the group element ab corresponds is in fact $\pi_a\pi_b$. That is, we must show that $\pi_{ab} = \pi_a\pi_b$. (The symbol (=) here means equality of permutations.) Now $\pi_{ab}(x) = (ab)x$ by definition. On the other hand $\pi_a\pi_b(x) = \pi_a(\pi_b(x)) = \pi_a(bx) = a(bx)$. Since the associative law holds in G, the equality is proved. Note that this also proves that the set of permutations under consideration is closed under composition of permutations. It also shows that $(\pi_a)^{-1} = \pi_{a^{-1}}$ since $\pi_a\pi_{a^{-1}} = \pi_e = \iota$. Hence the set of permutations π on the group elements of the form $\pi(x) = ax$ is a group and is in fact isomorphic to the group G itself.

* * *

Example 20. For the group of three elements e, a, b we have

$$\pi_e : \begin{pmatrix} e & a & b \\ e & a & b \end{pmatrix}$$

$$\pi_a : \begin{pmatrix} e & a & b \\ a & b & e \end{pmatrix} \quad \text{and}$$

$$\pi_b : \begin{pmatrix} e & a & b \\ b & e & a \end{pmatrix}$$

	π_e	π_a	π_b
π_e	π_e	π_a	π_b
π_a	π_a	π_b	π_e
π_b	π_b	π_e	π_a

Note that the table "looks" exactly like the table for the group of three elements of Figure 4b.

Theorem 6 is an example of a "representation" theorem. This theorem tells how an abstract group may be represented in concrete terms; it says in effect that to study all groups it suffices to study all groups of permutations. In fact, in the early years of their investigation, groups were studied in this way. By regarding group elements as permutations, a powerful tool for research is developed. On the other hand, some proofs can be handled more easily from the abstract point of view. From the point of view expressed in the Prologue, a representation theorem for an abstract algebra means that the process of abstraction has come full circle. Whatever the motivation was for studying the algebraic system, a representation theorem prescribes a way to build a concrete model of all such systems.

EXERCISE 4

1. Write out a table of the 24 permutations on the symbols 1, 2, 3, 4. For each permutation π find the least positive integer n such that $\pi^n = \iota$. This table will be of use later as a source of examples.

The following exercises develop a useful way of writing and calculating with permutations.

Definition. Let π be a permutation on a set S. Let $(\overset{\pi}{\sim})$ be a relation on S defined by

$$a \overset{\pi}{\sim} b \text{ if and only if there is an integer } n \text{ such that } \pi^n(a) = b.$$

2. Show that for every permutation π, $(\overset{\pi}{\sim})$ is an equivalence relation. The equivalence classes are called the *orbits* of S under π.

Example 21. $\begin{pmatrix} 1234567 \\ 7241653 \end{pmatrix}$ has orbits $(1, 7, 3, 4)$, $(5, 6)$, and (2). Each orbit can be pictured as points on a circle (see Figure 5).

3. Find the orbits of the following permutations.

1. $\begin{pmatrix} 1 & 2 & 3 & 4 \\ 2 & 3 & 4 & 1 \end{pmatrix}$ 2. $\begin{pmatrix} 1 & 2 & 3 & 4 \\ 4 & 3 & 2 & 1 \end{pmatrix}$

3. $\begin{pmatrix} 1 & 2 & 3 & 4 \\ 3 & 4 & 2 & 1 \end{pmatrix}$ 4. $\begin{pmatrix} 1 & 2 & 3 & 4 \\ 3 & 2 & 1 & 4 \end{pmatrix}$

5. $\begin{pmatrix} 1 & 2 & 3 & 4 \\ 1 & 4 & 2 & 3 \end{pmatrix}$ 6. $\begin{pmatrix} 1 & 2 & 3 & 4 \\ 3 & 4 & 1 & 2 \end{pmatrix}$

7. $\begin{pmatrix} 1 & 2 & 3 & 4 \\ 1 & 2 & 3 & 4 \end{pmatrix}$ 8. $\begin{pmatrix} 1 & 2 & 3 & 4 & 5 \\ 4 & 5 & 1 & 3 & 2 \end{pmatrix}$

Definition. A permutation π on a set S is called a *cycle* if S has at most one orbit containing more than one element. If a cycle moves exactly k elements it is called a *k-cycle*. 2-cycles are called transpositions.

4. Which of the permutations in Problem 3 are cycles? Which are transpositions?

5. Show that if π is a permutation that moves only a finite number of symbols, then π is a cycle if and only if we can order the symbols moved $x_1, \ldots, x_n$ so that $\pi(x_i) = x_{i+1}$ for $i = 1, \ldots, n-1$ and $\pi(x_n) = x_1$. In this case we write $\pi = (x_1, \ldots, x_n)$. If π moves an infinite number of symbols, then π is a cycle if and only if we can order the symbols moved $\ldots x_{-1}, x_0, x_1, \ldots$ so that

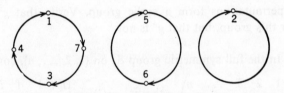

Figure 5

$\pi(x_i) = x_{i+1}$ for all integers i. In this case we write $\pi = (\ldots x_{-1}, x_0, x_1, \ldots)$. Write those permutations in Problem 3 that are cycles in the form $(x_1, \ldots, x_n)$.

6. Let A be an orbit of S under π. Show that the permutation π_A on S defined by

$$\pi_A(x) = \begin{cases} \pi(x) & \text{if } x \in A \\ x & \text{if } x \notin A \end{cases}$$

is a cycle.

7. Let π have orbits A and B. Show that $\pi_A \pi_B = \pi_B \pi_A$.

8. Let π be a permutation on S with only a finite number of orbits $A_1, \ldots, A_n$. Show that $\pi = \pi_{A_1} \pi_{A_2} \ldots \pi_{A_n}$.

9. Write the following permutations as the product of disjoint cycles:

1. $\begin{pmatrix} 1 & 2 & 3 \\ 1 & 3 & 2 \end{pmatrix}$

2. $\begin{pmatrix} 1 & 2 & 3 & 4 & 5 & 6 \\ 3 & 2 & 1 & 5 & 4 & 6 \end{pmatrix}$

3. $\begin{pmatrix} 1 & 2 & 3 & 4 \\ 2 & 1 & 4 & 3 \end{pmatrix}$

4. $\begin{pmatrix} 1 & 2 & 3 & 4 & 5 & 6 \\ 6 & 5 & 2 & 1 & 3 & 4 \end{pmatrix}$

5. $\begin{pmatrix} 1 & 2 & 3 & 4 & 5 & 6 & 7 & 8 \\ 4 & 1 & 8 & 6 & 5 & 2 & 3 & 7 \end{pmatrix}$

6. $\begin{pmatrix} a & b & c & d & e & f & g \\ b & a & d & c & e & g & f \end{pmatrix}$

10. Show that for a cycle $(x_1, \ldots, x_n)$ and any permutation π on a set of symbols including $x_1, \ldots, x_n$ the product $\pi(x_1, \ldots, x_n)\pi^{-1} = (\pi(x_1), \ldots, \pi(x_n))$.

1.7. CYCLIC GROUPS

Definition — A group G is called *cyclic* if there exists $g \in G$ such that for every $x \in G$ there is an integer n such that $g^n = x$. Here, g is called a *generator* for G, and G is denoted $\langle g \rangle$.

Example 22. In the full symmetric group S_4 on $\{1, 2, 3, 4\}$, consider the permutations

$$g = \begin{pmatrix} 1 & 2 & 3 & 4 \\ 2 & 3 & 4 & 1 \end{pmatrix} \qquad g^2 = \begin{pmatrix} 1 & 2 & 3 & 4 \\ 3 & 4 & 1 & 2 \end{pmatrix}$$

$$g^3 = \begin{pmatrix} 1 & 2 & 3 & 4 \\ 4 & 1 & 2 & 3 \end{pmatrix} \qquad g^0 = g^4 = \begin{pmatrix} 1 & 2 & 3 & 4 \\ 1 & 2 & 3 & 4 \end{pmatrix} = \text{identity}.$$

These four permutations form a cyclic group. Verify that g^3 is another generator for this group, but that g^2 is not.

Example 23. In the full symmetric group S_n on $\{1, 2, \ldots, n\}$, consider

$$g = \begin{pmatrix} 1 & 2 & 3 & \ldots & n \\ 2 & 3 & 4 & \ldots & 1 \end{pmatrix}, \quad \text{that is,} \quad g(i) = \begin{cases} i + 1 & \text{if } i \neq n \\ 1 & \text{if } i = n \end{cases}.$$

It is easy to verify that $g, g^2, \ldots, g^{n-1}, g^n$ are distinct and that g^n is the identity permutation. Indeed,

$$g^i = \begin{pmatrix} 1 & 2 & 3 & \cdots & n \\ 1+i & 2+i & 3+i & \cdots & i \end{pmatrix}, \quad \text{that is,}$$

$$g(k) = \begin{cases} k+i & \text{if } 1 \le k \le n-i \\ (k+i)-n & \text{if } n-i < k \le n \end{cases}.$$

There is a nice geometric representation of this group. Let N denote a regular n-sided polygon. Number the position of the vertices, in a clockwise fashion, $1, 2, 3, \ldots, n$ as shown in Figure 6. Let g be a clockwise rotation of $2\pi/n$ radians. Clearly this results in a symmetry of N described by the permutation g given above.

As a consequence of Example 23, we have proved the following existence theorem.

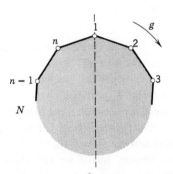

Figure 6

Theorem 7. For every integer n there is a cyclic group with n distinct elements.

Example 24. (*Infinite Cyclic Group*). We define a permutation on integers as follows:

$$g = \begin{pmatrix} \cdots & -2 & -1 & 0 & 1 & 2 & \cdots \\ \cdots & -1 & 0 & 1 & 2 & 3 & \cdots \end{pmatrix}: \text{ that is, } g(i) = i+1 \text{ for all } i.$$

This is clearly a permutation and we calculate that $g^k(i) = k + i$. Thus $g^h = g^k$ if and only if $h = k$. Moreover the set of all powers $\{g, g^2, \ldots; g^0; g^{-1}, g^{-2}, \ldots\}$ forms an infinite group generated by g.

Note that a cyclic group seems to be completely determined once we are given the generator g and the number of distinct elements in the group.

Theorem 8. If $G = \langle g \rangle$ is an infinite cyclic group then $g^r = g^s$ implies that $r = s$. If $G = \langle g \rangle$ is a finite cyclic group with m elements then

1. $g^m = 1$ and if $0 \le i < j < m$ then $g^i \ne g^j$
2. $G = \{1, g, \ldots, g^{m-1}\}$.

PROOF. If $g^r = g^s$ with $r \ne s$, then Theorem 3 implies that G is finite. If G is finite with m elements and if, for some i and j such that $0 \le i < j < m$, we have $g^i = g^j$, then Theorem 3 would imply that G had fewer than m elements. Thus $G = \{1, g, \ldots, g^{m-1}\}$, and so, in particular, $g^m = g^i$ for some i such that $0 \le i < m$. It follows that $g^{m-i} = 1$ and if $i > 0$ then we should have a contradition to the distinctness of the elements $1, g, \ldots, g^{m-1}$, which we have just established.

*   *   *

Theorem 9. Any two cyclic groups with the same number of elements are isomorphic.

PROOF. Let $G = \langle g \rangle$ and $H = \langle h \rangle$ be two cyclic groups with the same number of elements. The most natural way to set up the isomorphism would be to define

$$\varphi(g^n) = h^n.$$

Note that every element of H appears as the image of an element of G, and moreover $\varphi(g^n g^m) = \varphi(g^{n+m}) = h^{n+m} = \varphi(g^n)\varphi(g^m)$. Thus φ must be an isomorphism! But we have proved too much, for our argument has not yet used the hypothesis that G and H have the same number of elements. Indeed we seem to have proved that any two cyclic groups are isomorphic!

The argument fails for we have not established that φ is a function; we have not yet shown that if $g^r = g^s$ then $h^r = h^s$, nor have we shown that φ is one-to-one, but if we can show these we shall have shown that φ is a 1–1 mapping from G onto H which preserves the group operation.

To show that φ is a function we must show that $g^r = g^s$ implies that $h^r = h^s$. If G is infinite, Theorem 8 shows that $r = s$ and thus that $h^r = h^s$. Suppose G and H were finite with m elements. From Theorem 8 we have that $g^m = 1$ and $h^m = 1$. Now, if $g^r = g^s$, then from Theorem 3 it follows that $m \mid r - s$ since from Theorem 8 it is clear that m is the least-positive integer such that $g^m = 1$. Thus $r = mq + s$, and hence $h^r = h^{mq}h^s = 1h^s = h^s$. Thus φ is a function from G onto H, and by interchanging the roles of g and h in the preceding argument, it follows that φ is 1–1. This completes the proof that φ is an isomorphism.

1.8.   DIHEDRAL GROUPS

The class consisting of those groups which are the group of symmetries of a regular n-sided polygon are called the dihedral groups. We have studied this group for the equilateral triangle in Example 9 and for the square in Problem 1 of Exercise 1.

For convenience we orient the regular n-gon as in Figure 6 by locating a vertex at the top whose position we label 1, and continuing, we number the positions of the other vertices in clockwise order. First let us count the number of distinct symmetries of the n-gon. Observe that a symmetry σ is completely determined (1) by the position of the image, $\sigma(1)$, of the vertex at 1 under the symmetry, and (2) by the position of the image, $\sigma(2)$, of the vertex at 2 relative to $\sigma(1)$—whether it is clockwise or counterclockwise of

$\sigma(1)$. There are n choices for the vertex at 1 and for each choice, there are two choices for the image of the vertex at 2. Thus there are $2n$ symmetries of the regular n-gon.

We denote a clockwise rotation of $2\pi/n$ radians by R and a reflection about the vertical diameter through the vertex at 1 by A as is indicated in Figure 7. From what we have just observed any symmetry can be obtained by

1. A rotation of $2\pi k/n$ radians. The corresponding group element is R^k where $0 \le k < n$.

2. A reflection or no reflection about the vertical diameter. The corresponding group element is denoted A^e where $e = 1$ or $e = 0$.

A typical situation is pictured in Figure 8, where we have labeled the vertices $\alpha, \beta, \gamma, \delta, \ldots$, to show the effect of the symmetries. Remember the integers $1, 2, \ldots, n$ denote the positions of the vertices, not the vertices themselves. If we denote the identity symmetry by J, we have the relations

$$R^n = J = A^2 \quad \text{and} \quad RA = AR^{-1}.$$

Figure 7

This last relation takes only a bit of visualization to verify, and it is shown in Figure 9.

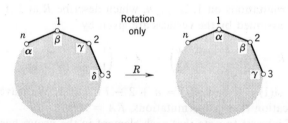

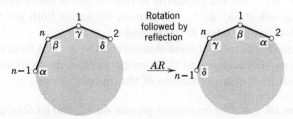

Figure 8

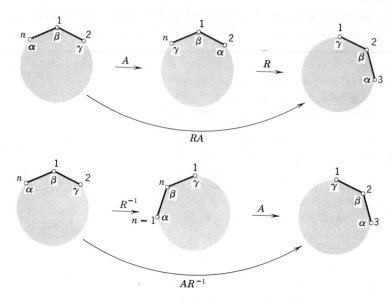

Figure 9

From the relation $RA = AR^{-1}$ we have $R^k A = AR^{-k}$. This follows after k applications of the given relation:

$$R^k A = \underbrace{R \ldots RA}_{k} = \underbrace{R \ldots RAR^{-1}}_{k-1} = \ldots = AR^{-k}.$$

The permutations on $1, 2, \ldots, n$, which describe R and A in terms of the positions assumed by the vertices are given by

$$R = \begin{pmatrix} 1 & 2 & \ldots & n \\ 2 & 3 & \ldots & 1 \end{pmatrix} \qquad A = \begin{pmatrix} 1 & 2 & 3 & \ldots & n \\ 1 & n & (n-1) & \ldots & 2 \end{pmatrix}.$$

We have $A(1) = 1$ and $A(i) = n + 2 - i$ if $i \neq 1$. We leave as an exercise the verification that, as permutations, $RA = AR^{-1}$.

It is of interest to note that each element in the group has the form $R^k A^e$ where $0 \leq k < n$ and $0 \leq e < 2$. There are precisely $2n$ elements of this form and we prove that all must be distinct. If $R^k A^e = R^h A^f$, then we should have that $R^{k-h} = A^{f-e}$. But the geometric import of this is that a rotation, R^{k-h}, is equal to a reflection, A^{f-e}. This cannot be unless both are the identity permutation—that is, unless $R^k = R^h$ and $A^f = A^e$.

Actually the distinctness of these elements can be derived from the relations given above without recourse to the geometry, and in doing so we can obtain a complete abstract characterization of the dihedral group.

Theorem 10. Let n be an integer greater than 2 and let G be a group containing elements r and a such that

Definition –
Dihedral
Group

1. $r^n = a^2 = 1$ and $r^k \neq 1$ if $0 < k < n$, and $a \neq 1$.
2. $ra = ar^{-1}$.

Then G contains at least $2n$ elements of the form $r^k a^e$ where $0 \leq k < n$ and $e = 0$ or 1. The multiplication rule for these elements is given by

3. $(r^k a^e)(r^h a^f) = \begin{cases} r^{k+h} a^f & \text{if } e = 0 \\ r^{k-h} a^{e+f} & \text{if } e = 1. \end{cases}$

PROOF. As was shown above the relations

4. $r^h a = ar^{-h}$ (or equivalently $r^{-h} a = ar^h$)

follow quite formally from h applications of relation 2. Relation 4 suffices to prove the multiplication law (relation 3) of the theorem. Relation 3 is trivial if $e = 0$. If $e = 1$ then

$$(r^k a^e)(r^h a^f) = r^k(a^e r^h)a^f = r^k(r^{-h} a^e)a^f = r^{k-h} a^{e+f}.$$

Relation 3 shows that the set $\{r^k a^e : 0 \leq k < n, e = 0 \text{ or } 1\}$ is closed under multiplication and contains the identity as $1 = r^0 a^0$

Thus to complete the proof we need only show that the $2n$ elements $r^k a^e$ are all distinct. Suppose that $r^k a^e = r^h a^f$. We show first that this implies $r^{k-h} = 1$ and that $a^{e-f} = 1$. In any event we have, by multiplying on the left by r^{-h} and on the right by a^{-f},

$$r^{k-h} a^{e-f} = 1.$$

To simplify notation, let $k - h = x$ and $e - f = y$. We want to show that $r^x a^y = 1$ implies that $r^x = 1$ and $a^y = 1$. If $y = 0$, then we are done. If $y = \pm 1$, then, since $a^2 = 1$, $a^y = a$, and we have $r^x a = 1$ or that $r^x = a$. But then, $ra = rr^x = r^x r = ar$. From relation 2 we have $ra = ar^{-1}$. Hence we can conclude that $r = r^{-1}$ or that $r^2 = 1$. This is a contradiction of the relations (1), since we are assuming that $n > 2$.

Finally relations (1) imply that if $0 \leq k, h < n$, and if $r^{k-h} = 1$, then it must be that $k = h$; similarly $a^{e-f} = 1$ yields $e = f$. Thus the distinctness is proved and the theorem is established.

* * *

Corollary. (*Dihedral groups*) For every integer $n > 2$, there is a group of order $2n$ with properties 1 and 2. This group is unique up to isomorphism.

PROOF. The existence is given by the groups of symmetries of a regular n-sided polygon. The uniqueness is the content of Theorem 10 which gives the precise structure of the group table of such a group.

1.9. SUBGROUPS

We are now going to select subsets of a group that will help us understand the structure of the whole group. We want subsets that reflect some of the properties of the group and yet permit us to localize our investigation of the group. In addition we shall want to be able to state how various subsets interact within the group. For these reasons we must place some restrictions on the subsets selected.

We have seen several instances of subsets of a group which are groups themselves under the operation of the parent group. For example, if $\langle G, \circ \rangle$ is a group and $g \in G$ then $\{g^n : n$ an integer$\}$ is a group under the operation $(\circ)$. Example 22 is a group and is a subset of S_4. The subsets of a group $\langle G, \circ \rangle$ which are groups under $(\circ)$ are natural candidates for special study since they appear to have a chance of satisfying the properties we hold desirable.

Definition. A nonempty subset S of a group $\langle G, \circ \rangle$ is called a *subgroup* of G if S is closed under $(\circ)$ and if $\langle S, \circ \rangle$ is a group.

Lemma 6. A nonempty subset S of a group $\langle G, \circ \rangle$ is a subgroup if and only if the following two conditions hold:

1. Whenever $a \in S$ and $b \in S$, then $a \circ b \in S$.
2   Whenever $a \in S$, then $a^{-1} \in S$ also.

Here the inverse is the inverse existing in G.

PROOF. First, suppose that S is a subgroup of G. (1) holds for it is but a restatement of the condition that S is closed under $(\circ)$. Since $\langle S, \circ \rangle$ is a group it has an identity that must satisfy $x^2 = x$. However, as Lemmas 1 and 2 showed, such an element must be the identity of G. Since the identity of S is the identity of G, it now follows from Lemma 5 that the inverse of a in S is the inverse of a in G, which we have denoted by a^{-1}. Thus (2) holds.

Conversely, suppose that (1) and (2) hold for a nonempty subset S of G. From (1) it follows that S is closed under $(\circ)$. We show that $1 \in S$. As S is nonempty, let $a \in S$. Then by (2) $a^{-1} \in S$, and so, by (1), $a \circ a^{-1} = 1 \in S$. Since the associative law holds for all of G, it holds automatically on the subset S. Thus all the group axioms are verified for S under the operation $(\circ)$.

* * *

Lemma 7. If G is a finite group then (2) is implied by (1).

PROOF. Since G is finite, the elements $a, a^2, a^3, \ldots,$ are not all distinct. Suppose that $a^r = a^s$ where $r > s$. By cancellation we have $a^{r-s} = 1$, or $a(a^{(r-s)-1}) = 1$. Hence $a^{-1} = a^{(r-s)-1}$.

Thus for finite groups, a nonempty subset is a subgroup if and only if it is closed under the group operation.

Lemma 8. A nonempty subset S of a group G is a subgroup of G if and only if whenever a, b belong to S then ab^{-1} belongs to S.

PROOF. The necessity of this condition is apparent from Lemma 6, combining both (1) and (2). Let us suppose that the condition holds. Then it must be that if $a \in S$, then $aa^{-1} = 1 \in S$. But then, since $a \in S$, it must follow that $1a^{-1} = a^{-1}$ belongs to S. Thus condition (2) holds. Finally, to show closure, suppose that a and b are members of S. Thus it follows that $b^{-1} \in S$. Hence the condition tells us that $a(b^{-1})^{-1} = ab \in S$. Hence condition (1) of Lemma 6 holds and so S must be a subgroup.

Example 25. For any group G, G is itself a subgroup of G. The singleton subset $\{1\}$ is a subgroup, $\langle 1 \rangle$. A <u>subgroup</u> S of G is called _proper_ if $S \neq G$ and $S \neq \langle 1 \rangle$.

Example 26. Let G be the group of vectors in the plane under vector addition (see Example 5). Let $\vec{v}$ be a fixed vector. The subset of vectors consisting of the scalar multiples of $\vec{v}$ form a subgroup S. $S = \{r\vec{v} : r$ is a real number$\}$. This subgroup can be pictured as a line through the origin (see Figure 10).

Example 27. In the <u>full symmetric group</u> S_4 on 1, 2, 3, 4, the following four permutations form a subgroup which is isomorphic to the four-group of Example 15:   All permutations of the group.

$$\iota = \begin{pmatrix} 1234 \\ 1234 \end{pmatrix}; \quad (12)(34) = \begin{pmatrix} 1234 \\ 2143 \end{pmatrix}; \quad (13)(24) = \begin{pmatrix} 1234 \\ 3412 \end{pmatrix}; \quad (14)(23) = \begin{pmatrix} 1234 \\ 4321 \end{pmatrix}.$$

Example 28. If $g \in G$, the set of powers $\langle g \rangle = \{g^n : n$ an integer$\}$ form a subgroup, the cyclic group generated by g.

Definition. The order of an element $g \in G$ shall be the order of $\langle g \rangle$.

Theorem 3 states that if $g^t = 1$ then t is divisible by the order of g, and that the order of g is the least-positive integer m such that $g^m = 1$.

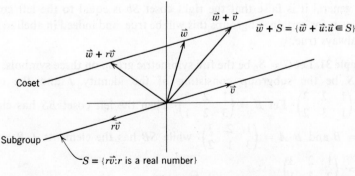

Figure 10

The notion of a subgroup carries with it, in a very natural way, an equivalence relation.

> **~ Theorem 11.** If S is a subgroup of G, then the relation given by $a \ R \ b$ if and only if $ab^{-1} \in S$ is an equivalence relation.

PROOF. We have $a \ R \ a$ since $aa^{-1} \in S$. If $a \ R \ b$, then $ab^{-1} \in S$ and so $(ab^{-1})^{-1} \in S$. Hence $(ab^{-1})^{-1} = ba^{-1} \in S$. Hence $b \ R \ a$. If $a \ R \ b$ and $b \ R \ c$, then $ab^{-1} \in S$ and $bc^{-1} \in S$. Hence $(ab^{-1})(bc^{-1}) = ac^{-1} \in S$. Thus $a \ R \ c$.

$$* \quad * \quad *$$

The resulting equivalence classes from this equivalence relation are called *right cosets*. We can and do define these in another way.

Definition. Let S be a subgroup of a group G and let $b \in G$. The *right coset* Sb of S in G is the set $Sb = \{sb : s \in S\}$.

$a \in Sb$ if and only if $a \ R \ b$. For if $a \in Sb$, then $a = sb$ for some $s \in S$, and so $s = ab^{-1} \in S$, hence $a \ R \ b$. Conversely, if $a \ R \ b$, then $ab^{-1} \in S$ and so $ab^{-1} = s$, or $a = sb$.

In an analogous way, left cosets are defined $bS = \{bs : s \in S\}$, and similarly the relation L defined by $a \ Lb$ if and only if $a^{-1}b \in S$ is an equivalence relation.

If the group operation is "addition" we shall write a right coset of S in $G = \langle G, + \rangle$ in a more suggestive notation which reflects the group operation:

$$S + b = \{s + b : s \in S\}.$$

Similarly left cosets in additive groups shall be written $b + S$.

Example 29. In the group of vectors in the plane, if S is a subgroup which is a line through the origin as in the example above, then a right coset is $S + \vec{v} = \{\vec{w} : \vec{w} = \vec{s} + \vec{v}, \text{ some } \vec{s} \in S\}$, and the coset $S + \vec{v}$ can be pictured as a line parallel to the line representing the subgroup S (see Figure 10).

Example 30. If S is a subgroup of G then $S = S1 = 1S$ is both a left and right coset of S in G.

In general it is false that the right coset Sb is equal to the left coset bS. However, for certain subgroups this will be true, and indeed in abelian groups it is always true.

Example 31. Let $G = S_3$ be the full symmetric group on three symbols, 1, 2, 3. Let S be the subgroup consisting of the identity J and the element $A = \begin{pmatrix} 1 & 2 & 3 \\ 1 & 3 & 2 \end{pmatrix}$. Let $B = \begin{pmatrix} 1 & 2 & 3 \\ 3 & 2 & 1 \end{pmatrix}$. Then the left coset BS has elements $B \cdot J = B$ and $B \cdot A = \begin{pmatrix} 1 & 2 & 3 \\ 3 & 1 & 2 \end{pmatrix}$, while SB has the elements $J \cdot B = B$ and $A \cdot B = \begin{pmatrix} 1 & 2 & 3 \\ 2 & 3 & 1 \end{pmatrix}$.

Lemma 9. The mapping φ defined by $\varphi(aS) = Sa^{-1}$ is a 1–1 mapping from the left cosets of S in G onto the right cosets of S in G. $\forall\, aS\,,\ \exists\, Sb\, : aS = Sb$

PROOF. We first show that φ is a function. If $aS = bS$ then $b \in aS$, or $b = as$, where $s \in S$. Hence $b^{-1} = s^{-1}a^{-1}$, or $b^{-1} \in Sa^{-1}$. Hence $Sb^{-1} = Sa^{-1}$, and so $\varphi(aS) = \varphi(bS)$. Conversely the same argument shows that if $Sb^{-1} = Sa^{-1}$ then $aS = bS$. The mapping given here is *onto* the set of right cosets since $\varphi(a^{-1}S) = Sa$ under this mapping.

$*\quad*\quad*$

From this lemma we conclude that the number of distinct left cosets is the same as the number of distinct right cosets.

Definition. The number of distinct right (or left) cosets of S in G is called the *index* of S in G, denoted $[G:S]$. Note that $|G| = [G:1]$.

The next theorem, attributed to J. L. Lagrange (1736–1813), is of fundamental importance for it introduces arithmetic relationships into group theory.

Theorem 12. (*Lagrange*). If S is a subgroup of a group G then the order of G is the product of the order of S and the index of S in G, $|G| = |S| \cdot [G:S]$.

PROOF. The equivalence relation of Theorem 6, given by $a \mathrel{R} b$ if and only if $ab^{-1} \in S$, splits G into a set union of disjoint equivalence classes, which we have called right cosets of S. $G = Sa_1 \cup Sa_2 \cup \cdots$.

The elements of S can be mapped onto the right coset Sa by θ_a, where $\theta_a(s) = sa$ if $s \in S$. It is easy to verify that θ_a is a 1–1 mapping from S onto Sa. From this it follows that each coset has as many elements as S. Hence $G = Sa_1 \cup Sa_2 \cup \cdots$ represents G as the disjoint set union of a number of right cosets. Since the number of elements in each coset is $|S|$ and there are $[G:S]$ distinct cosets the theorem follows.

Corollary. If G has finite order, then the order of any $g \in G$ divides $|G|$, and in particular $g^{|G|} = 1$.

PROOF. The order of an element in a group was defined as the order of the cyclic subgroup it generates and so the corollary follows immediately.

$*\quad*\quad*$

The converse of this theorem and the corollary is a matter of interest. In general the converses are false. For an arbitrary divisor of the group there need be no subgroup, hence no element, with that order. An example of this is given in Problem 11 of Exercise 5. However it is true, though we do not prove it in this first chapter on groups, that if p is a *prime* dividing the order of the group, then there is an element of the group whose order is p. More is true—namely that if p^e is any power of the prime p which divides the order of the group, then there is a subgroup of order p^e (see Theorem 9.7).

~Theorem 13. If p is a prime then any group of order p is cyclic.

PROOF. Since G has order p, there is an element $g \neq 1$ in G. Consider the cyclic subgroup $\langle g \rangle$ generated by g. By the theorem of Lagrange, the order of this subgroup must divide p. Since the order is not 1, the order of $\langle g \rangle$ must be p. That is, $\langle g \rangle = G$.

* * *

From Theorem 9 it follows that any two groups of prime order p are isomorphic.

The determination of all subgroups of a group is for most groups a very difficult problem. However it is easy to do this for cyclic groups.

~Theorem 14. Every subgroup of a cyclic group $G = \langle g \rangle$ is cyclic.

PROOF. Let S be a subgroup. Let a be chosen so that a is the smallest positive integer such that $g^a \in S$. We claim that $S = \langle g^a \rangle$. Now every element of G, hence also of S, has the form g^b, thus it will suffice to show that if $g^b \in S$ then $b = ah$, for then $g^b = (g^a)^h$. Now, if a does not divide b then we have $b = aq + c$ where $0 < c < a$. But then $g^b = g^{aq+c} = g^{aq}g^c$, or $g^c = g^b(g^{aq})^{-1}$. Since $g^a \in S$ it follows that g^{aq} and $(g^{aq})^{-1}$ belong to S. But since $g^b \in S$ by assumption, it follows that $g^c \in S$, contrary to the choice of a.

* * *

~Theorem 15. In an infinite cyclic group all subgroups except $\{1\}$ are infinite.

PROOF. Let g be a generator of an infinite cyclic group. If S is a subgroup then, by Theorem 14, $S = \langle g^a \rangle$. Since $S \neq \{1\}$ we may assume that $a > 0$. If S were finite, this would imply that $(g^a)^b = 1$ for some $b > 0$. This in turn implies that g has finite order, contrary to assumption.

* * *

Note that this theorem in connection with Theorem 9 tells us that any two proper subgroups of an infinite cyclic group are isomorphic, even isomorphic to the group itself. The situation for finite cyclic groups is somewhat more complicated; the subgroups are in 1–1 correspondence with the divisors of $|G|$. From Lagrange's theorem we know that the order of every subgroup divides the order of the group. The next theorem is an existence theorem for subgroups of a cyclic group. Its proof is constructive in that a generator is constructed for each subgroup.

━ ***Theorem* 16.** Let $G = \langle g \rangle$ be a finite cyclic group of order n. For every divisor d of n there is a unique subgroup of order d.

PROOF (*Existence*). Let $n = dr$. We shall show that $\langle g^r \rangle$ has order d. Let us call k the order of g^r. Now we have that $(g^r)^d = g^n = 1$ so that $k \mid d$ and hence, by Theorem 0.1, $k \leq d$. On the other hand $(g^r)^k = 1$ by definition of k, but if $k < d$ then $rk < rd = n$ and $g^{rk} \neq 1$ since g was assumed to have order n. Thus $k = d$.

Uniqueness. Suppose that $\langle g^s \rangle$ has order d where $n = dr$. We shall show that $\langle g^s \rangle = \langle g^r \rangle$. (This does not imply that $g^s = g^r$.) From Theorem 0.2 we have $s = rm + t$ where $0 \leq t < r$. Hence $sd = rmd + td$ where $0 \leq td < rd = n$ and so $g^{sd} = g^{rdm}g^{td}$ or $1 = g^{td}$, which is impossible unless $t = 0$. If $t = 0$, we have that r divides s, say $s = ru$ so that $g^s = (g^r)^u$. But this says that g^s belongs to $\langle g^r \rangle$ and hence even $\langle g^s \rangle \subseteq \langle g^r \rangle$. Since both subgroups were assumed to have the same number of elements, we must have $\langle g^s \rangle = \langle g^r \rangle$.

* * *

The set of all subgroups of a group G can be ordered in a natural way by set inclusion. We write

$$A \subseteq B \quad \text{or} \quad B \supseteq A$$

if A and B are subgroups of G and A is a subset, hence even a subgroup, of B. By a maximal subgroup of G is meant a subgroup M such that $M \neq G$, but $M \subseteq N \subseteq G$ implies that $M = N$ or $N = G$.

Given two subgroups A and B of a group G it is interesting to ask what is the largest subgroup contained in each and what is the smallest subgroup containing both A and B. Of course, $\langle 1 \rangle$ is contained in both A and B, and G contains both A and B. As we show, in Theorem 17, the set intersection $A \cap B$ is a subgroup of G, and so $A \cap B$ is clearly the largest subgroup contained in both A and B. The smallest subgroup containing both A and B must contain the set union $A \cup B$, of course, but because of the closure requirement for subgroups it will usually contain more than just $A \cup B$. For example, if $a \in A$ and $b \in B$, there is no reason why, in general, ab should belong to $A \cup B$. We denote the smallest subgroup containing both A and B by $A \vee B$ and call it the *join* of A and B. We establish the existence of $A \vee B$ and give a useful characterization for its elements in Theorem 19.

━***Theorem* 17.** If A and B are subgroups of G, then $A \cap B$ is a subgroup of G.

PROOF. Clearly $1 \in A \cap B$. Let x and y belong to $A \cap B$. Thus x and y both belong to A, and x and y both belong to B. Hence xy^{-1} belongs both to A

and to B, and therefore to $A \cap B$, and so it follows from Lemma 8 that $A \cap B$ is a subgroup.

In exactly an analogous way we can prove a stronger theorem:

Theorem 18. Let $\mathscr{A}$ be a set of subgroups A of G. $\cap \mathscr{A}$ is a subgroup and is the largest subgroup contained in every subgroup $A \in \mathscr{A}$.

We omit the proof of this theorem.

Theorem 19. Let A and B be subgroups of group G. Let $D = \{x :$ There exists a nonempty sequence of elements, $s_1, \ldots, s_n$, from $A \cup B$ such that $x = s_1 \ldots s_n.\}$. Then D is a subgroup of G and $D = A \vee B$, the smallest ~~group~~ G containing $A \cup B$.

products (multiply) → subgroup of

PROOF. First, note that $D \supseteq A \cup B$ since, for example, if $a \in A$ then a is already in the desired form for an element of D by choosing $n = 1$ and $s_1 = a$. We prove that D is a subgroup. Let $x = s_1 \ldots s_n$ and $y = r_1 \ldots r_m$ where all s_i and r_j belong either to A or to B. As A and B are subgroups it follows that $r_j^{-1} \in A \cup B$ and so $xy^{-1} = s_1 \ldots s_n r_m^{-1} \ldots r_1^{-1} \in D$. Thus D is a subgroup.

If U is any subgroup containing both A and B, it must contain every element of the form $s_1 \ldots s_n$ where s_i belongs to either A or B since U will be closed under the group operation. Hence $U \supseteq D$.

$$* \quad * \quad *$$

An alternate characterization of $A \vee B$ can be given as

$$A \vee B = \cap \{T : T \text{ is a subgroup of } G \text{ and } A \cup B \subseteq T\}.$$

This characterization holds even if A and B are not subgroups of G. In fact, we can introduce the following notation.

Definition. Let S be a nonempty subset of G:

$$\langle S \rangle = \cap \{T : T \text{ is a subgroup of } G \text{ and } S \subseteq T\}.$$

Clearly $\langle S \rangle$ is a subgroup and it is the smallest subgroup that contains the set S. We say that S generates $\langle S \rangle$. More generally we say that a subset S of G generates a subgroup H of G if $H = \langle S \rangle$. This is a natural extension of the notion of a cyclic group which is generated by a single element. By a proof analogous to the proof of Theorem 19, we can prove Theorem 20.

Theorem 20. Let S be a subset of a group G:

$$\langle S \rangle = \{x : x = s_1^{e_1} \ldots s_n^{e_n} \quad \text{where} \quad s_i \in S, e_i = \pm 1, \quad \text{and} \quad n = 1, 2, \ldots\}.$$

The details of this proof are left as an exercise.

Example 32. For the full symmetric group S_3 on $\{1, 2, 3\}$, using the notation of Example 9, we have

$$\{J, A\} \vee \{J, B\} = \{J, A, B, AB, BA, ABA\} = S_3.$$

It is often suggestive to draw a diagram of the subgroups of a group G. In Figure 11 we do this for S_3 and for the cyclic group $\langle g \rangle$ of order 6.

Definition. Let A and B be subsets of a group G. The *complex* $A \cdot B$ is the set $\{ab : a \in A \text{ and } b \in B\}$.

Note that for this definition A and B need not be subgroups, and that even if they are subgroups, $A \cdot B$ is usually not a subgroup. $A \cdot B$ is usually not closed under the group operation. However, the following counting theorem is true when A and B are groups.

Theorem 21. If A and B are finite subgroups of a group G then

$$|A \cdot B| = \frac{|A|\,|B|}{|A \cap B|}.$$

PROOF. Quite formally, the number of products xy we can form where x comes from A and y comes from B is, of course, $|A|\,|B|$. The trouble is that there may well be some duplication; $ab = a_1 b_1$ is possible for distinct a, b, a_1, b_1. This suggests that we consider the cartesian product $A \times B$, which has $|A|\,|B|$ elements, and on $A \times B$ we define a relation as follows:

$$(a_1, b_1) \sim (a_2, b_2) \quad \text{if and only if} \quad a_1 b_1 = a_2 b_2.$$

The relation $(\sim)$ is an equivalence relation and it is easy to see that $|A \cdot B|$ is the number of distinct equivalence classes as each equivalence class corresponds to an element of $A \cdot B$. To prove the theorem it suffices to show that each equivalence class has exactly $|A \cap B|$ elements. In fact, we prove that if E denotes the equivalence class to which (a, b) belongs then

$$E = \{(ax^{-1}, xb) : x \in A \cap B\}.$$

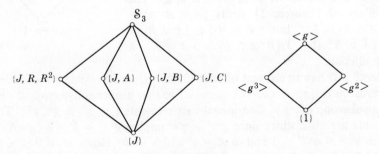

Figure 11

Clearly if $x \in A \cap B$, then $ax^{-1} \in A$ and $xb \in B$ so that $(ax^{-1}, xb) \in A \times B$ and $(a, b) \sim (ax^{-1}, xb)$. Conversely, if $(a, b) \sim (a_1, b_1)$, then $ab = a_1 b_1$ and so $x = a_1^{-1} a = b_1 b^{-1} \in A \cap B$. Thus $a_1 = ax^{-1}$ and $b_1 = xb$ and our assertion holds. Finally, if $(ax^{-1}, xb) = (ay^{-1}, yb)$ then $x = y$. Thus E has exactly $|A \cap B|$ elements and the proof is complete.

* * *

Corollary. If A and B are finite subgroups of a group G, then $[A \vee B : A] \geq [B : A \cap B]$.

PROOF. The inequality to be proved may be expressed

$$\frac{|A \vee B|}{|A|} \geq \frac{|B|}{|A \cap B|}, \quad \text{or} \quad |A \vee B| \geq \frac{|A| \, |B|}{|A \cap B|}.$$

Since $A \vee B \supseteq A \cdot B$, $|A \vee B| \geq |A \cdot B|$, and the corollary follows.

* * *

These theorems enable us to determine the abstract nature of all groups of small orders. As an example we shall determine, up to isomorphism, all groups of order 6.

Let G be a group of order 6. Let g be an element of G, $g \neq 1$. Then g may have order 2, 3, or 6 from the theorem of Lagrange.

If g has order 6 then $G = \langle g \rangle$ is the cyclic group of order 6 which we know exists.

If the order of g is 3, then there must exist another element $h \neq 1$ in G, $h \notin \langle g \rangle$.

Lemma 10. If G is a group of order 6, then G has at most one subgroup of order 3.

PROOF. Suppose G contains A and B, distinct subgroups of order 3. We know these are cyclic groups. We know $A \cap B = 1$, since $A \cap B$ is a subgroup of A, but A has only the trivial subgroups and since $A \neq B$, $A \cap B \neq A$. The Corollary of Theorem 21 yields $[A \vee B : A] \geq [B : A \cap B] = 3$. But $6 = |G| \geq |A \vee B| = |A| \cdot [A \vee B : A] \geq 3 \cdot [B : A \cap B] = 3 \cdot 3 = 9$, a contradiction.

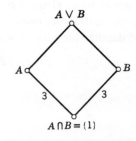

Hence if G has an element of order 3, then G has an element h of order 2. We must have $\langle g \rangle \cap \langle h \rangle = 1$ since $\langle h \rangle$ has no proper subgroup and $\langle h \rangle$ is not a subgroup of $\langle g \rangle$. Consider the six elements $1, g, g^2, h, gh, g^2 h$. These elements are all distinct since $g^e h^f = g^r h^s$ implies $g^{e-r} = h^{s-f} \in \langle g \rangle \cap \langle h \rangle$. Hence $g^{e-r} = h^{s-f} = 1$ and so $g^e = g^r$ and $h^f = h^s$. However, if $0 \leq e, r < 3$, and $0 \leq f, s < 2$, then $e = r$ and $f = s$. Thus $G = \{1, g, g^2, h, gh, g^2 h\}$.

But what about hg? hg must then be one of these elements. Now $hg = g^e$ implies $h \in \langle g \rangle$ while $hg = h$ implies $g = 1$. Thus two possibilities remain:

$$hg = gh \quad \text{or} \quad hg = g^{-1}h.$$

As shown by Theorem 10, the second case gives rise to the dihedral group of order 6, which is isomorphic to S_3. In the first case, $hg = gh$, and we can show that $\langle hg \rangle$ is the entire group G; that is, G is cyclic. Since h and g commute,

$$(hg)^n = h^n g^n.$$

Thus $(hg)^n = 1$ implies $h^n g^n = 1$, or $h^n \in \langle g \rangle$, hence $h^n = 1$ and so $g^n = 1$. Since h has order 2, we have $2 \mid n$ and since g has order 3 we have $3 \mid n$. Thus $6 \mid n$. But surely $(hg)^6 = h^6 g^6 = 1$. Thus (hg) has order 6.

So far we have found two abstract groups of order 6; the cyclic group and the dihedral group. These arguments all began on the assumption of one element of order 3. The alternative is that all elements of G, except 1, have order 2. We shall now show that this is impossible. Let a and b be two elements of order 2. Let $A = \langle a \rangle$ and $B = \langle b \rangle$. Since we are supposing that all elements of G have order 2 it must be that ab has order 2. Thus $(ab)(ab) = 1$. But $(ab)(ba) = ab^2 a = a1a = a^2 = 1$. Thus $(ab)(ba) = (ab)(ab)$ and so $ab = ba$. It is now easy to verify that $\{1, a, b, ab\}$ is closed under multiplication, hence a subgroup. This is a contradiction of Lagrange's theorem as $4 \nmid 6$.

Thus we have proved that any group of order 6 is isomorphic to either the cyclic group of order 6 or to the symmetric group on $\{1, 2, 3\}$.

EXERCISE 5

1. Find all subgroups of order 4 in the symmetric group S_4 on the four symbols $\{1, 2, 3, 4\}$.

2. If $x^{-1}yx = y^{-1}$ and $y^{-1}xy = x^{-1}$ for elements x, y of a group, prove that $x^4 = y^4 = 1$.

3. Let A and B be two finite subgroups of a group G. Show that if $|A|$ and $|B|$ have no common divisor then

$$A \cap B = \langle 1 \rangle \quad \text{(the identity subgroup)}.$$

4. Find all the subgroups of a cyclic group of order 8 and draw a diagram showing the set inclusions between subgroups. Draw a similar diagram for a cyclic group of order 12.

5. Show, by constructing an example that it is possible for a group G to be isomorphic to a proper subgroup of a group H and for H to be isomorphic to a proper subgroup G_1 of G. (For a harder problem, see Problem 8 Exercise 7.)

6. Show that for all elements g in a group G, g and g^{-1} have the same order.

7. Let G be a group. Show that if $|G| = 2n$ then G has an element of order 2. If n is odd and G is abelian show that G has only one such element.

8. Show that if $A \cup B = A \vee B$ for subgroups A and B of G then $A \subseteq B$ or $B \subseteq A$.

9. Let $G = \langle g \rangle$ be a cyclic group having subgroups $A = \langle g^a \rangle$ and $B = \langle g^b \rangle$. Show that $A \vee B = \langle g^c \rangle$ where c is the greatest common factor of a and b. Show that $A \cap B = \langle g^d \rangle$ where d is the least common multiple of a and b.

10. Show that for any three subgroups A, B, and C of a cyclic group

$$A \cap (B \vee C) = (A \cap B) \vee (A \cap C).$$

Show by example with the "four-group" that this result is not true for abelian groups in general.

11. The following 7 permutations together with their squares form a group called the alternating group, $\mathscr{A}_4$, on four symbols.

$$a = \begin{pmatrix} 1 & 2 & 3 & 4 \\ 2 & 3 & 1 & 4 \end{pmatrix}$$

$$r = \begin{pmatrix} 1 & 2 & 3 & 4 \\ 2 & 1 & 4 & 3 \end{pmatrix}$$

$$b = \begin{pmatrix} 1 & 2 & 3 & 4 \\ 2 & 4 & 3 & 1 \end{pmatrix}$$

$$t = \begin{pmatrix} 1 & 2 & 3 & 4 \\ 3 & 4 & 1 & 2 \end{pmatrix}$$

$$c = \begin{pmatrix} 1 & 2 & 3 & 4 \\ 3 & 2 & 4 & 1 \end{pmatrix}$$

$$s = \begin{pmatrix} 1 & 2 & 3 & 4 \\ 4 & 3 & 2 & 1 \end{pmatrix}$$

$$d = \begin{pmatrix} 1 & 2 & 3 & 4 \\ 1 & 3 & 4 & 2 \end{pmatrix}$$

(i) Find $a^2, b^2, c^2, d^2, r^2, s^2, t^2$.
(ii) What is the order of $\mathscr{A}_4$?
(iii) Find the order of each element.
(iv) Find a subgroup of order 4.
(v) Find a subgroup of order 3.
(vi) Show that $\mathscr{A}_4$ has no subgroup of order 6.

12. Let G be a group containing elements a and b such that

(1) a and b have order 4,
(2) $a^2 = b^2$,
(3) $ba = a^3b$, and
(4) $\{a\} \neq \{b\}$.

(i) Show that $Q = \langle a \rangle \vee \langle b \rangle$ has eight elements. Any group isomorphic with Q is called the quaternions.
(ii) Which of the subsets $\{1, a\}, \{1, b\}, \{1, a^2\}$ are subgroups of Q?

13. Determine, up to isomorphism, all groups of order 10.

*Definition

14. The *center* of a group G is the set of elements

$$Z = \{x : xg = gx \text{ for all } g \in G\}. \quad *Definition$$

Show that Z is an abelian subgroup of G.

15. Let G be a group. Let S be a subset of G. The *normalizer of S* is the set of elements

$$N_S = \{x : xS = Sx\}.$$

Show that N_S is a subgroup.

16. Let G be a group. Let $x \in G$. An element $y \in G$ is called a conjugate of x if there is a $g \in G$ such that $y = g^{-1}xg$.

(i) Show that the relation $x \rho y$ if and only if y is a conjugate of x is an equivalence relation on G.

(ii) Show that if G is a finite group the number of distinct conjugates of x is the index of the normalizer N_x of $\{x\}$ in G.

17. Show that if G has order p^a, p a prime, then the center of G contains more than the identity. (*Hint:* Split G into equivalence classes of conjugate elements and observe that an element is in the center if and only if it is its only conjugate.)

1.10. HOMOMORPHISMS

In this section we consider the group theoretical implications of the following situation. We have two groups G and $\bar{G}$ and a mapping from G into $\bar{G}$. Now an arbitrary mapping will tell us little about the group structure of either G or $\bar{G}$ unless we can relate it to the group operations of G and $\bar{G}$. We have already seen one special kind of mapping, an isomorphism. An isomorphism told us that G and $\bar{G}$, though perhaps different sets, were abstractly the same group.

The concept of group isomorphism was thrust upon us early in the consideration of examples of groups to answer the question, When are different groups intrinsically the same? Here, the first prerequisite was a 1–1 correspondence between the elements of the two groups. A second condition was the preservation of the group operation. The second condition is really more significant because, in some sense, when the group operation is preserved, some of the group structure will be preserved also. Let us retain this condition but drop the condition that the mapping be 1–1.

__Definition.__ Let $\langle G, \circ \rangle$ and $\langle \bar{G}, * \rangle$ be two groups. A mapping φ from G into $\bar{G}$ is called a *homomorphism* of G into G (or of G onto $\bar{G}$ if φ is an onto mapping) provided

$$\varphi(g_1 \circ g_2) = \varphi(g_1) * \varphi(g_2)$$

for all pairs (g_1, g_2) in $G \times G$.

This says that if the image of g_1 under φ is $\bar{g}_1$ and the image of g_2 is $\bar{g}_2$ then the image of $g_1 \circ g_2$ is $\bar{g}_1 * \bar{g}_2$. We shall call this the *homomorphism* *condition.* The range of φ is denoted by $\varphi(G)$ and is called the homomorphic image of G under φ. Note that an isomorphism is a special case of a homomorphism.

Example 33. Let $\langle G, + \rangle$ be the group of integers under addition. Let $\langle \bar{G}, \cdot \rangle$ be the multiplicative group whose elements are 1 and -1. Let φ be the mapping defined

$$\varphi(n) = \begin{cases} 1 & \text{if } n \text{ is even} \\ -1 & \text{if } n \text{ is odd} . \end{cases}$$

The condition $\varphi(n + m) = \varphi(n) \cdot \varphi(m)$ is easily verified.

Example 34. Let G be the full symmetric group S_3 on $\{1, 2, 3\}$. We continue the notation of Example 9. Let $\bar{G}$ be the subgroup $\{J, A\}$. Let

$$\varphi(J) = \varphi(R) = \varphi(S) = J$$
$$\varphi(A) = \varphi(B) = \varphi(C) = A.$$

The homomorphism condition can be checked by noting that the preimages of J form a subgroup K of S_3 and the preimages of A form a coset $KA = AK$ of that subgroup. Hence if g_1 and g_2 belong to K the homomorphism condition holds. If $g_1 \in K$ while $g_2 \in A$, then $g_1 g_2 \in KA$ so that $\varphi(g_1 g_2) = A$, whereas $\varphi(g_1)\varphi(g_2) = JA = A$. Similarly, if $g_1 \in KA = AK$ and $g_2 \in K$, the homomorphism condition holds. Finally we have to test the homomorphism condition for pairs (g_1, g_2) from the coset KA. A few calculations complete this check.

Our first theorem about homomorphisms has far-reaching consequences for groups. In addition it has an important analogue in the study of the algebras we shall consider in later chapters. It may help to review Example 34 as the proof progresses.

Theorem 22. Let φ be a homomorphism of G into $\bar{G}$. The elements of G, which are mapped into the identity of $\bar{G}$, form a subgroup K of G called the <u>kernel</u> of φ, such that

(1) $gK = Kg$ for all g in G,
(2) if $\bar{g} \in \bar{G}$, then $\{x : x \in G \text{ and } \varphi(x) = \bar{g}\}$
is either empty or is a coset of K.
φ is 1–1 if and only if $K = \langle 1 \rangle$.

PROOF. To simplify notation we shall use juxtaposition to denote the group operation of G and $\bar{G}$. Let 1 be the identity of G and $\bar{1}$ be the identity of $\bar{G}$. First we note that $\varphi(1) = \varphi(1 \cdot 1) = \varphi(1)\varphi(1)$, and so by Lemma 1 we have that $\varphi(1) = \bar{1}$. Since $\bar{1} = \varphi(1) = \varphi(xx^{-1}) = \varphi(x)\varphi(x^{-1})$, it follows from Lemma 5 that $[\varphi(x)]^{-1} = \varphi(x^{-1})$ for any $x \in G$.

Now we show that $K = \{x : x \in G \text{ and } \varphi(x) = \bar{1}\}$ is a subgroup of G. If x

and y belong to K then $\varphi(x) = \varphi(y) = \bar{1}$ so that $\varphi(y^{-1}) = [\varphi(y)]^{-1} = \bar{1}$, and hence $\varphi(xy^{-1}) = \varphi(x)\varphi(y^{-1}) = \bar{1}$. Thus K is a subgroup.

More generally, if $\varphi(x) = \varphi(y)$, then $\bar{1} = \varphi(x)[\varphi(y)]^{-1} = \varphi(x)\varphi(y^{-1}) = \varphi(xy^{-1})$; hence $xy^{-1} \in K$, or $x \in Ky$. Similarly, $\bar{1} = [\varphi(y)]^{-1}\varphi(x) = \varphi(y^{-1})\varphi(x) = \varphi(y^{-1}x)$, and so $y^{-1}x \in K$, or $x \in yK$. Hence $\{x : \varphi(x) = \varphi(y)\}$ is a subset of Ky and also of yK. On the other hand, if $x \in Ky$, that is, $x = ky$, we have $\varphi(x) = \varphi(k)\varphi(y) = \bar{1}\varphi(y) = \varphi(y)$, or, if $x \in yK$, we have, similarly, that $\varphi(x) = \varphi(y)$. It therefore follows that $\{x : \varphi(x) = \varphi(y)\} = Ky = yK$, and this proves both (1) and (2) of the theorem.

Finally, if φ is a 1–1 mapping and $\varphi(a) = \bar{1} = \varphi(1)$ then $a = 1$ and so $K = \langle 1 \rangle$. Conversely, suppose that $K = \langle 1 \rangle$. If $\varphi(a) = \varphi(b)$ then $\bar{1} = \varphi(a)\varphi(b)^{-1} = \varphi(ab^{-1})$, and so $ab^{-1} = 1$, or $a = b$. Thus φ is a 1–1 mapping.

$*$ $*$ $*$

Figure 12 gives a schematic picture of this theorem.

Definition. A subgroup S of G is called *normal* in G if $gS = Sg$ for all $g \in G$.

Example 35. In the group G, $\langle 1 \rangle$ and G are always normal subgroups.

Example 36. Every subgroup of an abelian group is a normal subgroup. It is not true that if every subgroup of a group is a normal subgroup then the group is abelian. The quaternion group of Problem 12 of Exercise 5 is an example of a non-abelian group in which every subgroup is normal.

Example 37. In the full symmetric group S_3 of Example 9, $\{J, R, S\}$ is a normal subgroup, as is shown by Example 34 and Theorem 22. It happens that the index of this subgroup is 2. The next theorem proves the general result of which this is an example.

Theorem 23. If H is a subgroup of index 2 in a group G, then H is a normal subgroup of G.

PROOF. If $a \in H$ then $H = aH = Ha$. If $a \notin H$, then aH is a left coset distinct from H and Ha is a right coset distinct from H. Since $[G : H] = 2$ we must

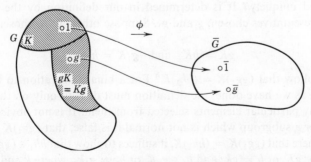

Figure 12

have, as coset decomposition of G, $G = H \cup aH = H \cup Ha$. Since $H \cap aH = \varnothing = H \cap Ha$ it follows that $aH = Ha$.

* * *

Theorem 22 tells us that the kernel of a homomorphism is a normal subgroup. It is remarkable that the converse is true.

> **Theorem 24.** Let K be a normal subgroup of G. Then there is a group $\bar{G}$ and a homomorphism of G *onto* $\bar{G}$ whose kernel is K.

For the proof of the theorem we are required to construct a group $\bar{G}$. This is a "bootstraps" operation since we have at our disposal only the group G. The clue comes from Theorem 22 wherein we saw that the preimage of an element in $\bar{G}$ was a coset of K in G. This means that the cosets of K in G behave like elements of $\bar{G}$. How can we make the cosets of K in G into a group?

Let us further re-examine the proof of Theorem 22. Clearly the image of G is a subgroup of $\bar{G}$ onto which G is mapped by φ. To simplify our discussion let us suppose that this subgroup is all of $\bar{G}$, in other words, that φ is a mapping of G onto $\bar{G}$. Theorem 22 states that there is a 1–1 correspondence between elements of $\bar{G}$ and cosets of K. Call this mapping ψ, $\psi : \{\text{cosets of } K\} \rightarrow \bar{G}$ and $\psi(gK) = \varphi(g)$. Thus ψ is 1–1 and if $\psi(g_1 K) = \varphi(g_1)$, we have $\psi(gg_1)K = \varphi(gg_1) = \varphi(g)\varphi(g_1)$. This is essentially the second condition for a group isomorphism, except that we have not yet made a group out of the cosets of K. Certainly there is a strong suggestion that we should make the cosets into a group by defining an operation on cosets as follows: $(gK)(g_1 K) = gg_1 K$. We now make these ideas precise and prove Theorem 24.

PROOF. Consider the set of cosets of K in G. We shall define a binary operation on these cosets and verify that these cosets under this operation form a group, called the *quotient*, or *factor* group of G by K, denoted G/K.

DEFINITION: $(gK)(g_1 K) = (gg_1)K$. There is an important hitch in this definition. Ostensibly we are given two cosets and a third coset is determined. Is it determined uniquely? It is determined in our definition by the particular coset representatives chosen, g and g_1. Suppose others were chosen, suppose that

$$gK = hK \quad \text{and} \quad g_1 K = h_1 K.$$

Does it follow that $(gg_1)K = (hh_1)K$? For a binary operation to be defined on cosets, as we have done, the definition must depend only on the sets and not on any particular elements selected from them. It is not obvious, and in general for a subgroup which is not normal it is false, that $(gg_1)K = (hh_1)K$. To show here that $(gg_1)K = (hh_1)K$, it suffices to show that $hh_1 \in (gg_1)K$. Now we have $h \in gK$, or $h = gk$; and $h_1 \in g_1 K$, or $h_1 = g_1 k_1$, where k and k_1 belong to K. Hence $hh_1 = gkg_1k_1$. Since K is normal, the cosets Kg_1 and g_1K are equal, and since $kg_1 \in Kg_1 = g_1K$ we have for some $k_2 \in K$, that $kg_1 = g_1k_2$. Hence $hh_1 = gkg_1k_1 = gg_1k_2k_1$. Because k_2 and k_1 belong to the subgroup K we have $k_2k_1 \in K$, and so $hh_1 \in (gg_1)K$.

Now the verification that the cosets, under the definition of multiplication given above, form a group is easy and we leave the details to the reader. Finally, the mapping of G onto G/K given by $g \to gK$ is easily seen to be a homomorphism of G onto G/K. We shall call this mapping the natural homomorphism of G onto G/K.

Corollary. If G is mapped homomorphically onto $\bar{G}$ with kernel K, then $G/K \cong \bar{G}$.

PROOF. The 1–1 mapping sketched in the paragraph preceding the proof of Theorem 24 preserves the group operations, as is seen in the proof of Theorem 24.

$$* \quad * \quad *$$

We may summarize these results as follows:

> **Theorem 25.** A homomorphic image of a group G is determined up to isomorphism by the normal subgroup that is the kernel of the homomorphism. Conversely, for every normal subgroup N there is a homomorphism with N as its kernel.

A word of caution: a homomorphism is a mapping and homomorphisms may be different with different kernels, yet the homomorphic images may be isomorphic. On the other hand, if different homomorphisms have the same kernel K, then the images are isomorphic with G/K.

Example 37. Let G be the cyclic group of order 3. Say $G = \{1, x, x^2\}$ where $x^3 = 1$. Let the image $\bar{G}$ coincide with G. Let φ be the identity mapping and let ψ be given as follows: $\psi(1) = 1$, $\psi(x) = x^2$ and $\psi(x^2) = x$. It is easily seen that ψ is a homomorphism. We have that the kernels are equal, $K = \{1\}$ and indeed $G/K \cong G$. Note that ψ is an isomorphism of G which is not the identity.

Example 38. Let G be the four-group, $G = \{1, a, b, ab\}$. Then C_2, the cyclic group of order 2, can be obtained as the homomorphic image of G by at least two distinct homomorphisms. Let $C_2 = \{1, x\}$, with $x^2 = 1$. Two different homomorphisms are given by

$$\varphi(1) = 1, \quad \varphi(a) = 1, \quad \varphi(b) = x, \quad \varphi(ab) = x. \qquad \text{Kernel} = K_\varphi = \{1, a\}$$
$$\psi(1) = 1, \quad \psi(b) = 1, \quad \psi(a) = x, \quad \psi(ab) = x. \qquad \text{Kernel} = K_\psi = \{1, b\}.$$

We have $C_2 \cong G/K_\varphi \cong G/K_\psi$.

Another frequent characterization of normal subgroups is given by the following theorems.

Proved

Theorem 26. Let N be a subgroup of G. N is normal in G if and only if, for all $x \in G$ and all $n \in N$, it is true that $xnx^{-1} \in N$.

PROOF. (I) Suppose that N is normal. Let $x \in G$ and $n \in N$. Then $xN = Nx$ and $xn \in Nx$. Hence $xn = n_1 x$ for some $n_1 \in N$, and $xnx^{-1} = n_1 \in N$. (II) Let $xnx^{-1} \in N$ for all $x \in G$ and $n \in N$. We are to show that $gN = Ng$ for all $g \in G$. Now let $gn \in gN$. Then $gng^{-1} = n_1 \in N$ by hypothesis. Hence $gn = n_1 g$ and so $gN \subseteq Ng$. Conversely, suppose $ng \in Ng$; then $g^{-1}ng = (g^{-1})n(g^{-1})^{-1} = n_2 \in N$, by hypothesis. Therefore $ng = gn_2$ and so $ng \in gN$; consequently $Ng \subseteq gN$; hence $Ng = gN$.

* * *

Prove

If we write xNx^{-1} for the set $\{xnx^{-1} : n \in N\}$, we may restate Theorem 26 in the form: N is normal if and only if $xNx^{-1} \subseteq N$ for all $x \in G$.

Corollary. If N is normal then $xNx^{-1} = N$ for all $x \in G$.

PROOF. In view of Theorem 26 we have only to show that if N is normal, then $N \subseteq xNx^{-1}$ for all x in G. So let x be given. We are to show that $n \in xNx^{-1}$ for all $n \in N$. We have $n = x(x^{-1}nx)x^{-1}$, and since, from Theorem 26, $N \supseteq x^{-1}N(x^{-1})^{-1} = x^{-1}Nx$, it follows that $x^{-1}nx = n_1 \in N$. Hence $n = xn_1 x^{-1} \in xNx^{-1}$.

* * *

Prove

Our argument in brief is that $xNx^{-1} \subseteq N$ implies $N \subseteq x^{-1}Nx \subseteq N$, the last inclusion coming from Theorem 26 by choosing x^{-1} as the particular element in G.

Theorem 27. Let G be a group. Let $a \in G$. The mapping φ_a of G into G defined by

$$\varphi_a(g) = aga^{-1}$$

is an isomorphism of G onto G in which every normal subgroup is taken onto itself.

PROOF. To show that the mapping is 1–1, suppose that $aga^{-1} = ag_1 a^{-1}$. By cancellation $g = g_1$. φ_a maps G onto G since $\varphi_a(a^{-1}ga) = a(a^{-1}ga)a^{-1} = g$. Finally, $\varphi_a(gg_1) = agg_1 a^{-1} = (aga^{-1})(ag_1 a^{-1}) = \varphi_a(g)\varphi_a(g_1)$. Hence the mapping is an isomorphism.

If N is a normal subgroup, then $n \in N$ implies that $ana^{-1} \in N$ by Theorem 26. Thus the effect of φ_a on the elements of N is simply to permute them among themselves.

* * *

Definition. An *automorphism* is an isomorphism of G onto itself. An automorphism φ of G of the form $\varphi(g) = aga^{-1}$ is called an *inner automorphism* of G. All other automorphisms are called outer automorphisms of G. An *endomorphism* of G is a homomorphism of G into itself.

An exercise in terminology gives the next theorem.

> **Theorem 28.** A subgroup N of G is normal if and only if it is taken into itself by every inner automorphism of G.

It was alleged that some of the group structure of G would be preserved for study in a homomorphic image, $\bar{G}$. The extent to which this is true is indicated by the following theorem.

> **Theorem 29.** Let φ be a homomorphism from G onto $\bar{G}$, with kernel K. There is a natural 1–1 correspondence between subgroups $\bar{H}$ of $\bar{G}$ and subgroups H of G that contain K. In this correspondence normal subgroups correspond with normal subgroups. (Figure 13 sketches these relationships.)

PROOF. Let H be a subgroup of G such that $G \supseteq H \supseteq K$. It is easy to verify that

$$\bar{H} = \{\varphi(h) : h \in H\}$$

is a subgroup of $\bar{G}$. Moreover, if H is normal in G, then $\bar{H}$ is normal in $\bar{G}$. This can be shown as follows. Let $\bar{h} \in \bar{H}$ and $\bar{g} \in \bar{G}$ be arbitrary. We must show that $\bar{g}\bar{h}\bar{g}^{-1} \in \bar{H}$. Choose $h \in H$ and $g \in G$ such that $\varphi(h) = \bar{h}$ and $\varphi(g) = \bar{g}$. Then, as H is normal in G we have $ghg^{-1} \in H$. Hence $\varphi(ghg^{-1}) \in \bar{H}$, or $\varphi(ghg^{-1}) = \varphi(g)\varphi(h)\varphi(g^{-1}) = \bar{g}\bar{h}\bar{g}^{-1} \in \bar{H}$.

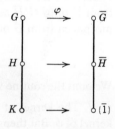

To prove the theorem it suffices to show that the mapping Φ on subgroups defined by $\Phi(H) = \bar{H}$ is a 1–1 mapping of those H such that $G \supseteq H \supseteq K$ onto the subgroups of $\bar{G}$.

First, we establish the 1–1 character. Suppose H and J are two such subgroups. Suppose further that $\Phi(H) = \Phi(J)$. Then let $h \in H$. Since $\varphi(h) \in \Phi(H) = \Phi(J)$, there must be a $j \in J$ such that $\varphi(j) = \varphi(h)$.

Figure 13

Hence $\bar{1} = [\varphi(j)]^{-1}\varphi(h) = \varphi(j^{-1})\varphi(h) = \varphi(j^{-1}h)$. Therefore $j^{-1}h \in K \subseteq J$, thus $j^{-1}h = k$ where $k \in K \subseteq J$. Hence $h = jk \in J$, so $H \subseteq J$. Similarly $J \subseteq H$, and thus equality is proved.

Second, we establish the onto character. Let $\bar{N}$ be a subgroup of $\bar{G}$. Let $N = \{x : \varphi(x) \in \bar{N}\}$. N is a subset of G which contains K, as $\bar{1} \in \bar{N}$ and $\Phi(K) = \langle \bar{1} \rangle$. Next N is a subgroup of G for if $\varphi(x)$ and $\varphi(y) \in \bar{N}$ then $\varphi(xy^{-1}) = \varphi(x)\varphi(y^{-1}) = \varphi(x)\varphi(y)^{-1} \in \bar{N}$ as $\bar{N}$ is a subgroup and so $xy^{-1} \in N$. Clearly $\varphi(N) = \bar{N}$. Finally, if $\bar{N}$ is normal in $\bar{G}$ then N is normal in G. We omit these details.

Corollary. Under the hypothesis of Theorem 29 and using the notations of the proof, we have

$$\bar{H} = \varphi(H) \cong H/K.$$

PROOF. The mapping φ can be restricted to a homomorphism of the subgroup H, whose kernel is K. Now apply the corollary of Theorem 24.

*   *   *

Theorem 30. Let φ be a homomorphism from G onto $\bar{G}$, with kernel K. Let H be normal in G, $H \supseteq K$, and let $\bar{H} = \varphi(H)$. Then $G/H \cong \bar{G}/\bar{H}$. (These relationships are sketched in Figure 14.)

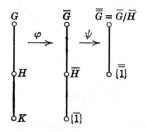

Figure 14

PROOF. We have that $\bar{H}$ is normal in $\bar{G}$. We construct the homomorphism ψ from $\bar{G}$ onto $\bar{G}/\bar{H}$ as in Theorem 24. Now we look at the composite homomorphism from G onto $\bar{G}/\bar{H}$ given by $(\psi\varphi)$ defined as

$$(\psi\varphi)(x) = \psi(\varphi(x)).$$

We omit the routine verification that $(\psi\varphi)$ is a homomorphism of G onto $\bar{\bar{G}} = \bar{G}/\bar{H}$. The kernel of $(\psi\varphi)$ must be H, for if $\psi(\varphi(x)) = \bar{\bar{1}}$, then $\varphi(x) \in \bar{H}$, the kernel of ψ. But then $x \in H$, by Theorem 29. Now the corollary to Theorem 24 yields $\bar{\bar{G}} \cong G/H$ when applied to G and $\psi\varphi$, and yields $\bar{\bar{G}} \cong \bar{G}/\bar{H}$ when applied to $\bar{G}$ and ψ.

*   *   *

This theorem takes the appealing form of a complex fraction manipulation when we view $\bar{G}$ as G/K and $\bar{H}$ as H/K. Then

$$\frac{G}{H} \cong \frac{G/K}{H/K}.$$

The homomorphism concept and mathematical induction form a powerful tool for studying finite groups. As an example, we prove the following weak converse of Lagrange's theorem for abelian groups. Later we shall prove this theorem without the hypothesis of commutativity.

Theorem 31. Let G be a finite abelian group. Let p be a prime. If $p \mid |G|$ then G has an element (hence a subgroup) of order p.

PROOF. The proof is by induction on $|G|$. We remark that if $|G|$ is a prime p then every element but the identity has order p. Now let $1 \neq g \in G$. Let g have order n. If $p \mid n$, then the cyclic group $\langle g \rangle$ has an element of order p by Theorem 16. If $p \nmid n$ we consider $\bar{G} = G/\langle g \rangle$. Since G is abelian, $\langle g \rangle$ is a normal subgroup of G, and as $p \nmid n$, $\langle 1 \rangle \subset \langle g \rangle \subset G$, hence $|\bar{G}| < |G|$. However, $p \mid |\bar{G}|$. By induction then, $\bar{G}$ has an element $\bar{h}$ of order p. Let h be a preimage of $\bar{h}$ under the natural mapping $\varphi : G \to G/\langle g \rangle$. $(\bar{h})^p = \bar{1}$ means $h^p \in \langle g \rangle$, so that $(h^p)^n = (h^n)^p = 1$. Thus either h^n has order p or $h^n = 1$. But if $h^n = 1$ then $\bar{h}^n = \bar{1}$, and since p is the order of $\bar{h}$ it would follow that $p \mid n$, contrary to assumption (see Figure 15).

* * *

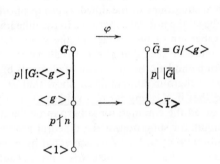

Figure 15

EXERCISE 6

1. Using the cyclic group $\langle g \rangle$ of order 12 in the role of G and the subgroup $\{1, g^4, g^8\}$ in the role of K in Theorem 24, specialize the proof given for Theorem 24 to this case. Exhibit explicitly the cosets and the multiplication in G/K.

2. Show that the homomorphic image of an abelian group is abelian.

3. Which of the subgroups in Problem 1 of Exercise 5 are normal subgroups of S_4?

4. Decide whether the subgroups found in parts (iv) and (v) of Problem 11 in Exercise 5 are normal.

5. Prove that all subgroups of the quarternions (Problem 12 of Exercise 5) are normal.

6. Show that the homomorphic image of a cyclic group is a cyclic group. Show that any finite cyclic group is a homomorphic image of the infinite cyclic group $\langle 1 \rangle$ of the integers under addition.

7. Let A and B be subgroups of a group G such that A is normal in $A \vee B$. Prove the following:

(i) $A \vee B = A \cdot B$,

(ii) $A \cap B$ is normal in B,

(iii) If C is a subgroup such that $A \subseteq C$ then $C \cap (A \vee B) = A \vee (C \cap B)$.

8. Let A, B, C, and D be subgroups of a group G.

(i) Show that if A is a normal subgroup of B, and C is a normal subgroup of D, then $A \cap C$ is a normal subgroup of $B \cap D$.

(ii) Show that if A is normal in B and A is normal in C, then A is a normal subgroup of $B \vee C$.

9. Prove that the set of all automorphisms of a group G forms a group under composition, and the set of all inner automorphisms forms a normal subgroup of this group.

10. Show that if φ is an isomorphism of G into $\bar{G}$ then $\varphi(g)^n = 1$ if and only if $g^n = 1$. What can be said if φ is assumed only to be a homomorphism?

11. Show that if S is a subgroup of a group G and N_S is its normalizer, then S is normal in N_S. Show that N_S is the largest subgroup of G in which S is normal.

⌖12. Find all normal subgroups of the dihedral group of order 10; of order 12. Generalize to describe all the normal subgroups in the dihedral group of order $2n$.

13. Let H be a subgroup of finite index of the group G; $[G:H] = n$. Show that there is a fixed integer e such that $g^e \in H$ for all $g \in G$.

14. Let G be a group and let Δ be the subset of elements of the form $x^{-1}y^{-1}xy$. Let D be the smallest subgroup containing Δ. Show that D is normal in G, that G/D is abelian, and that if K is any normal subgroup such that G/K is abelian, then $D \subseteq K$. (D is called the commutator subgroup or the derived group of G.)

15. Find the commutator subgroup of the dihedral group of order 10.

16. Let N be a subgroup of G. Let N be generated by a set $S \subseteq G$. Show that if $gsg^{-1} \in N$ for all $s \in S$ and all $g \in G$, then N is a normal subgroup of G.

1.11. DIRECT PRODUCTS

We have seen, given a group G, that other groups may be associated with G in a natural way. Thus we have studied subgroups of G and factor groups of G. We can regard these as new groups made from the given group G. There is another useful way of constructing new groups from old ones— the direct product.

Definition. Let A and B be groups. The set of ordered pairs $\{(a, b) : a \in A$ and $b \in B\}$ is made into a group, called the *direct product* of A and B by defining the group operation as

$$(a, b)(a', b') = (aa', bb').$$

Notation. The direct product of A and B shall be denoted $A \times B$. This is sometimes referred to as the *external* direct product.

Lemma 11. The set of ordered pairs under the componentwise group opera-
tion of the preceding definition forms a group whose order is $|A|\,|B|$. _times_

PROOF. The group operation, since it is done componentwise is a well-defined
binary operation, which is clearly associative. The identity is $(1, 1)$ and
$(a, b)^{-1} = (a^{-1}, b^{-1})$. $|A|\,|B|$ is the number of ordered pairs, hence the order
of $A \times B$.

* * *

Example 38. Let $\langle R, + \rangle$ be the real numbers considered as a group under
addition. Here, $R \times R$ is isomorphic to the vectors in the plane under addition
given as the group of Example 5.

$$\longrightarrow \{(r, s) : r, s \in R\}$$

Example 39. Let $A = B$ be the cyclic group C_2 of order 2. Here, $C_2 \times C_2$ is
isomorphic to the four-group of Example 15. If $C_2 = \{1, g : g^2 = 1\}$ then
$C_2 \times C_2 = \{(1, 1), (1, g), (g, 1), (g, g)\}$ and the isomorphism is given by
$\varphi(1, 1) = e$, $\varphi(1, g) = a$, $\varphi(g, 1) = b$ and $\varphi(g, g) = c$.

Lemma 12. Let A and B be groups. In $A \times B$, let $A_1 = \{(a, 1) : a \in A\}$, and
$B_1 = \{(1, b) : b \in B\}$. A_1 and B_1 are normal subgroups of $A \times B$ such that
$A_1 \cong A$, $B \cong B_1$, and each element $\bar{g} \in A \times B$ has a unique representation of
the form $\bar{g} = \bar{a}\bar{b}$ with $\bar{a} \in A_1$ and $\bar{b} \in B_1$.

PROOF. The details are left to the reader while we prove the converse.

morphic
_≅_

> **Theorem 32.** Let G be a group with normal subgroups A and B such
> that $g \in G$ has a unique representation of the form $g = ab$, with
> $a \in A$ and $b \in B$. Then $G \cong A \times B$.
>
> We say informally that G is the direct product of A and B, or that
> G is the *internal* direct product of A and B.

PROOF. Let φ be the mapping from $A \times B$ into G given by $\varphi(a, b) = ab$. We
shall show that this a group isomorphism. The mapping is 1–1, for if $ab =
a'b'$, by hypothesis, $a = a'$ and $b = b'$; hence $(a, b) = (a', b')$. It is *onto*, for,
by hypothesis, if $g \in G$, then a and b exist such that $g = ab$, and so
$\varphi(a, b) = ab = g$.

The unicity of the representation implies that $A \cap B = \{1\}$. For if $x \in A \cap B$
then x has two representations of the form ab; namely, $x = x1 = 1x$. Thus
it follows from the hypothesis that $x = 1$.

Moreover, if $a \in A$ and $b \in B$, then $ab = ba$, as we shall show. We prove
the equivalent statement, $aba^{-1}b^{-1} = 1$. Now since B is a normal subgroup
$aba^{-1} \in B$, $(aba^{-1})b^{-1} \in B$. Similarly, $ba^{-1}b^{-1} \in A$ and so $a(ba^{-1}b^{-1}) \in A$.
Thus $aba^{-1}b^{-1} \in A \cap B = \{1\}$. Hence $aba^{-1}b^{-1} = 1$ and so $ab = ba$.

Now to show $\varphi[(a, b)(a', b')] = \varphi(a, b)\varphi(a', b')$, we have to show that
$aba'b = aa'bb'$, which follows from $ba' = a'b$, as we have just shown.

* * *

Some of the details of the preceding proof can be collected in a useful lemma.

Lemma 13. Let A and B be subgroups of G. The following two conditions are equivalent.

1. A and B are normal subgroups of $A \vee B$, and $A \cap B = 1$.

2. For every $g \in A \vee B$ there is a unique pair (a, b) with $a \in A$ and $b \in B$ such that $g = ab$ and for every pair (a, b) with $a \in A$ and $b \in B$, $ab = ba$.

PROOF. First we prove that (1) implies (2). If $a \in A$ and $b \in B$, then $aba^{-1}b^{-1} = 1$; hence $ab = ba$, as shown by the argument in Theorem 32. Now if $g \in A \vee B$ then $g = s_1 s_2 \ldots s_n$ with $s_i \in A \cup B$, as shown by Theorem 19. Let $\{s_{i_1}, \ldots, s_{i_r}\}$ be the set of those s_i that belong to A, and let $\{s_{j_1}, \ldots, s_{j_t}\}$ be those s_i that belong to B. Since we have shown that any element of A commutes with any element of B, we have that $g = (s_{i_1} \ldots s_{i_r})(s_{j_1} \ldots s_{j_t}) = ab$. Finally, if $g = ab = a_1 b_1$ with a and a_1 in A and b and b_1 in B, then $a_1^{-1}a = b_1 b^{-1} \in A \cap B = 1$, so that $a_1^{-1}a = b_1 b^{-1} = 1$ or $a = a_1$ and $b_1 = b$. Thus all the conditions of (2) hold.

Now we show that (2) implies (1). If $g \in A \cap B$ then $g = 1g = g1$, and unless $g = 1$ we would have two distinct representations of g as a product of an element in A and an element from B. Thus $A \cap B = \{1\}$. To show that A is normal in $A \vee B$, let $a' \in A$ and $g = ab \in A \vee B$. Then $ga'g^{-1} = aba'b^{-1}a^{-1} = aa'bb^{-1}a^{-1} = aa'a^{-1} \in A$. Thus A is normal in $A \vee B$ and similarly B is normal in $A \vee B$. Thus (2) holds.

* * *

Theorem 33. If G has two normal subgroups A and B such that $A \cap B = 1$, $G = A \vee B$, then $G \cong A \times B$.

PROOF. The criteria of Theorem 32 hold by Lemma 13.

* * *

Theorem 34. If G has subgroups A and B such that each element of G has unique expression of the form $g = ab$ and $ab = ba$ for all $a \in A$ and $b \in B$, then $G \cong A \times B$.

PROOF. The criteria of Theorem 32 hold by Lemma 13.

We can generalize these results to several subgroups. We shall omit the proofs since they follow easily by mathematical induction on the number of subgroups involved.

* * *

Definition. Let $A_1, \ldots, A_n$ be groups. The set of ordered n-tuples $\{(a_1, \ldots, a_n) : a_i \in A_i\}$ is made into a group called the direct product of $A_1, \ldots, A_n$ by defining the group operation by

$$(a_1, \ldots, a_n)(a^*_1, \ldots, a^*_n) = (a_1 a^*_1, \ldots, a_n a^*_n).$$

The direct product of $A_1, \ldots, A_n$ shall be denoted $A_1 \times \ldots \times A_n$.

Theorem 35. Let G be a group with normal subgroups $A_1, \ldots, A_n$ such that every element of G has a unique representation of the form $g = a_1 a_2 \ldots a_n$ with each $a_i \in A_i$. Then $G \cong A_1 \times \ldots \times A_n$.

Lemma 14. Let $A_1, \ldots, A_n$ be subgroups of G. Each A_i is normal in $A_1 \vee \ldots \vee A_n$ and $A_i \cap (A_1 \vee \ldots \vee A_{i-1} \vee A_{i+1} \vee \ldots \vee A_n) = 1$ for all i, if and only if every $g \in A_1 \vee \ldots \vee A_n$ has a unique expression in the form $g = a_1 \ldots a_n$ with $a_i \in A_i$, and for all $i \neq j$, if $a_i \in A_i$ and $a_j \in A_j$ then $a_i a_j = a_j a_i$.

Theorem 36. If G has subgroups $A_1, \ldots, A_n$ such that

    (1) Each $g \in G$ has a unique expression as $g = a_1 \cdot a_2 \ldots a_n$, with $a_i \in A_i$,
    (2) For all $i \neq j$, $a_i \in A_i$, $a_j \in A_j$, imply $a_i a_j = a_j a_i$, then $G \cong A_1 \times \ldots \times A_n$.

Theorem 37. If G has subgroups $A_1, \ldots, A_n$ such that

    (1) Each A_i is normal in G,
    (2) $A_1 \vee \ldots \vee A_n = G$,
    (3) For each i, $A_i \cap (A_1 \vee \ldots \vee A_{i-1} \vee A_{i+1} \vee \ldots \vee A_n) = 1$, then $G \cong A_1 \times \ldots \times A_n$.

We can continue these constructions still further. For example let $\{S_1, S_2, \ldots\}$ be a sequence of groups. We may define $G = \{(s_1, s_2, \ldots) : s_i \in S_i\}$; that is, G is the set of sequences g of elements in $\bigcup S_i$ where the ith term of the sequence g is an element of the ith group on the sequence $\{S_1, S_2, \ldots\}$. G is made into a group by defining a product as follows:

If $g = (s_1, s_2, \ldots)$ $(s_i \in S_i)$
and $h = (t_1, t_2, \ldots)$ $(t_i \in S_i)$
then $gh = (s_1 t_1, s_2 t_2, \ldots)$ $(s_i t_i \in S_i)$.

Thus the ith term of the sequence of a product gh is the product of the ith terms of the sequences of the factors g and h. It is easy to verify that this definition makes G into a group. We write $G = S_1 \times S_2 \times \ldots$.

This type of construction plays an important role in the study of infinite groups. For us, it will serve as a method for constructing infinite groups with interesting properties. Problems 8 and 9 of the next exercise set show the usefulness of this construction.

EXERCISE 7

1. Show that the direct product of two groups is abelian if and only if both groups are abelian.

2. Let C_K denote a cyclic group of order K. Identify $C_2 \times C_2$, $C_2 \times C_3$, $C_4 \times C_3$.

3. Let S_3 be the symmetric group on 3 symbols. Let V be the four-group. Which of the following are isomorphic? $C_4 \times C_3$, $C_6 \times C_2$, $V \times C_3$, $S_3 \times C_2$.

4. When is a dihedral group the direct product of two proper subgroups.

5. Let G be the internal direct product of subgroup A and B, that is, $G = A \vee B \cong A \times B$. If N is a normal subgroup of A, show that $G/N \cong A/N \times B$.

6. Let G have normal subgroups A, B such that $A \cap B = 1$. Show that G is isomorphic to a subgroup of $G/A \times G/B$.

7. Let G have normal subgroups A, B such that $A \vee B = G$ and such that $ab = ba$ for all $a \in A$ and $b \in B$. Show that G is a homomorphic image of $A \times B$.

★8. Construct two nonisomorphic groups G and H such that each is isomorphic to a subgroup of the other.

★9. Construct two nonisomorphic groups G and H such that each is a homomorphic image of the other.

SUPPLEMENTARY READING

R. W. Ball, On the order of an element in a group, *American Mathematical Monthly*, **71** (1964), 784.

W. Burnside, *Theory of Groups of Finite Order* (Second Edition), reprinted by Dover Publications, New York, 1955.

Marshall Hall, Jr., *The Theory of Groups*, New York: Macmillan (1959), Chapters 1 and 2.

J. H. McKay, Another proof of Cauchy's group theorem, *American Mathematical Monthly*, **66** (1959), 119.

H. J. Zassenhaus, *The Theory of Groups* (Second Edition), New York: Chelsea (1958).

2 | Rings

2.1. DEFINITIONS

Many algebraic structures have two operations, usually called addition ($+$) and multiplication ($\cdot$). Examples are provided by the integers, the rational numbers, the real numbers, the complex numbers, and the functions from the real numbers into the real numbers. Here we shall collect some basic definitions and properties of algebraic systems with two operations.

Definition. A *ring* $\langle R, +, \cdot \rangle$ is a nonempty set of elements R with two binary operations (denoted here by ($+$) and ($\cdot$)) such that

1. $\langle R, + \rangle$ is an abelian group.
2. ($\cdot$) is associative.
3. The distributive laws hold; for all triples (a, b, c) from R,
$$a\cdot(b + c) = a\cdot b + a\cdot c \quad \text{and} \quad (b + c)\cdot a = b\cdot a + c\cdot a.$$

We shall follow the convention of using 0 to denote the identity of $\langle R, + \rangle$; we shall speak of ($+$) as addition, ($\cdot$) as multiplication, and frequently denote multiplication by juxtaposition. All the examples just cited are rings under the conventional interpretations of addition and multiplication.

Rings are further classified according to the following definitions:

Definition

1. A ring is called a *ring with identity* if the ring has a multiplicative identity, that is, there is an element e such that $a\cdot e = e\cdot a = a$ for all $a \in R$.

2. A ring is called *commutative* if ($\cdot$) is commutative.

3. A ring is called an *integral domain* if it is a commutative ring with identity in which if $ab = 0$ then $a = 0$ or $b = 0$.

4. A ring is called a *division ring* (skew field) if the nonzero elements of R form a multiplicative group under ($\cdot$).

5. A ring is called a *field* if the nonzero elements of R form a commutative group under ($\cdot$).

Example 1. Let R consist of a single element 0. Define $0 + 0 = 0$ and $0 \cdot 0 = 0$. (This is called the *nullring*.)

Example 2. Let R be any abelian group whose group operation we denote by $(+)$. Now define $ab = 0$ for all $a, b \in R$.

Example 3. The integers are an integral domain but not a field.

Example 4. The even integers are a commutative ring *without* identity.

Example 5. The rational numbers are a field.

Example 6. The functions from the real numbers into the real numbers form a commutative ring with identity which is not an integral domain under the definitions for $f + g$ and $f \cdot g$ given by

$$(f + g)(x) = f(x) + g(x)$$
$$(f \cdot g)(x) = f(x) \cdot g(x).$$

The constant function whose value at all real numbers is 0 is the zero function, $\hat{0}$. The constant function whose value at all real numbers is 1 is the multiplicative identity, $\hat{1}$. Finally, we note that if

$$f(x) = \begin{cases} x & \text{if } x \le 0 \\ 0 & \text{if } x > 0 \end{cases} \quad \text{and} \quad g(x) = \begin{cases} 0 & \text{if } x \le 0 \\ x & \text{if } x > 0 \end{cases}$$

then $f \ne \hat{0}, g \ne \hat{0}$, but $f \cdot g = \hat{0}$.

Example 7. Here is an example of a ring with four elements that has none of the additional properties of Definitions 1 through 5. We give the addition and multiplication tables. For $\langle R, + \rangle$ we take a four-group $\langle \{0, a, b, a + b\}, + \rangle$ and we define $0 \cdot x = x \cdot 0 = 0$ for all $x \in R$.

+	0	a	b	a + b
0	0	a	b	a + b
a	a	0	a + b	b
b	b	a + b	0	a
a + b	a + b	b	a	0

·	a	b	a + b
a	a	0	a
b	b	0	b
a + b	a + b	0	a + b

Note that $a \cdot b \ne b \cdot a$ and that both a and $a + b$ act as right multiplicative identities. We shall verify the ring axioms in detail.

1. PROOF OF ASSOCIATIVITY OF MULTIPLICATION: We are to show that $(xy)z = x(yz)$ for all x, y, z. If either x, y or z is 0 then both $(xy)z$ and $x(yz)$ are 0. If $z = b$, the $n(xy)b = 0$ and $x(yb) = x0 = 0$. If $z = a$, or $z = a + b$, then since these are right identities we have $x(yz) = xy = (xy)z$.

2. PROOF OF THE DISTRIBUTIVE LAW: $(y + z)x = yx + zx$. If $x = 0$, the law clearly holds. If $x = a$ or $a + b$ then $(y + z)x = y + z$ while $yx + zx = y + z$. If $x = b$ then $(y + z)b = 0 = 0 + 0 = yb + zb$.

3. PROOF OF THE DISTRIBUTIVE LAW: $x(y + z) = xy + xz$. If $y = z$, then $y + z = 0$ and $xy = xz$ so that $xy + xz = 0$. Thus, in this case, $x(y + z) = 0 = xy + xz$. If either x, y, or $z = 0$, the law clearly holds.

Taking into the account the commutivity of $(+)$ for each $x \neq 0$, we have three cases left:

$$x(a + b) = xa + xb \quad ?$$
$$x(b + (a + b)) = xb + x(a + b) \quad ?$$
$$x(a + (a + b)) = xa + x(a + b) \quad ?$$

From the rules for addition in the four-group these three cases reduce to the first. The first case is just the observation that in the multiplication table the third column (headed $(a + b)$) is the sum of the first two columns. This completes the proof of distributivity and thus all the ring axioms have been verified.

Example 8. Let P be the space of two-dimensional vectors, $\vec{v}$ with real coordinates. We consider the sets of mappings f of P into itself which satisfy

(L) $\qquad\qquad f(\vec{v} + \vec{u}) = f(\vec{v}) + f(\vec{u}) \quad$ all $\vec{v}, \vec{u}$ in P.

Such f exist; rotations about the origin or reflections about any line through the origin provide examples. S is made into a ring by defining $(+)$ and $(\cdot)$ by

$$(f + g)(\vec{v}) = f(\vec{v}) + g(\vec{v})$$
$$(f \cdot g)(\vec{v}) = f(g(\vec{v})).$$

The operations clearly give functions from P into itself and we know that composition is associative. We must, however, verify that $f + g$ and $f \cdot g$ satisfy (L) if f and g do. This is not difficult, and we shall omit the details. We have already seen from an earlier example that $\langle S, + \rangle$ is an additive group so that the only remaining axiom is distributivity:

$$f \cdot (g + h)(\vec{v}) = f((g + h)(\vec{v})) = f(g(\vec{v}) + h(\vec{v}))$$
$$= fg(\vec{v}) + fh(\vec{v}) = (fg + fh)(\vec{v}).$$

The next-to-last equality holds because f satisfies (L). Thus $f \cdot (g + h) = f \cdot g + f \cdot h$. Similarly,

$$(g + h) \cdot f(\vec{v}) = (g + h)(f(\vec{v})) = g(f(\vec{v})) + h(f(\vec{v}))$$
$$= (gf + hf)(\vec{v}).$$

Thus $(g + h) \cdot f = g \cdot f + h \cdot f$. (It is curious to note that condition (L) was needed only on the first of these distributive laws.)

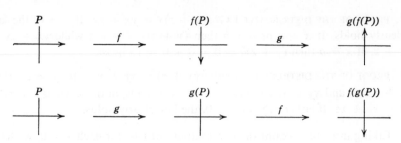

Figure 1

Finally, this ring is not commutative. Let f be a clockwise rotation by 90 degrees and g reflection about the x-axis.

Thus $f \cdot g \neq g \cdot f$ as shown in Figure 1.

It turns out that division rings that are not fields are somewhat hard to come by. We shall not give an example of a division ring that is not a field until Chapter 7. Part of this complication is indicated by a celebrated theorem of J. H. M. Wedderburn (1882–1948), which states that every finite division ring is a field. It is remarkable that the commutativity of multiplication should follow from the other field axioms and the finiteness of the number of elements in the system. We shall prove this theorem in Chapter 8.

Figure 2 may be helpful in comparing the various classes of algebraic structures. A line from one class A to a class B higher on the page indicates that every system in class A may be viewed as an algebraic system in class B. Definitions 1 through 5 (p. 73) show that one system differs from another by the addition of one or more axioms. This may not be apparent in transition from fields to integral domains, but the hiatus is resolved by Lemma 5 below.

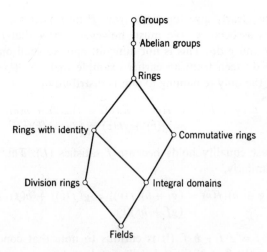

Figure 2

2.2. BASIC LEMMAS *Proofs*

We shall use $(-a)$ to denote the additive inverse of a and write $a - b$ for $a + (-b)$. All the lemmas suppose that $\langle R, +, \cdot \rangle$ is a ring.

Lemma 1. For all $a \in R$, $a \cdot 0 = 0 \cdot a = 0$.

PROOF. We have $a \cdot 0 + a \cdot 0 = a(0 + 0) = a \cdot 0$, hence $a \cdot 0 = 0$. Similarly $0 \cdot a = 0$.

* * *

Lemma 2. For all $a, b \in R$, $a(-b) = (-a)(b) = -(ab)$, $(-a)(-b) = ab$.

PROOF. We have $ab + (-a)b = [a + (-a)] \cdot b = 0 \cdot b = 0$. Thus $-(ab) = (-a)b$. Similarly, $b(-a) = -(ab)$. Finally, $(-a)(-b) = -[(a)(-b)] = -[-(ab)] = ab$, since in $\langle R, + \rangle$, the inverse of the inverse of x is x.

* * *

Lemma 3. In a ring with identity e, the identity is unique.

PROOF. If e and f are two identities we have $fe = ef = f$ and $ef = fe = e$. Thus $e = f$.

Lemma 4. If a ring that is not the nullring has a multiplicative identity e, then $e \neq 0$.

PROOF. If $e = 0$, then for all $a \in R$, $a = ae = a \cdot 0 = 0$. Thus $R = \{0\}$ contrary to the assumption that R was not the nullring.

* * *

Definition. Let R be a ring. An element $a \in R$ is called a left zero-divisor if $a \neq 0$ and if there is an element $b \neq 0$ such that $ab = 0$. Right zero-divisors are defined analogously; for commutative rings there is no difference.

Lemma 5. If R is a ring in which the left cancellation law, if $ab = ac$ and $a \neq 0$ then $b = c$, holds, then R has no left zero-divisors.

PROOF. If $ab = 0$ and $a \neq 0$, then $ab = 0 = a0$; hence $b = 0$.

* * *

If R is a division ring the left cancellation law holds, since for $a \neq 0$, a^{-1} exists; thus whenever $ab = ac$, we have $a^{-1}ab = a^{-1}ac$, or $b = c$. Similarly the right cancellation law holds. Thus, in particular, any field is an integral domain. The converse of Lemma 5 is true and Problem 2 of Exercise 1 asks for a proof.

Theorem 1. Any finite integral domain is a field.

PROOF. Since an integral domain is a commutative ring with identity (denoted by 1) and without zero divisors, to show the nonzero elements form a multiplicative group we need only show the existence of inverses. Let a be a nonzero element of the integral domain. Since the set is finite, not all $a, a^2, a^3, \ldots, a^n, \ldots$, can be distinct. Say $a^r = a^s$ with $r < s$. Then $a^r = a^r \cdot a^{s-r}$ with $s - r > 0$. Hence $a^r(1 - a^{s-r}) = 0$, and since $a \neq 0$, it follows that $(1 - a^{s-r}) = 0$. Thus $1 = a^{s-r}$ and since $s - r \geq 1$, we have $1 = a \cdot a^{(s-r)-1}$, with $(s - r) - 1 \geq 0$. Hence a^{-1} is $a^{(s-r)-1}$. Hence all axioms for a field hold. (Note how nice it is not to have to verify that the inverse is unique! Also note the similarity of this proof with that of Lemma 1.7.)

* * *

2.3. SUBRINGS

Definition. A subset S of a ring $\langle R, +, \cdot \rangle$ is called a subring of R provided S is closed under $(+)$ and $(\cdot)$ and forms a ring under these operations.

Lemma 6. A nonempty subset S of a ring $\langle R, +, \cdot \rangle$ is a subring if and only if

1. For all $a, b \in S$, $a - b \in S$.
2. For all $a, b \in S$, $a \cdot b \in S$.

PROOF. We recall that (1) is a necessary and sufficient condition for $\langle S, + \rangle$ to be a subgroup of $\langle R, + \rangle$. Condition (2) says that S is closed under multiplication and so $(\cdot)$ is a binary operation on S. Finally, since the other ring axioms are identities on R, they hold *a fortiori* on S.

* * *

Example 8. The even integers form a subring of the integers.

Example 9. The integers form a subring of the rational numbers.

Example 10. In Example 6, the set

$$T = \{f : f(x) \text{ is rational}\}$$

is a subring.

Example 11. $\{0\}$ and R are always subrings of R.

Example 12. In Example 7, $\{0, a\}$, $\{0, b\}$, $\{0, a + b\}$ are subrings.

If A and B are subrings of a ring R then the set intersection $A \cap B$ is a subring of R. More generally, if S is a set of subrings of R then $\bigcap S$ is a subring of R. These observations are easily proved.

As in groups, the dual notion of the smallest subring containing A and B is useful but more complicated. We call this ring the *join* of A and B and denote it $A \vee B$; in general it is not the set sum $A \cup B$.

$$A \vee B = \bigcap \{T : T \text{ is a subring of } R \text{ and } A \cup B \subseteq T\}.$$

$A \vee B$ is the set of all finite sums of elements in R which can be expressed as products of elements from A and B.

EXERCISE 1

1. What is wrong with the following string of equalities in the ring of integers?

$$1 = 2 - 1 = (6 - 4) - 1 = (6 + (-4)) - 1 = (6 + (-4)) + (-1)$$
$$= 6 + ((-4) + (-1)) = 6 - (4 - 1) = 6 - 3 = 3.$$

2. Prove that in every ring R with identity which has no left zero divisors, the left cancellation law;

$$\text{if } ab = ac \text{ and } a \neq 0, \text{ then } b = c,$$

holds.

3. Which of the following systems are rings? For those that are rings classify each according to Definitions 1 through 5.

(i) All real numbers of the form $a + b\sqrt{2}$ where a and b are integers under the usual addition and multiplication.

(ii) All real numbers of the form $a + b\sqrt[4]{2} + c\sqrt{2}$ where a, b, and c are rational numbers under the usual addition and multiplication.

(iii) The collection of all subsets of the positive integers where $(+)$ means set union and $(\cdot)$ means set intersection.

(iv) The elements 0, 1, 2, 3, 4, 5, where the addition and multiplication tables are as follows:

+	0	1	2	3	4	5
0	0	1	2	3	4	5
1	1	2	3	4	5	0
2	2	3	4	5	0	1
3	3	4	5	0	1	2
4	4	5	0	1	2	3
5	5	0	1	2	3	4

·	0	1	2	3	4	5
0	0	0	0	0	0	0
1	0	1	2	3	4	5
2	0	2	3	4	5	1
3	0	3	4	5	1	2
4	0	4	5	1	2	3
5	0	5	1	2	3	4

4. Let $\langle D, +, \cdot \rangle$ be a ring with identity. By considering $(1 + 1)(a + b)$, show that the assumption that $(+)$ is a commutative operation is superfluous.

5. Let D and E be integral domains. $D \times E$ can be made into a ring by defining addition and multiplication by components:

$$(a, b) + (c, d) = (a + c, b + d)$$
$$(a, b) \cdot (c, d) = (ac, bd).$$

Show that $D \times E$ is never an integral domain. List those axioms of an integral domain which do hold.

6. (i) Let p be a prime. Let D_p be the set of rational numbers which, when expressed in lowest terms, have form a/b where $b = p^k$ for some $k \geq 0$. Show that under ordinary addition and multiplication D_p is an integral domain.

(ii) Let $\hat{D}_p$ be the set of rational numbers which when expressed in lowest terms have the form a/b where $p \nmid b$. Show that $\hat{D}_p$ is an integral domain.

(iii) Generalize the examples of (i) and (ii).

7. Prove or disprove: There is an integral domain with exactly six elements.

8. Assuming only that the integers are an additive, infinite cyclic group with generator 1, show that the integers are not a field.

2.4. HOMOMORPHISMS

The main feature we need to know about rings at this time is their elementary homomorphism theory. This theory will be a very helpful tool in studying the integers, polynomials, and fields. The theory is easily developed as a direct analogy of group homomorphisms.

Definition. Let $\langle R, +, \cdot \rangle$ and $\langle \bar{R}, +, \cdot \rangle$ be two rings. A function φ mapping R into $\bar{R}$ is called a (ring) homomorphism of R provided for all $a, b \in R$.

     1. $\varphi(a + b) = \varphi(a) + \varphi(b)$.
     2. $\varphi(ab) = \varphi(a)\varphi(b)$.

→ Isomorphism

If φ is onto, $\bar{R}$ is called a homomorphic image of R. If φ is 1–1 and onto, φ is called a (ring) isomorphism and we write $R \simeq \bar{R}$. If $\langle R, +, \cdot \rangle = \langle \bar{R}, +, \cdot \rangle$ then φ is called an *endomorphism*. If φ is in fact 1–1 and onto then φ is called an automorphism. Conditions 1 and 2 show that the range of φ is a subring of $\bar{R}$ as the conditions of Lemma 6 are readily verified.

Condition 1 tells us that φ is a group homomorphism of $\langle R, + \rangle$ into $\langle \bar{R}, + \rangle$. If we use 0 as the symbol for the additive identity in both R and $\bar{R}$, the set $K = \{x : x \in R, \varphi(x) = 0\}$ is the kernel of φ and is a subgroup of $\langle R, + \rangle$. In addition, K is a subring of $\langle R, +, \cdot \rangle$ since if $\varphi(r) = \varphi(s) = 0$ then $\varphi(rs) = \varphi(r)\varphi(s) = 0$. But, just as in the group case, K is no ordinary subring. Indeed, we have that if $r \in K$ then for any $s \in R$, it follows that both rs and sr belong to K since $\varphi(rs) = \varphi(r)\varphi(s) = 0 \cdot \varphi(s) = 0 = \varphi(s) \cdot 0 = \varphi(s)\varphi(r) = \varphi(sr)$. In other words not only is K closed under multiplication, but even when we multiply an element in K by an arbitrary element of R we get an element in K.

Definition. A nonempty subset A of a ring $\langle R, +, \cdot \rangle$ is called an *ideal* provided A is a subring and

     1. For all $a \in A$ and $r \in R$, $ar \in A$ and $ra \in A$.

The condition "A is subring" may be replaced by
     2. If $a \in A$ and $b \in A$ then $a - b \in A$
since (2) implies $\langle A, + \rangle$ is a subgroup of $\langle R, + \rangle$ while (1) guarantees that A is closed under $(\cdot)$.

We may restate our observations about the kernel of a ring homomorphism as a theorem.

Theorem 2. Let φ be a homomorphism of the ring $\langle R, +, \cdot \rangle$ into the ring $\langle \bar{R}, +, \cdot \rangle$. The kernel $K = \{x : \varphi(x) = 0\}$ is an ideal of R. φ is a 1–1 mapping if and only if $K = \{0\}$.

PROOF. Only the last statement remains to be proved. If φ is 1–1 and $\varphi(a) = \bar{0}$, then $a = 0$ so that $K = \{0\}$. If $K = \{0\}$ and $\varphi(a) = \varphi(b)$ then $\bar{0} = \varphi(a) - \varphi(b) = \varphi(a - b)$ and so $a - b = 0$ or $a = b$. Thus φ is a 1–1 mapping.

Example 13. $\{0\}$ is an ideal, the zero ideal.

Example 14. R is an ideal, sometimes called the unit ideal.

Example 15. In Example 7 of a ring with 4 elements, $\{0, b\}$ is an ideal.

Example 16. Let $\langle I, +, \cdot \rangle$ be the ring of integers under the usual addition and multiplication. $\langle d \rangle = \{xd : x = 0, \pm 1, \ldots\}$ is an ideal.

Example 17. Let $\langle R, +, \cdot \rangle$ be the ring in Example 6, the ring of functions. Let S be any subset of real numbers.

Let $A = \{f : f(x) = 0 \text{ for all } x \in S\}$. A is an ideal. (The subring of Example 10 is not an ideal.)

Example 18. Let $\langle R, +, \cdot \rangle$ be the rational numbers under the usual addition and multiplication. Let I be the set of integers. I is a subring of R but *not* an ideal since, for example, $1 \in I$, $1/2 \in R$ but $1/2 \cdot 1 = 1/2 \notin I$.

Example 19. Let R be a commutative ring. Let $a \in R$ and $A = \{ra : r \in R\}$. A is an ideal, for if $ra \in A$ and $s \in R$, then $s(ra) = (sr)a \in A$ and $(ra)s = s(ra) \in A$, and if $ra \in A$ and $sa \in A$ then $ra - sa = (r - s)a \in A$. We write $A = Ra$.

It is worth noting that unless R has an identity, a need not be a member of this ideal. As an example consider the ideal consisting of the multiples of 4 in the ring E of even integers. This is clearly $E2$, but $2 \notin E2$.

Example 20. Let R be a commutative ring. Let $a \in R$. Let $\langle a \rangle = \{ra + na : r \in R \text{ and } n \in I\}$. It is easily verified that $\langle a \rangle$ is an ideal of R, in fact the smallest ideal containing a. $\langle a \rangle$ is called a *principal* ideal.

Note that $\langle a \rangle = Ra$ if R contains an identity e, since for every integer n we have $na = (ne)a$ and, of course, $ne \in R$.

It is easy to see that if A and B are ideals then $A \cap B$ is an ideal and $A \vee B$ is an ideal. When A and B are ideals, the join $A \vee B$ has a particularly easy characterization.

Lemma 7. If A and B are ideals of a ring R then $A \vee B = T$ where

$$T = \{a + b : a \in A \text{ and } b \in B\}.$$

PROOF. First we show that T is an ideal by verifying conditions 1 and 2 of the definition. Let $r \in R$, $a \in A$ and $b \in B$, then $r(a + b) = ra + rb$, and because A and B are ideals, $ra \in A$ and $rb \in B$. Similarly $(a + b)r \in T$, and so condition 1 holds for T. The identity $(a + b) - (a_1 + b_1) = (a - a_1) + (b - b_1)$ shows that condition 2 holds.

It is easy to see, just from condition 2 that any ideal containing $A \vee B$ must contain T, while $T \supset A \vee B$ trivially. Hence the lemma follows.

$$* \quad * \quad *$$

Definition. Let R be a commutative ring. An ideal A of R is called *principal* if there is an $a \in A$ such that $A = \langle a \rangle$.

Theorem 3. Every ideal in the ring of integers I is principal.

PROOF. Let A be an ideal. If $A = \{0\} = \langle 0 \rangle$ there is nothing more to prove; henceforth we assume that A contains some nonzero elements. A must contain some positive elements, for if $x \in A$, then $-x \in A$ as A is a subgroup under addition. Now select a as the smallest positive element of A. Now if $y \in A$, we have $y = aq + r$ where $0 \leq r < a$ by Theorem 0.2. As $r = y - aq$ and both y and aq belong to A, it follows that $r \in A$, also. The alternative $0 < r < a$ contradicts the choice of a, so that r must equal 0 and $aq = y \in \langle a \rangle$. Thus $\langle a \rangle = A$.

*   *   *

We now wish to prove analogues of the other group-theoretic theorems.

Theorem 4. Let A be an ideal of $\langle R, +, \cdot \rangle$. There is a ring $\bar{R}$ and a homomorphism φ of R onto $\bar{R}$ whose kernel is A.

PROOF. We begin with the information provided by the observation that $\langle A, + \rangle$ is a subgroup of $\langle R, + \rangle$ which is normal since $(+)$ is commutative. Hence we know there is a group homomorphism φ of $\langle R, + \rangle$ onto $\langle R/A, + \rangle$. We shall make R/A into a ring by defining a multiplication $(\cdot)$ on the cosets of A.

First let us recall how $(+)$ works in $\langle R/A, + \rangle$. We write the cosets additively and, by Theorem 1.24, we know

$$(r + A) + (s + A) = (r + s) + A.$$

We shall define our multiplication by

$$(r + A) \cdot (s + A) = (r \cdot s) + A.$$

As in the group case we must justify that this definition is independent of the coset representatives. It is at this crucial step we use the property that A is an ideal and not just a subring. We claim that if $r + A = r_1 + A$ and $s + A = s_1 + A$, then $rs + A = r_1 s_1 + A$. Remember that these are cosets of $\langle A, + \rangle$ in $\langle R, + \rangle$ so that this is equivalent to proving that if $r_1 \in (r + A)$ and $s_1 \in (s + A)$ then $r_1 s_1 \in (rs + A)$. Now,

$$r_1 \in (r + A) \text{ implies } r_1 = r + a_1, \text{ for some } a_1 \in A,$$
$$s_1 \in (s + A) \text{ implies } s_1 = s + a_2, \text{ for some } a_2 \in A.$$

Thus $r_1 s_1 = (r + a_1)(s + a_2) = rs + ra_2 + a_1 s + a_1 a_2$. Now ra_2, $a_1 s$, and $a_1 a_2 \in A$ since A is an ideal (property 1 of the definition). Hence $ra_2 + a_1 s + a_1 a_2 \in A$ since A is an additive group, and so $r_1 s_1 \in rs + A$.

We have thus defined, on the cosets of A, an addition and a multiplication. We have now to verify the ring axioms. We know $\langle R/A, + \rangle$ is an abelian group. The associativity of $(\cdot)$ and the distributive laws follow easily since the operations $(+)$ and $(\cdot)$ on the cosets are done by the corresponding operations on the coset representatives in R. Thus $\bar{R}$ shall be $\langle R/A, + \rangle$.

Finally to get the homomorphism φ we simply define for all $r \in R$, $\varphi(r) = r + A$. Clearly φ has the desired properties.

$$* \quad * \quad *$$

Terminology

The ring $\langle R/A, +, \cdot \rangle$ we have just constructed will be called the *residue class* ring. (The terms *factor ring*, *difference ring*, or *quotient ring* are also appropriate.) The cosets of A are now called residue classes. The mapping $\varphi : R \to R/A$ given by $\varphi(r) = r + A$ we shall call the *natural* homomorphism of R onto R/A.

Example 21. Let $\langle I, +, \cdot \rangle$ be the ring of integers under the usual addition and multiplication. Let A be the ideal $\langle 12 \rangle = \{12n : n = 0, \pm 1, \ldots\}$. I/A consists of 12 residue classes (cosets) $\{A = 0 + A, 1 + A, 2 + A, \ldots, 11 + A\}$. The residue classes are distinct since, if $r + A = s + A$, then $s = r + a$ for some $a \in A$, or $s = r + 12n$, or 12 divides $s - r$. But if $0 \le r, s < 12$, 12 cannot divide $s - r$, unless $s = r$.

On the other hand, for any integer m we have $m = 12q + r$ where $0 \le r < 12$, so that $m \in r + A$. Let us write $\bar{r}$ for $r + A$. Note that in I/A, $\bar{4} \cdot \bar{3} = \overline{4 \cdot 3} = \overline{12} = \bar{0} = A$; thus I/A is not an integral domain.

Example 21 shows that a homomorphic image of an integral domain need not be an integral domain. However, it is easy to see that if φ is a homomorphism of R *onto* $\bar{R}$ it follows that

(1) If R is a ring with identity 1, then $\bar{R}$ is a ring with identity $\bar{1}$, and $\bar{1} = \varphi(1)$,

(2) If R is commutative, then $\bar{R}$ is commutative.

Example 22. Example 21 can be generalized to a whole class of examples by choosing the ideal $\langle d \rangle$ of the integers described in Example 16. $\langle I, +, \cdot \rangle$ is the ring of integers, $I/\langle d \rangle$ consists of the d residue classes

$$\{a + \langle d \rangle : a = 0, 1, \ldots, (d - 1)\}.$$

Theorem 5. Let I be the ring of integers and $d \in I$. $I/\langle d \rangle$ is an integral domain if and only if $d = 0$ or d is a prime.

PROOF. For all d we know that $I/\langle d \rangle$ is a commutative ring with identity. If $d = 0$ then $I/\langle 0 \rangle \cong I$ and so $I/\langle 0 \rangle$ is an integral domain. Suppose that d is a prime. Suppose that for nonzero residue classes $\bar{a}$ and $\bar{b}$ it is true that $\bar{a}\bar{b} = \bar{0}$. Since $\overline{ab} = \bar{a}\bar{b}$ it follows that $ab \in \langle d \rangle$ and so $d \mid ab$. Since d is a prime, it follows from the definition in Chapter 0 that $d \mid a$ or $d \mid b$, and hence $a \in \langle d \rangle$ or $b \in \langle d \rangle$, that is, $\bar{a} = \bar{0}$ or $\bar{b} = \bar{0}$. Thus $I/\langle d \rangle$ is an integral domain.

On the other hand, suppose that $d \neq 0$ and $I/\langle d \rangle$ is an integral domain. If $d = ab$, where a and b are positive integers, then from Theorem 0.1 it follows that $a \leq d$ and $b \leq d$. As $d = ab$ we have $\bar{0} = \bar{d} = \overline{ab} = \bar{a}\bar{b}$. Since $I/\langle d \rangle$ is an integral domain, either $\bar{a} = \bar{0}$ or $\bar{b} = \bar{0}$. If $\bar{a} = \bar{0}$ then $a \in \langle d \rangle$ and so $d \mid a$; hence by Theorem 0.1, $d \leq a$. Thus $d = a$. Similarly if $\bar{b} = \bar{0}$, we conclude that $d = b$, and so it follows from Theorem 0.3 that d is a prime.

Corollary. $I/\langle d \rangle$ is a field if and only if d is a prime.

PROOF. This is an immediate consequence of Theorem 5 and Theorem 1.

$$* \quad * \quad *$$

We shall often denote $I/\langle d \rangle$ as simply I_d.

> **Theorem 6.** Let φ be a homomorphism of $\langle R, +, \cdot \rangle$ onto $\langle \bar{R}, +, \cdot \rangle$ with kernel K. Then $\bar{R} \cong R/K$.

PROOF. We know from the corresponding theorem for groups that $\langle \bar{R}, + \rangle \cong \langle R/K, + \rangle$ by the isomorphism ψ, $\psi(r + A) = \varphi(r)$. (See the proof of Theorem 1.20.) We have only to show that ψ preserves multiplication.
$$\psi[(r + A)(s + A)] = \psi(rs + A) = \varphi(rs) = \varphi(r)\varphi(s) = \psi(r + A) \cdot \psi(s + A).$$

> **Theorem 7.** Let φ be a homomorphism of $\langle R, +, \cdot \rangle$ onto $\langle \bar{R}, +, \cdot \rangle$ with kernel K. There is a 1–1 correspondence θ between the subrings of R containing K and the subrings of $\bar{R}$ such that for subrings A and B of R
> 1. If $R \supseteq A \supseteq B \supseteq K$ then $\theta(R) = \bar{R} \supseteq \theta(A) \supseteq \theta(B) \supseteq \theta(K) = \{\bar{0}\}$ and
> 2. If $R \supseteq A \supseteq K$ then A is an ideal of R if and only if $\theta(A)$ is an ideal of $\bar{R}$.

PROOF. The corresponding theorem for groups (Theorem 1.29) and its proof shows that if $\langle A, + \rangle$ is a subgroup of $\langle R, + \rangle$ and $A \supseteq K$, then the mapping θ given by $\theta(A) = \{\varphi(a) : a \in A\}$ is a 1–1 correspondence of the subgroups of R which contain K and the subgroups of $\bar{R}$. Thus, to prove the first part of our theorem and at the same time prove property 1, we need only show that $\theta(A)$ is a subring if and only if A is a subring, that is, that $\theta(A)$ is closed under multiplication if and only if A is closed under multiplication. First assume that A is closed under multiplication. Let $\bar{r}, \bar{s} \in \theta(A)$. Thus we have for some $r, s \in A$ that $\varphi(r) = \bar{r}$ and $\varphi(s) = \bar{s}$. But $\bar{r}\bar{s} = \varphi(r)\varphi(s) = \varphi(rs)$, and since $rs \in A$ it follows that $\bar{r}\bar{s} \in \theta(A)$. Thus $\theta(A)$ is closed under multiplication. Conversely, assume that $\theta(A)$ is closed under multiplication and let $r, s \in A$. Then $\varphi(r), \varphi(s) \in \theta(A)$ so that $\varphi(r)\varphi(s) = \varphi(rs) \in \theta(A)$. Now this means that there is some $a \in A$ such that $\varphi(a) = \varphi(rs)$ and thus $\varphi(rs - a) = 0$ so that

$rs - a \in K$. Now $K \subseteq A$ so that $rs - a \in A$, and since $a \in A$ and A is a subgroup, it follows that $rs \in A$. Thus A is closed under multiplication.

To prove property 2 suppose that $R \supseteq A \supseteq K$ and that A is an ideal. We now know that $\theta(A)$ is a subring; we shall show it is an ideal. Now suppose $\varphi(a) \in \theta(A)$ and $\bar{r} \in \bar{R}$. There exists an $r \in R$ such that $\varphi(r) = \bar{r}$. Then $\bar{r}\varphi(a) = \varphi(r)\varphi(a) = \varphi(ra)$. Since A is an ideal $ra \in A$ and so $\bar{r}\varphi(a) \in \theta(A)$. Similarly, $\varphi(a)\bar{r} \in \theta(A)$. Conversely, suppose that $\theta(A)$ is an ideal; we shall show that A is an ideal. Let $a \in A$ and $r \in R$. We have $\varphi(r)\varphi(a) = \varphi(ra) \in \theta(A)$. Thus there is an element $b \in A$ such that $\varphi(b) = \varphi(ra)$ and so $ra - b \in K \subseteq A$. Since A is a subring and $b \in A$, it follows that $ra \in A$. Similarly, we can show that $ar \in A$ and thus complete the proof that A is an ideal.

* * *

There is another way of viewing a ring homomorphism and the residue class ring. We introduce the notion of a congruence relation on a ring.

Definition. Let $\langle R, +, \cdot \rangle$ be a ring. A *congruence* relation ($\equiv$) on R is an equivalence relation such that

1. If $a \equiv b$ then $a + c \equiv b + c$ for all $c \in R$, and
2. If $a \equiv b$ then $ac \equiv bc$ and $ca \equiv cb$ for all $c \in R$.

Lemma 8. If ($\equiv$) is a congruence on R then

$$K = \{x : x \equiv 0\}$$

is an ideal, and the residue classes of K in R are the equivalence classes of R under the congruence ($\equiv$).

PROOF. The verification that K is an ideal is routine. It then suffices to prove that $a \equiv b$ if and only if $(b - a) \in K$, for then $a \equiv b$ if and only if $b \in a + K$. If $a \equiv b$ then $0 = a - a \equiv b - a$ and so $(b - a) \in K$. If $(b - a) \in K$ then $b - a \equiv 0$ and so $b \equiv a$.

* * *

In view of this lemma the following theorem is clear.

Theorem 8. The congruence relations on a ring are in 1–1 correspondence with the ideals of the ring.

It is standard practice to incorporate a symbol for the ideal K associated with a congruence in the notation, and instead of writing $a \equiv b$, we write more fully

$$a \equiv b \ (\text{modulo } K), \text{ or more briefly,}$$
$$a \equiv b \ (\text{mod } K), \text{ or more briefly,}$$
$$a \equiv b \ (K).$$

When R is the ring of integers, the notation is even simpler for Theorem 3 tells us that every ideal $K \subseteq I$ is principal, $K = \langle k \rangle$, and so we write

$$a \equiv b \ (\text{mod } k) \quad \text{for} \quad a \equiv b \ (\text{mod } \langle k \rangle).$$

Notice that $a \equiv b \ (\text{mod } k)$ if and only if $k \mid (a - b)$.

A consequence of Theorem 8 is that the theory of congruences could be subsumed under the theory of ring homomorphisms and residue class rings. Historically, congruences, as generalized equality on the integers, came first and each concept has its advantages. When our attention is focused on the homomorphic image $\bar{R}$ and we wish to study the properties of the image, the notation $\bar{b} = \bar{a}$ instead of $b \in a + A$ is more suggestive. When we are interested in R and are studying its properties, the notation $a \equiv b \ (\text{mod } A)$ often facilitates calculations because of its equality-like properties. This is particularly true when R is the ring of integers. As an example of both techniques we shall prove some standard number-theoretic results.

Theorem 9. (*Fermat's Little Theorem*). Let p be a prime in I. For all a not divisible by p,

$$p \mid a^{p-1} - 1.$$

Equivalent statements are

1. If $a \not\equiv 0 \ (\text{mod } p)$ then $a^{p-1} \equiv 1 \ (\text{mod } p)$ or
2. In the natural homomorphism $\varphi : I \to I/\langle p \rangle$, if $\bar{a} \neq \bar{0}$ then $(\bar{a})^{p-1} = \bar{1}$.

Statement 1 is the usual form in which it is found in the literature, and it varies from the statement of Theorem 9 only in vocabulary. Statement 2 says that a^{p-1} and 1 have the same image under φ.

PROOF. We shall prove statement 2. From Theorem 5 and its corollary we know that $I/\langle p \rangle$ is a field, and hence the nonzero elements form a multiplicative group M of order $p - 1$. If $\bar{a} \neq \bar{0}$ then $\bar{a} \in M$ and it follows from the corollary to the theorem of Lagrange applied to M that $(\bar{a})^{p-1} = \bar{1}$.

* * *

Corollary. For all integers a and all primes p, $a^p \equiv a \ (\text{mod } p)$.

PROOF. If $a \not\equiv 0 \ (\text{mod } p)$ then $a^{p-1} \equiv 1 \ (\text{mod } p)$ and hence $a^p \equiv a \ (\text{mod } p)$. If $a \equiv 0 \ (\text{mod } p)$ then $a^n \equiv 0 \equiv a \ (\text{mod } p)$ for all n, in particular $n = p$.

* * *

Another result from number theory, known as Wilson's theorem (Theorem 10), has an easy proof in these terms. We need the following lemma.

Lemma 9. If p is a prime integer greater than 2, then in $I/\langle p \rangle$ there are exactly two elements $\bar{x}$ such that $\bar{x}^2 = \bar{1}$.

PROOF. We see that $\bar{1}^2 = (-\bar{1})^2 = \bar{1}$. Since $p \neq 2$, it follows that $\bar{1} \neq -\bar{1}$ and so there are at least two elements $\bar{x}$ whose squares are $\bar{1}$. On the other hand, if $\bar{x}^2 = \bar{1}$ then $\bar{x}^2 - \bar{1} = (\bar{x} - \bar{1})(\bar{x} + \bar{1}) = \bar{0}$. Since $I/\langle p \rangle$ is an integral domain, it must be that $\bar{x} - \bar{1} = \bar{0}$ or $\bar{x} + \bar{1} = \bar{0}$. Hence there can be at most two solutions to the equation $\bar{x}^2 - \bar{1} = \bar{0}$.

*   *   *

Theorem 10. If p is a prime integer then $(p - 1)! \equiv -1 \pmod{p}$.

PROOF. If $p = 2$ we verify that $(2 - 1)! = 1! \equiv -1 \pmod{2}$. Henceforth we assume that $p > 2$. The statement of the theorem is equivalent to the statement that in $I/\langle p \rangle$ the product of all nonzero elements equals $(-\bar{1})$. Now with every nonzero element $\bar{a}$ in $I/\langle p \rangle$ we may associate its inverse $(\bar{a})^{-1}$, and as Lemma 9 shows, $(\bar{a})^{-1} \neq \bar{a}$ unless $\bar{a} = \bar{1}$ or $\bar{a} = -\bar{1}$. Thus in the product of all nonzero elements in $I/\langle p \rangle$, if $\bar{a} \neq \bar{1}$ or $-\bar{1}$, the element $\bar{a}$ cancels with $(\bar{a})^{-1}$. Hence the product of all elements in $I/\langle p \rangle$ must equal what is left after cancellation, which is $\bar{1}(-\bar{1}) = (-\bar{1})$.

*   *   *

It is possible to prove a representation theorem for rings which is similar to the representation theorem for groups. It will not be of particular use to us in this book but it does help to emphasize the analogue between groups and rings. The motivation for the theorem stems from the observation that the mapping φ_a defined on a ring by $\varphi_a(r) = ar$ yields an endomorphism of the additive group of the ring. This is so, since $\varphi_a(r) + \varphi_a(s) = ar + as = a(r + s) = \varphi_a(r + s)$. Moreover, composition of these endomorphisms obeys the following rule, $(\varphi_a \circ \varphi_b)(r) = \varphi_a(\varphi_b(r)) = \varphi_a(br) = a(br) = (ab)r = \varphi_{ab}(r)$. This suggests that the endomorphisms of the additive group can be made into a ring by defining $\varphi_a + \varphi_b$ and $\varphi_a \circ \varphi_b$ as follows:

1. $(\varphi_a + \varphi_b)(r) = \varphi_a(r) + \varphi_b(r)$,
2. $(\varphi_a \circ \varphi_b)(r) = \varphi_a(\varphi_b(r))$.

Theorem 11 (*Representation Theorem for Rings*). A ring $\langle R, +, \cdot \rangle$ with identity is isomorphic to a ring of endomorphisms of $\langle R, + \rangle$.

PROOF. For the set of endomorphisms we select $E = \{\varphi_a : a \in R, \varphi_a(r) = ar\}$. We define addition on E by (1) and define multiplication on E as composition of endomorphisms as given by (2). We now claim that $\langle R, +, \cdot \rangle$ is isomorphic to $\langle E, +, \circ \rangle$ by the mapping Φ defined by $\Phi(a) = \varphi_a$ for all $a \in R$. Clearly Φ is a function from R onto E. If $\varphi_a = \varphi_b$ then, in particular, $\varphi_a(1) = \varphi_b(1)$, that is, $1a = 1b$ and so $a = b$. Thus Φ is a 1–1 mapping.

To show that Φ preserves the ring operations we must show that $\Phi(a + b) = \Phi(a) + \Phi(b)$ and $\Phi(ab) = \Phi(a) \circ \Phi(b)$. The first means that

$\Phi_{a+b} = (\varphi_a + \varphi_b)$, which is true since $\varphi_{a+b}(r) = (a + b)r = ar + br = \varphi_a(r) + \varphi_b(r) = (\varphi_a + \varphi_b)(r)$. The second means that $\varphi_{ab} = \varphi_a \circ \varphi_b$, which is true since $(\varphi_a \circ \varphi_b)(r) = a(br) = (ab)r = \varphi_{ab}(r)$.

* * *

EXERCISE 2

1. Three mathematicians are discussing integral domains. One says: "If D is any system of numbers forming an integral domain, I can construct a new integral domain out of D. I simply define a new addition ($\oplus$) and a new multiplication ($*$) over D as follows:

$$a \oplus b = a + b - 1, \qquad a * b = ab - (a + b) + 2.$$

(Of course, I keep the old equality.)"

The second mathematician says: "You're crazy. According to *your* definition

$$a + 0 = a - 1,$$

so zero hasn't got the right properties."

The third mathematician says: "You're both crazy. Its an integral domain, all right, but the construction is trivial, because the new domain is isomorphic to the old one."

The first mathematician says: "We are all crazy then. I defy you to prove my new integral domain is isomorphic to the old one. Think of the integers."

Since mathematicians are not crazy, decide who is wrong and who is right in this dispute by proving these statements which are true.

2. Show that the following addition and multiplication tables for the set $D = \{0, 1\}$ make $\langle D, +, \cdot \rangle$ an integral domain by showing that this ring is isomorphic to $I/\langle 2 \rangle$.

+	0	1
0	0	1
1	1	0

·	0	1
0	0	0
1	0	1

3. Show that the only ideals in a division ring D are $\{0\}$ and D itself.

4. Prove the assertions about $\langle a \rangle$ in Example 20.

5. Solve the following congruences:

(i) $2x \equiv 1 \pmod 7$
(ii) $x^2 \equiv -1 \pmod{10}$
(iii) $x^2 \equiv -1 \pmod 5$
(iv) $3x + 5 \equiv 6x + 6 \pmod 8$

6. Show that the multiplicative group of nonzero elements in $I/\langle 11 \rangle$ is cyclic by finding a generator.

7. Let R be a commutative ring with identity. Prove that if $a \equiv b \pmod{\langle n \rangle}$ then $\sum_{i=0}^n c_i a^i \equiv \sum_{i=0}^n c_i b^i \pmod{\langle n \rangle}$.

8. In I, prove that 3 (or 9) divides m if and only if when m is written in the usual decimal notation, 3 (or 9) divides the sum of the digits. *Hint:* $10 \equiv 1 \pmod 3$ and $10 \equiv 1 \pmod 9$.

9. Find and prove a criterion for divisibility by 11.

10. What are the ideals of $I/\langle 6 \rangle$?

11. Let $\langle A, + \rangle$ be a finite abelian group of order $2n$ where n is odd. Let t be the unique element of order 2 in A (Exercise 1.5, Problem 7). Show that $\sum_{a \in A} a = t$.

2.5. INTEGRAL DOMAINS

In this section we shall investigate some properties of *division* in an integral domain.

Definition. If R is a commutative ring and a, b are elements of R, we say that *a divides b*, ($a \mid b$), or b is divisible by a, or a is a *factor* of b, if $a \neq 0$ and if there exists $c \in R$ such that $b = ac$. We write $a \nmid b$ if a does not divide b.

We select an integral domain for our investigations for several reasons. To begin with it is commutative; thus we do not have to speak of left divisors and right divisors of b (in an arbitrary ring there is no reason why if $b = ac$ there should exist d such that $b = da$). We do not consider a field because every nonzero element has an inverse so that every nonzero element divides every other element: $b = a(a^{-1}b)$. In an integral domain, partly because it has no zero divisors and partly because we do not assume the existence of multiplicative inverses, division and the resulting arithmetic theory play an important role in the study of its structure.

In this section, except for certain definitions, which we prefer to have available for arbitrary commutative rings, we suppose that all elements belong to an integral domain D. We begin by stating as a lemma some elementary results whose proofs we omit.

Lemma 10. If $a \mid b$ then there is a unique c such that $b = ac$. We denote this element by b/a. If $a \neq 0$ then $a \mid 0$. If $a \mid b$ then $a \mid sb$ for all $s \in D$. If $a \mid b$ and $a \mid c$ then $a \mid b + c$. If $a \mid b$ and $b \mid c$ then $a \mid c$.

Definition. Let R be a commutative ring with identity, 1. An element u of R is called a *unit* if $u \mid 1$.

Observe that 1 and -1 are units in any integral domain. More generally in any field, every nonzero element is a unit.

Example 23. In the integral domain whose elements are $\{a + b\sqrt{2} : a, b \in I\}$ the units include ± 1 and $\pm(1 + \sqrt{2})$ and $\pm(1 - \sqrt{2})$ and consist of elements of the form $a + b\sqrt{2}$ where $a^2 - 2b^2 = \pm 1$. For example,
$$(1 + \sqrt{2})(-1 + \sqrt{2}) = 1.$$

Lemma 11. If $a \mid b$ and $b \mid a$, then $a = be$ where e is a unit.

PROOF. From $a \mid b$ it follows that $b = ac$. From $b \mid a$, it follows that $a = bd$. Hence $b \cdot 1 = b = ac = (bd)c = b(dc)$. Since $b \neq 0$, it follows by the cancellation law that $dc = 1$, hence that $d \mid 1$, or that d is a unit.

* * *

Definition. Let R be a commutative ring with identity. A element a is called an *associate* of b if $a = be$, where e is a unit.

Lemma 12. The relation ($\sim$) on D, defined by $a \sim b$ if and only if a is an associate of b, is an equivalence relation.

The proof is left to the reader.

Definition. In an integral domain an element b is called *irreducible* if $b \neq 0$ and b is not a unit, but $a \mid b$ implies a is a unit or an associate of b. Otherwise b is called *reducible*.

Definition. In an integral domain an element $a \neq 0$ is called a *prime* if it is not a unit and if whenever $a \mid bc$, $a \mid b$ or $a \mid c$.

Lemma 13. If p is a prime, then p is irreducible.

PROOF. Suppose $a \mid p$. Then $p = ab$. Hence $p \mid a$ or $p \mid b$. If $p \mid a$, then, by Lemma 11, a is an associate of p. If $p \mid b$, then $b = cp$ and so $1 \cdot p = p = ab = acp = (ac)p$ and hence $1 = ac$. Thus a is a unit.

$$* \quad * \quad *$$

The converse of Lemma 13 is false, as Problems 13 and 14 in Exercise 5.2 show.

Definition. If one of b or c is nonzero and if $a \mid b$ and $a \mid c$, then a is called a *common* divisor of b and c. If u is a common divisor of b and c, and if $a \mid u$ for all common divisors a of b and c, then u is called a *greatest common divisor* (GCD) of b and c.
If b and c are nonzero, $b \mid a$ and $c \mid a$, then a is called a common multiple of b and c. If v is a common multiple of b and c and if $v \mid a$ for all common multiples a of b and c, then v is called a *least common multiple* (LCM) of b and c.

Lemma 14. If b and c have a greatest common divisor or a least common multiple, each is unique to within multiplication by a unit.

PROOF. Let u and u_1 be two greatest common divisors of b and c. We have $u \mid u_1$ and $u_1 \mid u$, hence by Lemma 11, $u_1 = ue$, where e is a unit. A similar proof holds for the least common multiple.

$$* \quad * \quad *$$

In view of Lemma 14 we shall, for now, use an ambiguous notation for a greatest common divisor of b and c denoting it by (b, c). Similarly, we denote a least common multiple by $[b, c]$. There is no guarantee that these exist for all pairs of elements. We shall study for the most part, integral domains where GCD and LCM exist. In any event the next lemma is true.

Lemma 15. If nonzero elements b and c have a GCD (b, c) and an LCM $[b, c]$, then $bc \sim [b, c](b, c)$. Moreover, if b and c have a LCM then $[b, c] \mid bc$ and $bc/[b, c]$ is a GCD of b and c.

PROOF. Since any two GCD's of b and c are associates, it suffices to prove the last sentence of the lemma. Certainly bc is a common multiple of b and c, hence assuming $[b, c]$ exists, $bc = [b, c]d$. It remains to see that d is a GCD of b and c. Since $b \mid [b, c]$ we have $[b, c] = bb_1$ and hence $bc = bb_1d$, or, by cancellation, $c = b_1d$. Hence $d \mid c$. Similarly $d \mid b$, and so d is a common divisor of b and c. Let a be a common divisor of b and c. We have, then, $b = ab_2$ and $c = ac_2$. Thus ab_2c_2 is a common multiple of b and c. Hence $[b, c]e = ab_2c_2$. But now $bc = ab_2ac_2 = (ab_2c_2)a = [b, c]ea$. Thus $[b, c]d = [b, c]ea$ or $d = ea$; hence $a \mid d$. Thus d is a GCD of b and c and so $(b, c) \sim d$.

Lemma 16. If b and c are elements in an integral domain that possess a GCD, say $(b, c) = d$, then $(b/d, c/d) = 1$.

PROOF. Let $b = db_1$ and $c = dc_1$. Let u be a common divisor of b_1 and c_1. It suffices to show that u is a unit. To this end we write $b_1 = ub_2$ and $c_1 = uc_2$. Hence $b = db_2u$ and $c = dc_2u$, and du is a common divisor. But then $du \mid d$, as d was assumed to be the greatest common divisor. However, $d \mid du$ trivially and, by Lemma 11, $d = due$, or $1 = ue$.

* * *

For integral domains we can prove a generalization of Theorem 5.

Theorem 12. Let $\langle D, +, \cdot \rangle$ be an integral domain and let $a \in D$. $D/\langle a \rangle$ has zero divisors if a is not irreducible. If a is a prime, then $D/\langle a \rangle$ is an integral domain.

PROOF. If a is not irreducible then $a = xy$ where x and y are neither units nor associates of a. This means that $x \notin \langle a \rangle$ and $y \notin \langle a \rangle$. However under the natural homomorphism $D \rightarrow D/\langle a \rangle$, we have $\bar{0} = \bar{a} = \overline{xy} = \bar{x}\bar{y}$ and, since $x \notin \langle a \rangle$, $\bar{x} \neq \bar{0}$ and similarly $\bar{y} \neq 0$. Hence $\bar{x}$ is a zero divisor.

Now suppose that a is a prime and $\bar{u}\bar{v} = \bar{0}$ in $D/\langle a \rangle$. Then $\bar{0} = \bar{u}\bar{v} = \overline{uv}$, or $uv \in \langle a \rangle$. Thus $a \mid uv$ and as a is prime, by definition $a \mid u$ or $a \mid v$, hence $\bar{u} = \bar{0}$ or $\bar{v} = \bar{0}$.

The generalization of the Corollary of Theorem 5 to integral domains turns out to depend not on the finiteness of the set of residue classes of $D/\langle a \rangle$, as it would appear from the proof given for the corollary, but on the fact that the ideal, which is the kernel of the homomorphism, is a *maximal* ideal. A maximal ideal of a ring R is an ideal A such that $A \neq R$, and if T is an ideal such that $A \subset T \subseteq R$, then $T = R$.

EXERCISE 3

1. In a commutative ring show (i) that no unit is a zero divisor, and (ii) that the units form a multiplicative group.

2. Find the units in the integral domains D_p and $\hat{D}_p$ of Problem 6 in Exercise 1.

3. Prove that, in an integral domain, if $b \mid c$ then b is a greatest common divisor and c is a least common multiple of b and c.

4. Let D be an integral domain. Suppose that 1 is the GCD of a and b. Suppose further that ae and be possess a GCD. Show $(ae, be) = e$.

5. Given that $D = \{a + b\sqrt{2} : a \text{ and } b \text{ integers}\}$ is an integral domain. Let $g(a + b\sqrt{2}) = |a^2 - 2b^2|$.

(i) Show that if $\alpha, \beta \in D$ then $g(\alpha\beta) = g(\alpha)g(\beta)$.

(ii) Show that $1 + 2\sqrt{2}$ is an irreducible element in D.

6. If $a \mid b$ and $a \mid c$ prove that $a \mid (bx + cy)$ for any x and y. List those axioms used in your proof.

7. In an integral domain if $ab \mid ac$, then $b \mid c$. Prove this and list all axioms used in the proof.

8. Let D be an integral domain. Let $Q = \{(a, b) : a, b \in D; \ b \neq 0\}$. Define $(a, b) \equiv (c, d)$ if and only if $ad = cb$. Prove that $(\equiv)$ is an equivalence relation on Q.

9. Let I denote the integers. Consider the set of all ordered pairs (a, b) of elements from the integers I. Addition and multiplication are defined:

$$(a, b) + (a, c) = (a + c, \ b + d)$$
$$(a, b) \cdot (c, d) = (ad + bc, \ bd - 2ac).$$

It is known that under these definitions the ordered pairs form an integral domain. Is this still true if I is replaced by $I/\langle 3 \rangle$? By $I/\langle 5 \rangle$?

10. Determine the nature of the multiplicative group of units in $I/\langle n \rangle$ where $n = 6, 7, 8$.

11. Let R be an integral domain. Show that if M is a maximal ideal then R/M is a field.

SUPPLEMENTARY READING

N. Jacobson, *Lectures in Abstract Algebra*, Vol. 1, Princeton, N.J.: Van Nostrand (1951), Chapter II.

N. H. McCoy, Rings and ideals, *Carus Monography*, no. 8, Mathematical Association of America, Buffalo, N.Y., 1948.

I. Niven and H. S. Zukerman, *An Introduction to the Theory of Numbers*, New York: John Wiley & Sons (1960), Chapter 2.

3 | The Integers

3.1. INTRODUCTION

In this chapter we shall put on a firm axiomatic foundation the properties of the system that we call the integers. In Chapter 5 we shall discuss a class of integral domains which is obtained as a generalization of the integers by selecting as axioms only those particular properties of the integers which we need for further work.

The attitude we have adopted up to now has been that we know what the integers are and we know their basic properties, some of which we explicitly listed in Chapter 0. In this chapter we shall for the first time set down a complete list of axioms for the integers. Subsequently we shall prove from this list of axioms all properties of the integers we use. Moreover we shall prove that any two systems satisfying these axioms are isomorphic. But we shall not give a construction of the integers from basic set theory. Such a construction is the domain of axiomatic set theory and formal logic and we refer to the books of Halmos, Suppes, and Bernays and Fraenkel (see Supplementary Reading). The position we take in this chapter is this: however the set of integers is conceived, the set satisfies the axioms listed. The proof that any two such systems are isomorphic is the strongest kind of a uniqueness theorem we can have.

This attitude places certain requirements on us. In dealing with integral systems we shall be very careful not to use any intuitive property of the integers in a *proof* or in stating a definition unless that property has been formally proved for our system. This is particularly true in the proof of the uniqueness theorem. We will, of course, in making formal definitions, in stating axioms, and in posing problems draw upon our intuition of what should be true for the integers. Moreover, when a new concept is introduced we shall cite familiar examples of the concept, including our experience with the integers. We rely on the sophistication of the reader to appreciate the detachment of the axiomatic treatment. Special care must be taken to determine from the context whether we are using the integers as a familiar source of examples or as an object of an abstract mathematical theory.

All of Section 3.5 of this chapter may be omitted without harm to the continuity of the book provided that the axioms and the subsequent properties are accepted as true in whatever system the integers are conceived to be. Chapter 5 on euclidean domains is indispensible for our later work.

The axioms for a system of integers break up into two parts. The first set of axioms concern their ring properties; we assume that we are considering a ring which is an integral domain. The second set of axioms postulate the existence of a relation, order, on the integral domain and state the properties assumed about this relation and about its connection with the addition and multiplication operations of the integral domain. Our first definition is quite general.

3.2. ORDER

This definition pertains to an abstract set, not necessarily one on which operations have been defined. Later we shall have to link together the concepts of order and the binary algebraic operations of an integral domain.

Definition. A set S is called *partially ordered* by a relation ρ if the relation ρ is defined on S and satisfies

1. $a \rho a$ for all $a \in S$ (ρ is said to be reflexive).
2. If $a \rho b$ and $b \rho a$ then $a = b$ (ρ is said to be antisymmetric).
3. If $a \rho b$ and $b \rho c$, then $a \rho c$ (ρ is said to be transitive).

The set S is said to be *totally ordered by* ρ if in addition ρ satisfies

4. For all $a, b \in S$, either $a \rho b$ or $b \rho a$.

Example 1. Let S be the rational numbers. Let $a \rho b$ mean $a \le b$. S is totally ordered by ($\le$).

Example 2. Let S be the set of *positive* integers. Let $a \rho b$ mean that $a \mid b$. The positive integers are partially ordered by division.

Example 3. Let S be the set of all subsets of a set S_0. Let $a \rho b$ mean that a is a subset of b. The set S is partially ordered by ρ.

Example 4. Let S be the set of all subgroups of a group G. Let $a \rho b$ mean that a is a subgroup of b. The set S is partially ordered by ρ.

3.3. ORDER IN INTEGRAL DOMAINS

Our experience with the "greater than–less than" relation in the integers and rational numbers tells us that if a is less than b then $a + c$ is less than $b + c$. This is not an automatic property of order relations with respect to addition, for if our system is that of the positive integers ordered by division, then $2 \mid 4$ but $2 + 1 \nmid 4 + 1$. Thus, to further characterize the properties of order, we must further postulate the connection between the order relation and previously defined operations.

Definition. An *ordered integral domain*, $\langle D, +, \cdot, \leq \rangle$ is an integral domain $\langle D, +, \cdot \rangle$ on which a relation $(\leq)$ has been defined such that D is totally ordered by $(\leq)$ and the following two axioms hold:

O1. For all triples of (a, b, c) from D, if $a \leq b$, then $a + c \leq b + c$.

O2. For all pairs (a, b) from D, if $a \leq b$ then $ac \leq bc$ whenever $0 \leq c$.

Immediately we can see that both the integers and the rational numbers, as we are familiar with them, are ordered integral domains in which $(\leq)$ means "is less than."

We want to emphasize that *both* integers and rational numbers satisfy the axioms. The search for a set of axioms that characterizes either the integers or the rational numbers is not yet finished, indeed, the lemmas and the theorems of this section hold for the integers, the rational numbers, and the real numbers.

Here are some notations and some easy lemmas that will be useful. We assume that all elements come from an ordered integral domain $\langle D, +, \cdot, \leq \rangle$. We write

$a < b$ in case $a \leq b$, but $a \neq b$,

$a \geq b$ in case $b \leq a$,

$a > b$ in case $b < a$.

Lemma 1. If $a < b$ then $a + c < b + c$.

PROOF. Here, $a < b$ implies $a \leq b$, hence $a + c \leq b + c$. If $a + c = b + c$, then $a = b$, contrary to $a < b$.

Lemma 2. If $a < b$ and $0 \leq c$, then $ac \leq bc$ with $ac = bc$ if and only if $c = 0$.

PROOF. $a < b$ implies $a \leq b$, hence if $0 \leq c$ then $ac \leq bc$. If $c = 0$, then $ac = 0 = bc$. If $ac = bc$ then $(a - b)c = 0$; however $a \neq b$, and so $a - b \neq 0$, from which it follows that $c = 0$.

$$* \quad * \quad *$$

Lemma 3. If $a \leq b$ and $c \leq d$, then $a + c \leq b + d$.

PROOF. $a \leq b$ implies $a + c \leq b + c$; $c \leq d$ implies $c + b \leq d + b$, or $b + c \leq b + d$. By transitivity, $a + c \leq b + d$.

$$* \quad * \quad *$$

Warning. From $a \leq b$ and $c \leq d$, it does not follow that $a - c \leq b - d$! Give a counterexample from the integers!

Theorem 1. In a totally ordered integral domain, if $0 < a$, then $-a < 0$, and if $a < 0$, then $0 < -a$.

PROOF. Add $-a$ to both sides of $0 < a$ and $a < 0$. Then apply Lemma 1.

* * *

The significance of this theorem is that in an ordered integral domain, the elements are divided into three mutually disjoint sets:

$$P = \{x : 0 < x\}, \quad Z = \{0\}, \quad N = \{x : x < 0\}.$$

Moreover axioms O1 and O2 may be restated as

O1′. P is closed under addition.
O2′. P is closed under multiplication.

Theorem 2. In an ordered integral domain, $ab > 0$ if and only if either $a > 0$ and $b > 0$ or $a < 0$ and $b < 0$, that is, $ab > 0$ if and only if a and b have "like signs."

PROOF. (*If*). If $a > 0$, then $b > 0$ implies $ab > b \cdot 0 = 0$. If $-a > 0$, then $-b > 0$ implies $(-a)(-b) > (-b) \cdot 0 = 0$ or $ab > 0$.

(*Only if*). Suppose $ab > 0$. Then $ab \neq 0$, and so $a \neq 0$ and $b \neq 0$. Suppose by way of contradiction that $a > 0$ but $b < 0$. Then $-b > 0$ and so $a(-b) > a \cdot 0 = 0$; or $-(ab) > 0$. But then $ab + -(ab) > 0$, or $0 > 0$—a contradiction.

* * *

Corollary 1. $a^2 \geq 0$.

PROOF. $a^2 = a \cdot a = (-a)(-a)$.

Corollary 2. $1 > 0$.
PROOF. $1 \neq 0$, by Lemma 2.4, and $1 = 1 \cdot 1$.

* * *

We turn now to an elementary theory of absolute value in totally ordered integral domains.

Definition. Let $\langle D, +, \cdot, \leq \rangle$ be an ordered integral domain. If $a \in D$, the *absolute value* of a, denoted $|a|$, is defined as follows:

$$|a| = \begin{cases} a \text{ if } a \geq 0 \\ -a \text{ if } a \leq 0 \end{cases}$$

This definition makes sense in view of Theorem 1, since $a \geq 0$, or $-a \geq 0$; and both hold if and only if $a = 0$.

Lemma 4. $|0| = 0$ and if $a \neq 0$, $|a| > 0$.

PROOF. This is a trivial consequence of the definition, as is the next lemma.

Lemma 5. $|a| \geq a$ and $|a| \geq -a$.

Lemma 6. $a \leq b$ and $-a \leq b$ if and only if $|a| \leq b$.

PROOF (*If*). If $|a| = a$, then $0 \leq a = |a| \leq b$, and also $-a \leq 0$. Hence $a \leq b$ and $-a \leq b$. Similarly, if $|a| = -a$, then $0 \leq -a \leq b$ and so $a \leq 0 \leq b$.

(*Only if*). If $a \leq b$ and $-a \leq b$, then, since $|a| = a$ or $-a$, $|a| \leq b$.

* * *

Theorem 3. $|ab| = |a| \, |b|$.

PROOF. The theorem is trivial if $a \geq 0$ and $b \geq 0$, but

$$|ab| = |(-a)(-b)| = |-(ab)| = |(-a)b| = |a(-b)|$$

and since one of four underlined forms contains all nonnegative terms, the general theorem holds.

* * *

Theorem 4 (*Triangle Inequality*). $|a + b| \leq |a| + |b|$.

PROOF. We shall use Lemma 6 and show $-(a + b) \leq |a| + |b|$ and $(a + b) \leq |a| + |b|$. In any event, $a \leq |a|$ and $b \leq |b|$; hence by Lemma 3, $a + b \leq |a| + |b|$. Similarly $-a \leq |a|$ and $-b \leq |b|$; hence $-a - b = -(a + b) \leq |a| + |b|$.

* * *

This inequality is well named because, stated for vectors, where $|\vec{a}|$ denotes the length of $\vec{a}$ this law states that the length of one side of a triangle (Figure 1) is shorter than the sum of the lengths of the other two.

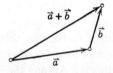

Figure 1

Theorem 5. $\big| \, |a| - |b| \, \big| \leq |a - b|$.

PROOF. We have $|a| = |b + (a - b)| \leq |b| + |a - b|$. By adding $-|b|$ to both sides we have $|a| - |b| \leq |a - b|$. Replacing a by b we have $|b| - |a| \leq |b - a|$. But as $|b| - |a| = -(|a| - |b|)$ and $|b - a| = |-(a - b)| = |a - b|$, we have $-(|a| - |b|) \leq |a - b|$. The theorem follows from Lemma 6.

* * *

EXERCISE 1

1. Let S be a set on which a relation ρ has been defined which satisfies (1) and (3) of the definition of a partial ordering (p. 94). Show that an equivalence relation ($\equiv$) can be defined by $a \equiv b$ if and only if $a \rho b$ and $b \rho a$. Call $\bar{S}$ the resulting set of equivalence classes and show that a relation $\bar{\rho}$ defined by $\bar{a} \bar{\rho} \bar{b}$ if and only if $a \rho b$ is independent of the choice of representatives $a \in \bar{a}$ and $b \in \bar{b}$ and that $\bar{S}$ is partially ordered by $\bar{\rho}$. When this is done for S, the set of all integers and $a \rho b$ meaning $a \mid b$, describe an equivalence class $\bar{a}$.

2. For what sets A will the set S of all subsets of A be totally ordered by set inclusion?

3. For what finite groups G will the set S of all subgroups of G be totally ordered by set inclusion?

4. Let S be the set of all subgroups of the full symmetric group on $\{1, 2, 3, 4\}$. Let $a \rho b$ mean that a is a *normal* subgroup of b. Is S partially ordered by ρ?

5. Let $\langle D, +, \cdot, \le \rangle$ be an ordered integral domain. Under what conditions does $a < b$ and $c < d$ imply $ac < bd$?

6. Let $\langle D, +, \cdot \rangle$ be an integral domain. Let P be a subset of D such that

   (i) $0 \notin P$,
   (ii) For all $a \neq 0$, either $a \in P$ or $-a \in P$,
   (iii) P is closed under addition 01′,
   (iv) P is closed under multiplication 02′.

Show that the relation ρ defined by

$$a \rho b \quad \text{if and only if} \quad b - a \in P \quad \text{or} \quad a = b$$

totally orders D, and $\langle D, +, \cdot \rho \rangle$ is an ordered domain. What is the set of positive elements of D under ρ?

3.4. WELL-ORDERED SETS

We shall now separate the integers from other integral domains by adding one further axiom which will concern order. At first glance it may seem improbable that this crucial axiom should entail order, but at second glance recall how we often say "2 is the first integer after 1." Another way to say this is "Among the integers larger than 1, 2 is the smallest." In contrast, for the rational numbers, the question "what is the first rational number after 1?" has no answer. This will be the distinction that makes the integers unique. To belabor our point still further, we know that *between* any two distinct rational numbers there is another rational number—"between" talks about order. Thus if a and b are rational numbers and $a < b$, then $a/2 < b/2$ and so $a = a/2 + a/2 < a/2 + b/2 < b/2 + b/2 = b$, or $a < (a + b)/2 < b$. If it were alleged that b were the smallest rational larger than 1, then $(1 + b)/2$ would provide a counterexample. We can define the element $(a + b)/2$ in the set of rational numbers because we can divide by 2. We cannot always divide by 2 among the integers. This, too, is a key distinction between the integers and the rationals, but it turns out that stating our condition on order is more convenient than stating it on divisibility.

To get a statement about order we once more turn to the abstract setting, and make a general definition.

Definition. Let S be a set which is totally ordered by a relation ρ. S is said to be _well ordered_ by ρ if every nonempty subset of S has a "least" element. More precisely S is well ordered by ρ if for every nonempty subset $T \subseteq S$, then there is a distinguished element, $t_0 \in T$, such that $t_0 \rho t$ for all $t \in T$.

This is a tricky definition for it places a condition on _every_ nonempty subset of S. To verify that ρ does well order S, we must prove the condition for _every_ nonempty subset.

Example 5. Let S be the set of positive integers. Our experience tells us that S is well ordered by "less than or equal to," ($\leq$).

Example 6. Let S be the set of all integers. S is _not_ well ordered by ($\leq$) for S itself has no least element.

Example 7. Let S be the set of all nonnegative rational numbers (this includes 0). Then S is _not_ well ordered by ($\leq$). Here S has a least element 0, but, as we noted, the set T of rationals larger than 1 has no least element.

Example 8. Let S be the set of ordered pairs (r, s) of nonnegative integers. S is well ordered by the relation ρ defined

$$(r, s)\, \rho\, (u, v) \quad \text{if (1) } r < u \text{ or}$$
$$\text{if (2) } r = u \text{ and } s \leq v.$$

This is a rather interesting example, and Problems 1, 2, and 3 of Exercise 2 verify the requisite properties. ρ is called the lexicographic ordering. It is convenient to think of S as the points in the plane with nonnegative integer coordinates and ρ as serving as a way to list them in a "dictionary."

> **Theorem 6.** If S is well ordered by ρ and T is any subset of S, then T is well ordered by ρ.

PROOF. T is well ordered by ρ, since all of the conditions for ρ to meet already hold because all elements of T belong to S.

* * *

EXERCISE 2

1. In Example 8 of this section, verify that ρ partially orders S.
2. In Example 8, verify that ρ totally orders S.
3. In Example 8, let T be any nonempty subset of S. Let T' be the subset of integers that appear as first coordinates of the points of T. T' has a least element,

t_0. Why? Let $T'' = \{v : (t_0, v) \in T\}.T''$ has a least element v_0. Why? Show that $(t_0, v_0) \in T$ and is the least element of T.

4. Use Theorem 6 and Example 8 to conclude that the set of nonnegative rational numbers can be well ordered. State explicitly what the ordering relation is.

5. Let $\langle S, \leq \rangle$ be a totally ordered set. Show that if S is finite, then $(\leq)$ well orders S.

6. Let $S = \{1, 2, 3, \ldots\}$. Define a relation δ on S so that $\langle S, \delta \rangle$ is a totally ordered set, but so that δ does not well order S.

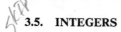

3.5. INTEGERS

At long last we may now formulate the axioms which characterize the integers.

Definition. A set E will be called an *integral system* if E is an ordered integral domain, $\langle E, +, \cdot, \leq \rangle$, in which $E_+ = \{a : 0 < a\}$ is well ordered by $(\leq)$.

The main result of this section is Theorem 10, which states that any two integral systems are isomorphic. Throughout this section, 0 and 1 shall denote the additive and multiplicative identities of an integral domain E.

> **Theorem 7.** In an integral system E there is no element a such that $0 < a < 1$.

PROOF. Let $T = \{a : 0 < a < 1\}$. If T is nonempty, then since it is a subset of E_+, T has a least member; call it m. Then $0 < m < 1$ implies $m^2 = m \cdot m < m$ by axiom O2. Since $m \neq 0$, $m^2 \neq 0$, and we have $0 < m^2 < m < 1$, contrary to the choice of m. Hence T must be empty.

* * *

Corollary 1. If $n \in E$, then there is no element a such that $n < a < n + 1$.

PROOF. If $n < a < n + 1$, then, using axiom O1, $n - n = 0 < a - n < 1$, contrary to Theorem 7.

* * *

Corollary 2. The only units in an integral system are 1 and -1.

PROOF. Let u be a unit. Hence there is a v such that $uv = 1$, and so $|uv| = |u| |v| = |1| = 1$. Now $u \neq 0$, hence $|u| > 0$, and $|u| \geq 1$. If $|u| > 1$, then $|u| |v| > 1 \cdot |v| = |v| > 0$, or $1 > |v| > 0$, a contradiction. Thus $|u| = 1$; but $|u| = u$ or $-u$. Hence $u = 1$ or $-u = 1$; equivalently $u = 1$ or $u = -1$. Clearly 1 and -1 are units.

* * *

Corollary 3. In an integral system, if $a \mid b$ and $b \neq 0$ then $|a| \leq |b|$.

PROOF. Here, $a \mid b$ means $b = aq$, hence $|b| = |a| \, |q|$. Now, since $b \neq 0$, $q \neq 0$, hence $|q| \geq 1$. Hence, by axiom O2,

$$|a| \, |q| \geq |a|, \quad \text{or} \quad |b| \geq |a|.$$

*　*　*

Lemma 7. Let E be an integral system and $k \in E$. The set $K = \{a : k \leq a, a \in E\}$ is well ordered by $(\leq)$.

PROOF. Since $K \subseteq E$, there is no question but that $(\leq)$ totally orders K. Does $(\leq)$ *well* order K? Let T be any nonempty subset of K. If $T \subseteq E_+$, then, by assumption, T has a least element. More generally by adding $-(k - 1)$ to each element of T we simply translate T into a set H which we can guarantee to be contained in E_+. Then, naturally, if h_0 is the least element of H then $h_0 + (k - 1)$ is the least element of T.

Here are the details. Let $H = \{t - (k - 1) : t \in T\}$. Since $k - 1 < k \leq t$ when $t \in T \subseteq K$ it follows that $t - (k - 1) > 0$ and so $H \subseteq E_+$. If h_0 is the least element of H, say $h_0 = t_0 - (k - 1)$ for some $t_0 \in T$, then $t_0 = h_0 + (k - 1) \in T$. Moreover if $t \in T$ then $t - (k - 1) \in H$ and so $h_0 < t - (k - 1)$; hence $h_0 + (k - 1) < t$. Thus $h_0 + (k - 1)$ is the least element of T.

*　*　*

Theorem 8. (*Principle of Induction*). Let an integral system E contain a subset T with the following properties:

　　1. $k \in T$.
　　2. If $a \in T$, then $a + 1 \in T$.
　Then $T \supseteq \{a : k \leq a\}$.

PROOF. Suppose that $T \not\supseteq \{a : k \leq a\}$. Then the set $Q = \{a : k \leq a \text{ and } a \notin T\}$ is a nonempty subset of $\{a : k \leq a\}$. The latter set is well ordered by $(\leq)$ (Lemma 7), hence Q has a least element q_0. Now $k \leq q_0$ and since $k \in T$, in fact $k < q_0$. By Corollary 1 of Theorem 7, $k + 1 \leq q_0$, hence $k \leq q_0 - 1$. Since q_0 is the least element of Q, $(q_0 - 1) \notin Q$; hence $(q_0 - 1) \in T$. But by (2), then, $(q_0 - 1) + 1 = q_0 \in T$; hence $q_0 \notin Q$, a contradiction. Thus T must contain $\{a : k \leq a\}$, as was to be proved.

*　*　*

The conventional use of this theorem in mathematics follows the scheme outlined in Chapter 0. We consider a statement or property that depends on an integer n. Symbolically we might write this $P(n)$. To prove, by induction, that $P(n)$ is true for all positive integers n we

　　(A) give a proof that $P(1)$ is true, and
　　(B) prove the lemma: For every positive integer a if $P(a)$ is true then $P(a + 1)$ is true.

We could have said, let $T = \{n : P(n)$ is true$\}$. From (A) we know that $1 \in T$, and from (B) we know that if $a \in T$ then $a + 1 \in T$. Theorem 8 guarantees that T is the set of all positive integers. The informal form of induction consisting of steps (A) and (B) is just a paraphrase of Theorem 8.

Condition 2 of the hypothesis of Theorem 8 corresponds to the inductive step, and "$a \in T$" corresponds to the inductive hypothesis.

Induction utilizes the fact that the positive integers may be generated in the form $1, 1 + 1, \ldots, m, m + 1, \ldots$. It is easy to see that every positive element can be written in the form $m + 1, m \geq 0$; but the effect of Theorem 8 is that starting from 1, by successive additions of 1, all positive elements are generated.

In induction proofs it is sometimes preferable to replace condition 2 by

2* If $a \in T$ for all $k \leq a < b$, then $b \in T$.

This gives a stronger hypothesis in establishing the inductive step. We can surely replace (2) by (2*) and obtain valid theorems by the same proof as that for Theorem 8. We use this form of induction later in proving Theorem 11.

The next theorem contains all the difficulties in proving that two integral systems E and $\bar{E}$ are isomorphic. The theorem establishes the validity of defining functions by induction, and consequently is of extreme importance in itself. More correctly it gives conditions under which an inductive definition does give rise to a function. Recall the example in Chapter 0, section 0.5. Given a set A and a binary operation $+$ on A we want to define $a_1 + a_2 + \cdots + a_n$. We have, of course, $a_1 + a_2$ and we define $a_1 + a_2 + a_3 = (a_1 + a_2) + a_3$. Inductively we define $a_1 + \cdots + a_{n-1} + a_n = (a_1 + \cdots + a_{n-1}) + a_n$. In actuality we have been given a sequence $(a_1, a_2, \ldots, a_n, \ldots)$ and we are defining a function φ from $\{n : n \in I, n \geq 2\}$ into A by the inductive scheme: $\varphi(2) = a_1 + a_2$ and for $n > 2$, $\varphi(n) = \varphi(n - 1) + a_n$. (Of course $\varphi(n)$ is more usually written $\sum_{i=1}^{i=n} a_i$ or, more informally still, $\sum a_i$.) But as we said in Chapter 0, when a function is defined by induction the set of ordered pairs that constitute the function are not exhibited. Theorem 9 describes explicitly in set theoretic terms what the ordered pairs are, assuming of course that the conditions of its hypothesis are met.

> **Theorem 9** (*Definition by Induction*) Let $\langle E, +, \cdot, \leq \rangle$ be an integral system. Let A be a nonempty set and let $a \in A$. Let g be a function from $E_+ \times A$ into A. There is a unique function f from E_+ into A such that
>
> 1. $f(1) = a$, and
> 2. $f(n + 1) = g(n, f(n))$ for all $n \in E_+$.

PROOF OF EXISTENCE OF f. We seek a set f of ordered pairs in $E_+ \times A$ such that (1), $(1, a) \in f$ and, (2), writing $f(n) = y$ if $(n, y) \in F$ then $(n + 1, g(n, y)) \in f$. We begin by defining the set C of all sets $T \subseteq E_+ \times A$ that have the properties 1 and 2. If f is to exist it must belong to C and, intuitively, f must be the smallest set in C. We shall accomplish this by definition!

We define $C=\{T:T \subseteq E_+ \times A, (1, a) \in T$, and whenever $(n, y) \in T$ then $(n + 1, g(n, y)) \in T\}$ and let $f = \bigcap C$. We shall show that f is the desired function. At least f is a well-defined set of ordered pairs belonging to $E_+ \times A$. Note that C is nonempty, for surely $E_+ \times A \in C$.

First we show that $f \in C$. Surely $(1, a) \in f$ as $(1, a) \in T$ for all $T \in C$. If $(n, y) \in f$ then $(n, y) \in T$ for all $T \in C$, and so $(n + 1, g(n, y)) \in T$ for all $T \in C$, and thus $(n + 1, g(n, y)) \in f$. This shows that if f is a function, it has the properties claimed by the theorem.

Second we prove the following property for f.

(P):   If $(n, y) \in f$ and $(n, y) \neq (1, a)$ then there is a pair
    $(u, v) \in f$ such that $(n, y) = (u + 1, g(u, v))$.

If this property does not hold for f then f contains an ordered pair (m, x) such that $(m, x) \neq (1, a)$ and for no pair $(u, v) \in f$ does $(m, x) = (n + 1, g(u, v))$. But then consider the set $k = f - \{(m, x)\}$. We shall show that $k \in C$. Now $(1, a) \in k$ as $(m, x) \neq (1, a)$. In addition, if $(n, y) \in k$ then $(n, y) \in f$ and so $(n + 1, g(n, y)) \in f$, and it must follow from the choice of (m, x) that $(n + 1, g(n, y)) \neq (m, x)$. Hence $(n + 1, g(n, y)) \in k$. Thus k satisfies the conditions for a set to belong to C. But then $f = \bigcap C$ is a subset of k contradicting the definition of k as a *proper* subset of f. Thus (P) holds for f.

Third we prove that f is a function. To do this we need to prove for all pairs x, y from A that if (n, x) and (n, y) belong to f then $x = y$. The proof will be an induction proof, with induction on n. We show first that if $(1, y) \in f$ then $y = a$. If $y \neq a$ then $(1, a) \neq (1, y)$, and by property (P) we should have $(1, y) = (u + 1, g(u, v))$ for some $(u, v) \in f$. This says that $1 = u + 1$, or that $u = 0$; however, $(0, v) \notin E_+ \times A$, and so no such (u, v) exists in f. Thus $y = a$. The inductive hypothesis states that for all pairs (c, d) from A, if (n, c) and (n, d) belong to f then $c = d$. Now suppose that $(n + 1, x)$ and $(n + 1, y)$ belong to f. As $n + 1 > 1$ it follows from property (P) that

$$(n + 1, x) = (u + 1, g(u, v)) \quad \text{for some } (u, v) \in f,$$
and $$(n + 1, y) = (w + 1, g(w, z)) \quad \text{for some } (w, z) \in f.$$

In particular, $u + 1 = n + 1 = w + 1$, $x = g(u, v)$, and $y = g(w, z)$. Hence $u = n = w$, and it follows that $(n, v) \in f$ and $(n, z) \in f$; thus from this and the induction hypotheses we conclude that $v = z$. Then, $(u, v) = (w, z)$, and because g is a function from $E_+ \times A$ into A, we have $g(u, v) = g(w, z)$, or $x = y$. Thus our induction is complete.

Finally we prove that the domain of f is E_+. We have $1 \in \mathscr{D}_f$ and if $n \in \mathscr{D}_f$ then $n + 1 \in \mathscr{D}_f$ so, by Theorem 8, $\mathscr{D}_f = E_+$.

The uniqueness of f is easily established by proving by an induction on m

that if f and h are two functions from E_+ into A such that $h(1) = a = f(1)$ and $h(n + 1) = g(n, h(n))(= f(n + 1))$ for all $n \in E_+$ then $h(m) = f(m)$ for all $m \in E_+$. We leave the details to the reader.

$$* \quad * \quad *$$

Theorem 10. Let $\langle E, +, \cdot, \leq \rangle$ and $\langle \bar{E}, \oplus, *, \leqslant \rangle$ be two integral systems. There is a function $\Phi : E \to \bar{E}$ which is a ring isomorphism such that whenever $x \leq y$ then $\Phi(x) \leqslant \Phi(y)$.

PROOF. We denote by 0 and 1 the additive and multiplicative identities of E, and by $\bar{0}$ and $\bar{1}$ the corresponding identities of $\bar{E}$. We denote the additive inverse of $\bar{a} \in \bar{E}$ by $\ominus \bar{a}$ and write $\bar{a} \ominus \bar{b}$ for $\bar{a} \oplus (\ominus \bar{b})$. By Theorem 9, there is a function $\varphi : E_+ \to \bar{E}_\oplus$ such that

$$\varphi(1) = \bar{1}, \quad \text{and} \quad \varphi(n + 1) = \varphi(n) \oplus \bar{1} \quad \text{for all } n \in E_+.$$

For this application of Theorem 9 we take $A = \bar{E}_\oplus$, $a = \bar{1}$ and $g(u, \bar{v}) = \bar{v} + \bar{1}$. By a straightforward application of Theorem 8 the range of φ is $\bar{E}_\oplus$. We extend φ to a function from E onto $\bar{E}$ by defining

$$\Phi(x) = \begin{cases} \varphi(x) & \text{if } x > 0 \\ \bar{0} & \text{if } x = 0. \\ \ominus\varphi(-x) & \text{if } x < 0 \end{cases}$$

The verifications that Φ is a 1–1 function from E onto $\bar{E}$ and that $\Phi(-x) = \ominus\Phi(x)$ for all $x \in E$ are straightforward, and we leave this to the reader. We shall show that Φ has the desired isomorphism properties.

First, it is easy to prove, by induction on x, that for all x and $y \in E_+$, $\varphi(x + y) = \varphi(x) \oplus \varphi(y)$ and $\varphi(xy) = \varphi(x) * \varphi(y)$. These details we omit. To show $\Phi(x + y) = \Phi(x) \oplus \Phi(y)$, we note that it is trivial if $x = 0$ or $y = 0$, and so we distinguish the cases $x + y = 0$, $x + y > 0$, and $x + y < 0$. The first case is an immediate consequence of $\Phi(-x) = \ominus \Phi(x)$. The second case reduces to the function φ if $x > 0$ and $y > 0$. The remaining possibility is that $x > 0$ and $y < 0$ and $x + y > 0$. Then $\Phi(x + y) = \varphi(x + y) = \varphi(x + y) \oplus \varphi(-y) \ominus \varphi(-y) = \varphi((x + y) + (-y)) \ominus \varphi(-y) = \varphi(x) \ominus \varphi(-y) = \Phi(x) \oplus \Phi(y)$.

If $x + y < 0$ then $-(x + y) > 0$ and so $\Phi(x + y) = \ominus\Phi(-(x + y)) = \ominus\Phi((-x) + (-y)) = \ominus[\Phi(-x) \oplus \Phi(-y)] = \ominus\Phi(-x) \ominus \Phi(-y) = \Phi(x) \oplus \Phi(y)$.

To show $\Phi(xy) = \Phi(x) * \Phi(y)$ we treat the cases $xy = 0$, $xy > 0$, and $xy < 0$ separately. If $xy = 0$ then $x = 0$ or $y = 0$, and the result is trivial. If $xy > 0$ and $x > 0$ and $y > 0$, the result reduces to that for the function φ. If $xy > 0$ and $x < 0$ and $y < 0$ then $\Phi(xy) = \Phi((-x)(-y)) = \Phi(-x) * \Phi(-y) = (\ominus \Phi(x)) * (\ominus \Phi(y)) = \Phi(x) * \Phi(y)$. If $xy < 0$ we may assume that $x < 0$ and $y > 0$, and so $\Phi(xy) = \ominus\Phi(-xy) = \ominus\Phi((-x)y) = \ominus[\Phi(-x) * \Phi(y)] = \Phi(x) * \Phi(y)$.

Finally, to show that $x \leq y$ implies $\Phi(x) \leqslant \Phi(y)$, it suffices to show that if $0 \leq z$ then $\Phi(0) = \bar{0} \leqslant \Phi(z)$ since $x \leq y$ if and only if $0 \leq y - x$ and $\Phi(y - x) = \Phi(y) \ominus (x)$. It is clear, however, that $0 \leq z$ implies $\bar{0} \leqslant \varphi(z)$ and so $0 \leq z$ implies $\bar{0} \leqslant \Phi(z)$.

$$* \quad * \quad *$$

We now know that all integral systems are isomorphic, but we do not know that any exist. This situation may well be intolerable to one who has been using integers for years and he may feel we have, like ostriches, put our heads in the sand. But he cannot be too offended if we catch up with him by assuming that there is at least one integral system. Let each of us assume the existence of the integral system that seems most natural, but let us all use a common notation and call the selected system $\langle I, +, \cdot, \leq \rangle$. Hereafter let us agree that the symbol "I" shall denote that specific set that is an ordered integral domain in which the positive elements are well ordered by ($\leq$).

EXERCISE 3

1. Let π be a permutation on $1, \ldots, n$. Let ρ_i be the transposition $(i, i + 1)$ on $1, \ldots, n$. (See Problems 2–11 in Exercise 1.4 for notation.) Show that

$$\pi\rho_i(a) = \begin{cases} \pi(a) & \text{if} \quad a \neq i, i + 1 \\ \pi(i + 1) & \text{if} \quad a = i \\ \pi(i) & \text{if} \quad a = i + 1 \end{cases}.$$

Show that there exists a sequence of transpositions $\rho_{i_1}, \ldots, \rho_{i_r}$ such that $\pi\rho_{i_1} \ldots \rho_{i_r} = \iota$ and so $\pi = \rho_{i_r} \ldots \rho_{i_1}$.

Example: $\begin{pmatrix} 1 & 2 & 3 & 4 & 5 \\ 2 & 1 & 5 & 3 & 4 \end{pmatrix}(3, 4) = \begin{pmatrix} 1 & 2 & 3 & 4 & 5 \\ 2 & 1 & 3 & 5 & 4 \end{pmatrix}$

and $\begin{pmatrix} 1 & 2 & 3 & 4 & 5 \\ 2 & 1 & 5 & 3 & 4 \end{pmatrix}(3, 4)(4, 5)(1, 2) = \begin{pmatrix} 1 & 2 & 3 & 4 & 5 \\ 1 & 2 & 3 & 4 & 5 \end{pmatrix}$

Find a bound on the number m needed to represent π as a product of cycles of the form $(i, i + 1)$. [*Hint:* Move n to the extreme right, then proceed by induction.]

2. Suppose $0 < a_1 \leq a_2 \leq \cdots \leq a_n$ and that $a_1 < a_n$, where the a_i are real numbers. Define for $r = 1, 2, \ldots$

$$A_r = \frac{1}{r}(a_1 + a_2 + \cdots + a_r)$$

$$G_r = (a_1 \cdot a_2 \cdot \ldots \cdot a_r)^{1/r}.$$

Show, by induction, that $A_n > G_n$. [*Hint:* Show that $A_r = A_{r-1} + (a_r - A_{r-1})/r$ and raise each side to the rth power. Use the fact that for $x > 0$, $n > 1$, $(1 + x)^n > 1 + xn$.]

3. Let $a_1, a_2, \ldots, a_n$ be letters of an "alphabet." (We regard a_i as distinct from a_j if $i \neq j$.) A word is any finite string of symbols $x_1 x_2 x_3, \ldots, x_m$ where each x_i is some a_j. Thus $a_1, a_1 a_2, a_1 a_2 a_1, a_3 a_1, a_3 a_2 a_2 a_3, a_2 a_3 a_1 a_2 a_1 a_2$ are words. Two words A and B are called *adjacent* if one of the words, say A, has the form $RWWS$ and the other, B, has the form RWS. That is, in A the subword W has been repeated, while in B one of the repetitions is deleted. Thus $a_1 a_1$ and a_1 are adjacent, $a_3 a_1 a_2$ and $a_3 a_1 a_2 a_1 a_2$ are adjacent, $a_1 a_2 a_1$ and $a_1 a_2$ are *not* adjacent. Two words A and B are called *equal* if there is a finite sequence of words $W_1, \ldots, W_s$ such that W_1 is A, W_s is B, and W_i and W_{i+1} are adjacent for $i = 1, 2, \ldots, S - 1$. Thus $a_1 a_1 a_2 a_3 = a_1 a_2 a_3 = a_1 a_2 a_3 a_2 a_3 a_1 a_2 a_3$.

    (i) Show that the relation "adjacent" is not transitive.

    (ii) Show that the relation "equal" is an equivalence relation.

    (iii) Prove that if x is a word in which all n alphabet letters occur and if y is any word, then x is equal to a word w in which y occurs as a subword. [*Hint:* Use induction on the number of symbols in y.]

4. In the proof of Theorem 9 considerable space was used to show that if $f = \bigcap C$ then $f \in C$. What is wrong with the following "simple" argument? Since C is a collection of sets with a certain property, the intersection of these sets must have this property. In symbols: Since $f = \bigcap C$, then $f \in C$ is obvious! Show by a counterexample that it is not only *not* obvious but that it is false.

5. (R. C. Buck) Show that the following scheme cannot define a function from I_+ into I_+ : $f(1) = 1$, $f(2n + 1) = n^2 - n + 1$, and $f(3n + 1) = 2n + f(2n + 1)$. [*Hint:* Try to compute $f(13)$.]

6. Let R be a ring and let $\{a_1, \ldots\}$ be a sequence of elements in R. Show that the inductive definition of $\sum a_i$, suggested on p. 102, does in fact meet the requirements of Theorem 9 by finding a set A and appropriate functions g and f.

★ **7.** Prove that, under the definition of $\sum a_i$ suggested on p. 102, if π is any permutation of $(1, \ldots, n)$ then $\sum_{i=1}^{i=n} a_i = \sum_{i=1}^{i=n} a_{\pi(i)}$. (Assume that the elements $a_1, \ldots, a_n$ belong to a ring.)

3.6. ARITHMETIC IN THE INTEGERS

Our next theorem has perhaps the most far-reaching consequences of any we prove about the integers. It is the jumping-off place for the class of euclidean domains we study in Chapter 5. It is a slight strengthening of Theorem 0.2. It says in effect that we can "keep dividing" one integer by another until we obtain a remainder smaller than the divisor.

    Theorem 11 (*Division Algorithm*). Let a and b belong to I. If $b \neq 0$ then there exists a unique ordered pair (q, r) from I such that

$$a = bq + r \quad \text{and} \quad 0 \leq r < |b|.$$

PROOF OF EXISTENCE. We shall give a proof which, while somewhat inelegant from the standpoint of the number of cases we must consider, displays the essential algorithmic nature of the theorem. We treat first the case $a \geq b > 0$. This we prove by induction on $a - b$. (Here we use the form 2* on p. 102.) If $a - b = 0$, then we have $q = 1$ and $r = 0$. In general, if $a > b$ we have $a = b + (a - b)$. If $b > (a - b)$ (≥ 0), we are finished; if not, then $a - b \geq b > 0$ and since $a - 2b < a - b$ it follows by induction $a - b = bg + r$ where $0 \leq r < b$; thus it follows that $a = b(g + 1) + r$.

Now we treat the case $b > a \geq 0$ by noting $a = b0 + a$ trivially. Next we treat the case $b > 0$ and $a < 0$. Thus $-a > 0$ and by our first two cases we have $-a = bq + r$, or $a = b(-q) - r$. If $r = 0$ we are finished; if not, we write $a = b(-q - 1) + (b - r)$ and as $0 < r < b$ it follows that $0 < b - r < b$.

Finally if $b < 0$ then $-b > 0$ and so we have $a = (-b)q + r$ for some q and r such that $0 \leq r < (-b) = |b|$. We may rewrite this as $a = b(-q) + r$, and thus we have established the existence part of the proof in all cases. The induction step displays the recursive nature of the algorithm and guarantees that the process of repeated subtractions of b ends in a finite number of steps.

PROOF UNIQUENESS. Suppose $a = bq + r = bq_1 + r_1$. We may suppose $r \leq r_1$ and we have that $b(q + q_1) = r_1 - r$. Hence $b|(r_1 - r)$ and, by Corollary 3 of Theorem 7, if $r_1 - r \neq 0$, $|b| \leq |r_1 - r| = r_1 - r$. But $0 \leq r \leq r_1 < |b|$, hence $r_1 - r < |b|$—a contradiction. Hence $r_1 = r$ and $b(q - q_1) = 0$. Since $b \neq 0$ it follows that $q = q_1$.

$$* \quad * \quad *$$

We now want to derive some consequences of this division algorithm.

First, from Theorem 2.3 every ideal in I is principal. The proof given there rested chiefly on the division algorithm (it was called Theorem 0.2 at that time). From this it is but an easy exercise to see that for any two integers, $a, b \in I$, the smallest ideal containing both of them is $\{ax + by : x, y \in I\}$, which is therefore a principal ideal $\langle d \rangle$. Moreover $d = GCD(a, b)$. An important corollary of these remarks is that if $d = GCD(a, b)$ then there exist integers u and v such that $d = au + bv$. We shall have much more to say about these important matters in Chapter 5. Right now, just for variety, we shall establish first the existence of a least common multiple for a and b. It will then follow from Lemma 2.15 that $GCD(a, b)$ exists. From this it follows that every irreducible integer is a prime, and from this the unique factorization theorem for integers. It should not be forgotten during this string of results that the lead role is played by the division algorithm.

Lemma 8. If $a, b \in I_+$, then a and b have a least common multiple.

Before we prove this, recall that the definition of least common multiple did not refer to an order, but to division. This lemma will essentially establish the identification of these two uses of the word "least."

PROOF. Let T be the set of positive common multiples of a and b. $ab \in T$, hence T is nonempty. Let v be the least element in T. We claim $v = [a, b]$.

By definition, v is a common multiple. We must show that if $t \in T$, then $v \mid t$. By the division algorithm, $t = vq + r$ with $0 \le r < v$. We claim $r = 0$. In any event, $r = t - vq$, and since a and b both divide $t(t \in T)$ and v, a and b both divide $t - vq = r$. Hence, if r is not zero, $r \in T$ and $r < v$—a contradiction.

* * *

For integers a, b we shall hereafter use $[a, b]$ to denote the nonnegative least common multiple.

> **Theorem 12.** If $a, b \in I$ and not both are zero, then a and b have a greatest common divisor.

PROOF. Since multiplication by a unit does not affect the GCD we may suppose that $a \ge 0$ and $b \ge 0$. If $a = 0$ or $b = 0$ then the nonzero one is the GCD. If a and b are both nonzero, the result follows from Lemmas 8 and 2.15.

* * *

For integers a, b we shall hereafter use (a, b) to denote the nonnegative greatest common divisor.

Lemma 9. In I, any irreducible element is a prime.

PROOF. Let a be irreducible and let $a \mid bc$. We must show that $a \mid b$ or $a \mid c$. Let us suppose that $a \nmid b$. Since $d = (a, b)$ exists we may inquire into what it is. Since $d \mid a$ by definition and a is irreducible, d must either be an associate of a or a unit. If d is an associate of a, since $d \mid b$, this would imply that $a \mid b$; a contradiction. Hence d is a unit and we suppose $d = 1$. Hence $[a, b] = ab/(a, b) = ab$. Now $a \mid bc$ by assumption. Moreover $b \mid bc$ and so $[a, b] \mid bc$ by definition of the LCM. Thus $ab \mid bc$ or $bc = abe$, hence $c = ae$ ($a \nmid b$ implies $b \ne 0$) and so $a \mid c$.

The next theorem is often called the fundamental theorem of arithmetic.

> **Theorem 13.** (*Unique Factorization Theorem*). Every nonzero integer is either a unit or can be written as a finite product of primes, which is unique in the following sense: if $a = p_1 \ldots p_n = q_1 \ldots q_m$ where each p_i and q_j is a prime, then $n = m$, and on proper numbering p_i is an associate of q_i.

PROOF OF EXISTENCE. Since factorization is unaffected by multiplication of a unit we may suppose that the element to be factored belongs to I_+. Let $a \in I_+$. We proceed by induction (using form 2* on p. 102) on a. If $a = 1$, then a is a unit. Now suppose that the theorem is true for all positive elements less than a. If a is irreducible it is a prime and we are done. If a is not irreducible, then $a = bc$ where, because of Corollary 3 of Theorem 7, we may assume

$0 < b < a$ and $0 < c < a$. Hence, the induction hypothesis gives a decomposition of b and c into a product of primes and so gives a factorization of a into a product of primes.

PROOF OF UNIQUENESS. Let $a = p_1 \ldots p_n = q_1 \ldots q_m$. To eliminate some complications which really do not affect the essentials of the proof we shall suppose that $a > 1$ and that the p_i and q_j are all positive primes. We shall prove by induction on a that $n = m$ and that, on proper numbering, $p_i = q_i$. If a is a prime then clearly $n = m = 1$ and $p_1 = q_1$. If a is not a prime let $1 < x = p_2 \ldots p_n$ and $1 < y = q_2 \ldots q_m$. We have $p_1 x = q_1 y$, and hence that $p_1 \mid q_1$ or that $p_1 \mid y$.

Case 1. $p_1 \mid q_1$. Since p_1 and q_1 are primes it follows that $p_1 = q_1$ and $x = y$. By induction, the two factorizations for x and y must imply that $n = m$ and that, on proper renumbering, $p_i = q_i$.

Case 2. $p_1 \mid y$. Let $y = p_1 z$. By induction z has a unique factorization $z = s_1 \ldots s_t$. But by induction y also has a unique factorization and as $y = q_2 \ldots q_m = p_1 s_1 \ldots s_t$ it must be that $p_1 = q_i$ for some i. Thus on proper numbering $q_2 = p_1$. Hence $a = p_1 \ldots p_n = q_2 q_1 q_3 \ldots q_m$, and we repeat the argument in Case 1.

                   *   *   *

We conclude this section on arithmetic by stating some of the elementary facts concerning primes. For the remainder of this section a prime will mean a positive prime integer. In the first place there are an infinite number of them.

Theorem 14. There are an infinite number of prime integers.

PROOF (*Euclid*). Let $p_1, p_2, \ldots, p_n$ be the first n primes. Consider the number $N = p_1 p_2 \ldots p_n + 1$. If N were divisible by any of $p_1, \ldots, p_n$, say p_1, then p_1 would divide 1—a contradiction. Hence N must be divisible (Factorization Theorem) by some prime not yet listed. Thus for any finite set of primes we have proved that there is a prime not in the set.

                   *   *   *

A colleague once remarked that he thought the power of a mathematician could be judged by the number of different proofs he knew for this theorem. A nice one is to prove that the series $1/2 + 1/3 + 1/5 + 1/7 + 1/11 + \cdots = \sum 1/p$ of the reciprocals of the primes *diverges*. Proofs appear in the books by Niven and Zukerman, and Hardy and Wright, mentioned in the reading list at the end of the chapter. In Hardy and Wright the divergence appears as a consequence of a method of proof for Theorem 14.

The question of the density of the primes among the integers is answered by the following result, known as the prime number theorem. Let $\pi(x)$ denote the number of primes less than or equal to x. It is true that

$$\lim_{x \to \infty} \pi(x) \frac{\log_e x}{x} = 1.$$

That is, for large x, $\pi(x) \sim x/\log_e x$. The original proof is due to J. Hadamard (1865–1963) and de la Vallée Poussin (1866–1962).

The technique of the proof of Theorem 14 can be extended to show, for example, that there are an infinite number of primes of the form $4k - 1$. Examples are 7, 19, 23. Let $p_1, p_2 \ldots, pn$ be the primes of the form $4k - 1$. Consider $N = 4p_1, p_2 \ldots p_n - 1$; note that a product of primes of the form $4k + 1$ is again of that form. A more general and considerably deeper theorem was   proved by Dirichlet (1805–1859): If a and b are relatively prime, then there are infinitely many primes of the form $ak + b$.

The determination of whether a given integer is prime or composite is traditionally done by two elementary procedures. The first is a "sieve" method attributed to Eratosthenes. This method finds all primes less than or equal to the given number. An example will suffice.

Is 37 a prime? Write out all the integers 2–37:

$$
\begin{array}{cccccccccc}
 & 2 & 3 & \cancel{4} & 5 & \cancel{6} & 7 & \cancel{8} & \cancel{9} & \cancel{10} \\
11 & \cancel{12} & 13 & \cancel{14} & \cancel{15} & \cancel{16} & 17 & \cancel{18} & 19 & \cancel{20} \\
\cancel{21} & \cancel{22} & 23 & \cancel{24} & \cancel{25} & 26 & \cancel{27} & 28 & 29 & \cancel{30} \\
31 & \cancel{32} & \cancel{33} & \cancel{34} & \cancel{35} & \cancel{36} & 37 & & &
\end{array}
$$

We know 2 is a prime thus 4, 6, . . ., and every second number thereafter will be divisible by 2, hence composite. We may then cross out every second number after 2. (These numbers go "through the sieve.") The next number not crossed out is 3. We may claim it is a prime since, were it composite, it would have been divisible by a prime smaller (in this case, 2) and would thus have been crossed out. We now cross out every third number after 3. These numbers are divisible by 3, hence composite. Now the next number not crossed out is 5. A similar argument shows 5 is prime. We continue in this manner until we have reached 37. It should be clear that we are really done after we pass the half-way point, 19, since, in testing 19, the next number to cross out would be 38, which is not in our table. We conclude that 37 is a prime and moreover that the primes in the 2–37 range are 2, 3, 5, 7, 11, 13, 17, 19, 23, 29, 31, 37.

The second method for determining whether a number n is prime is to find out whether there is a prime less than n which divides n. One labor-saving device is at our disposal: If $ab = n$ then surely $a \le \sqrt{n}$ or $b \le \sqrt{n}$, the contrary implying $ab > n$. This method of course requires a list of the primes $p \le \sqrt{n}$. Hence to decide whether 37 is prime we need only test for divisibility of 37 those primes $\le \sqrt{37} < 7$, that is, 2, 3, 5.

EXERCISE 4

1. Express in prime factors 104976, 857375, 97344.

2. A simple nickel slot machine has two wheels w_1 and w_2. On w_1 are the equally spaced numbers 1, 2, . . ., 8. On w_2 are the equally spaced numbers 1, 2, . . ., 10.

Each time the lever is pulled, wheel w_2 advances 26 numbers. Wheel w_1 advances two numbers (without stopping) each time wheel w_2 makes a complete revolution (regardless of the starting position). A jackpot occurs when wheel w_1 shows 6 and w_2 shows 9. Assuming the machine has just shown 6 and 9, how much money is collected before the next jackpot? Can initial positions of the wheels be found so that no jackpot will occur? Prove your answer.

3. Let $G = \langle g \rangle$ be a cyclic group of order n. Prove that the order of g^a is $n/(a, n)$.

4. The number of integers a such that $0 < a \leq n$ and $(a, n) = 1$ is denoted $\varphi(n)$. The function φ is called the Euler φ-function. Show that $\varphi(n)$ is the number of generators in a cyclic group of order n. By classifying the elements in a cyclic group according to their order prove that $n = \sum_{d|n} \varphi(d)$.

5. In $I/\langle n \rangle$ consider $I^*_n = \{\bar{a} : (a, n) = 1\}$. Show that I^*_n is a multiplicative group of order $\varphi(n)$. [*Hint:* Recall Lemma 1.7.] Prove the following generalization of the Fermat's little theorem due to Euler:

$$\text{If } (a, n) = 1 \quad \text{then} \quad a^{\varphi(n)} \equiv 1 \ (\text{mod } n).$$

6. Let p be a prime in I_+. Show that $n \mid \varphi(p^n - 1)$ for all n. [*Hint:* $(p, p^n - 1) = 1$. Find the order of $\bar{p}$ in $I^*_{(p^n - 1)}$.]

7. Another useful number-theoretic function is the greatest integer or "bracket" function. If r is a real number define $[r]$ as the greatest integer less than or equal to r. Thus $[r] \leq r < [r] + 1$. For example, $[r] = r$ if $r \in I$, $[\sqrt{2}] = 1$, $[5/2] = 2$, $[\pi] = 3$, and $[-\sqrt{3}] = -2$.

  (i) Prove that $[[r]] = [r]$.
  (ii) Prove that $[r + n] = [r] + n$ if $n \in I$.
  (iii) What is the relation of q and $[a/b]$ where a, b, and q are as defined in Theorem 11?
  (iv) Evaluate $[x] + [-x]$.
  (v) Prove that $[r + s] \geq [r] + [s]$.
  (vi) Prove that $\left[\dfrac{[r]}{n}\right] = \left[\dfrac{r}{n}\right]$ if $n \in I_+$.

8. Find the exponent of 3 in the decomposition of 100! into prime factors. Generalize to $n!$ and any prime p.

SUPPLEMENTARY READING

P. Bernays and A. A. Fraenkel, *Axiomatic Set Theory*, Amsterdam; North-Holland (1958).

R. C. Buck, Mathematical induction and recursive definitions, *American Mathematical Monthly*, **70** (1963), 128–135.

S. Fefferman, *The Number Systems*, Reading, Massachusetts: Addison-Wesley (1964).

P. R. Halmos, *Naive set theory*, Princeton, N.J.: Van Nostrand (1960).

G. H. Hardy and E. M. Wright, *Theory of Numbers* (Fourth Edition), Oxford: The University Press (1960).

R. R. Stoll, *Set Theory and Logic*, San Francisco: Freeman (1961).

P. Suppes, *Axiomatic Set Theory*, Princeton, N.J.: Van Nostrand (1960).

E. Landau, *Foundation of Analysis*, New York: Chelsea (1948).

I. Niven and H. S. Zukerman, *An Introduction to the Theory of Numbers*, New York: John Wiley & Sons (1960).

4 | Fields

4.1. INTRODUCTION

In this chapter we give special attention to the elementary properties of fields. We have already seen in earlier chapters a number of different examples of fields—some finite and some infinite. A field may be viewed as a generalization of the rational numbers. Recall that a field is an integral domain in which the nonzero elements form a multiplicative group; the field axioms assume enough to guarantee a solution to every linear equation, $ax = b$ in which $a \neq 0$. The generalization from the rationals is achieved by dropping the concept of order from the axiomatic structure. Our first results show in particular how the rational numbers can be constructed from the integers by a process which may be carried out in any integral domain.

4.2. FIELD OF QUOTIENTS

The basic problem is this: Given an integral domain D, we should like to be able to solve equations of the form $ax = b$. Now we know no solution is possible if $a = 0$ and $b \neq 0$. On the other hand, if $a = 0$ and $b = 0$, the equation has at least two solutions, $x = 0$ and $x = 1$. To gain both the existence and unicity of a solution it seems plausible to suppose that $a \neq 0$. But even so, a solution does not always exist within D. Thus $2x = 1$ has no solution in integers. To solve this equation we need a multiplicative inverse for a. We seek to construct a larger system Q, which will contain D or at least an isomorphic copy of D, and in which we can solve such an equation.

The idea for the construction of Q comes from simply saying "Let's invent a new "number," called a solution of the equation $ax = b$. Let us denote it by the ordered pair of elements from D, (a, b)."†

---

† An equally suitable motivation comes from *supposing* that the larger system Q has been constructed in which a^{-1} exists. Then the solution becomes $a^{-1}b$, and we are led to the ordered pair (a, b) or, as is more customary, the "fraction" b/a.

112

Thus we might let $Q^* = \{(a, b) : a, b \in D, a \neq 0\}$ and try to discover how to "add" and "multiply" ordered pairs. We cannot proceed quite this casually because of the problem of equality. Clearly we shall want equations $ax = b$ and $cax = cb$ (provided $c \neq 0$) to have the same solution. That is, we want to say $(a, b) = (ca, cb)$ if $c \neq 0$. Our first task is then to define an equivalence relation on $Q^* = \{(a, b) : a, b \in D, a \neq 0\}$. We shall then try to make the resulting set of *equivalence classes* into the desired system Q. Remember, in this section (a, b) denotes an ordered pair, not a GCD.

Thus we are first tackling the problem of why $1/2 = 3/6$. $1/2$ and $3/6$ are *different fractions*, but they are *names* of the *same rational number*.

The clue for the definition of equivalence for ordered pairs is this: If $ax = b$ and $cx = d$ have the same solution, then so do $cax = cb$ and $acx = ad$. Since $ac = ca$, however, it should follow that $cb = ad$.

Definition. In Q^*, $(a, b) \equiv (c, d)$ if and only if $ad = bc$.

Lemma 1. ($\equiv$) is an equivalence relation on Q^*.

PROOF. (1) $(a, b) \equiv (a, b)$ since $ab = ba$. (2) If $(a, b) \equiv (c, d)$, then $(c, d) \equiv (a, b)$, also because multiplication in D is commutative. (3) If $(a, b) \equiv (c, d)$ and $(c, d) \equiv (e, f)$, then $(a, b) \equiv (e, f)$. From the first, $ad = bc$; from the second, $cf = de$. Multiply the first equality by e and the second by a to obtain $ade = bce$ and $acf = ade$. Hence $acf = bce$. As $c \neq 0$, we may cancel c to obtain $af = be$, the condition for $(a, b) \equiv (e, f)$.

* * *

We shall denote by b/a the equivalence class $\{(c, d) : (c, d) \equiv (a, b)\}$ of elements of Q^*. Let Q be the set of equivalence classes.

We now set about defining $(+)$ and $(\cdot)$ in Q, identifying a subset of Q which is isomorphic to D, and showing that Q is a field; hence all equations of the form $Ax = B$, $A \neq 0$ have unique solutions in Q.

Multiplication. What should it mean to multiply b/a by d/c? b/a and d/c are equivalence classes. Take (a, b) from the first and (c, d) from the second. (a, b) means the solution to $ax = b$. Similarly (c, d) means the solution to $cy = d$. The different choice of the dummy symbols x and y is intentional and suggestive, since, speaking informally, $x = (a, b)$ and $y = (c, d)$. Thus to find what $(a, b) \cdot (c, d)$ should be, we want to find an equation whose solution is xy; that is, $acxy = bd$, since, again informally, $ax = b$ and $cy = d$.

Definition. If b/a and d/c belong to Q, define $b/a \cdot d/c = bd/ac$.

As was the case in defining a group operation on the cosets of a normal subgroup, we must show that this definition makes sense by showing that the product of the classes is independent of the choice of equivalence class representative. First, since $a \neq 0$ and $c \neq 0$, $ac \neq 0$ and so $(ac, bd) \in Q^*$, hence $bd/ac \in Q$. Next we prove a lemma which demonstrates the required independence.

Lemma 2. If $(a, b) \equiv (r, s)$ and $(c, d) \equiv (u, v)$, then $(ac, bd) \equiv (ru, sv)$.

PROOF. We are assuming $as = br$ and $cv = du$ from whence it follows that $ascv = brdu$, or that $(ac, bd) = (ru, sv)$.

$$* \quad * \quad *$$

Addition. Assuming as before that $ax = b$ is one equation, and $cy = d$ is another, we want an equation for which $x + y$ is a solution. If $ax = b$, then $cax = cb$, and if $cy = d$, $acy = ad$. Hence, adding both equations, $acx + acy = cb + ad$, or $ac(x + y) = cb + ad$.

Definition. If b/a and d/c belong to Q, define $b/a + d/c = (bc + ad)/ac$.

Again we must make the verifications that this is a definition of a binary operation on Q. Since $a \neq 0$ and $c \neq 0$, $ac \neq 0$, in any event we know that $(bc + ad)/ac$ is an element of Q.

Lemma 3. If $(a, b) \equiv (r, s)$ and $(c, d) \equiv (u, v)$, then $(ac, ad + bc) \equiv (ru, rv + su)$.

PROOF. We have $as = br$ and $cv = du$. Hence $ac(rv + su) = ac\underline{rv} + ac\underline{su} = ard\underline{u} + b\underline{rc}u = ru(ad + bc)$, which was to be proved.

$$* \quad * \quad *$$

Theorem 1. Under the definitions for $(+)$ and $(\cdot)$, the set of quotients Q is a field in which

$$D^* = \{b/1 : b \in D\} \text{ is isomorphic to } D.$$

Moreover Q is the smallest subfield of Q containing D^*.

PROOF. We verify all the field axioms. The calculations appear routine, but remember a/b stands for a set of ordered pairs.

1. Addition is associative:

$$\frac{a}{b} + \left(\frac{c}{d} + \frac{e}{f}\right) = \frac{a}{b} + \frac{cf + ed}{df} = \frac{adf + b(cf + ed)}{bdf} = \frac{(ad + bc)f + bed}{bdf}$$

$$= \frac{ad + bc}{bd} + \frac{e}{f} = \left(\frac{a}{b} + \frac{c}{d}\right) + \frac{e}{f}.$$

Similarly multiplication is associative.

2. Addition and multiplication are commutative: This follows readily from the definition, since addition and multiplication are commutative in D.

3. $0/1$ is an additive identity: $a/b + 0/1 = (a \cdot 1 + 0 \cdot b)/b \cdot 1 = a/b$. Similarly $1/1$ is the multiplicative identity.

4. $-a/b$ is the additive inverse of a/b: $a/b + -a/b = (ab - ab)/b^2 = 0/b^2 = 0/1$.

5. If $a/b \neq 0/1$, $(a/b)^{-1} = b/a$: If $a/b \neq 0/1$ then $b \cdot 0 \neq a \cdot 1$, and so $a \neq 0$. Since $a \neq 0$, $(a, b) \in Q^*$ and so b/a is meaningful. Calculation shows $a/b \cdot b/a = ab/ba = 1/1$. (Note that the commutativity of multiplication in D is used here.)

6. Multiplication is distributive over addition: $(a/b)(c/d + e/f) = (a/b)$ $(cf + ed/df) = a(cf + ed)/bdf = acf/bdf + aed/bdf = (a/b)(c/d) + (a/b)(e/f)$.

7. $D^* = \{d/1 : d \in D\}$ is isomorphic to D: We claim the mapping $\varphi : D \to D^*$ given by $\varphi(d) = d/1$ is an isomorphism. It is clearly 1–1, since $\varphi(d) = \varphi(e)$ implies $d/1 = e/1$; hence $d = e$. φ clearly maps D^* onto D. Moreover

$$\varphi(d + e) = \frac{d + e}{1} = \frac{d}{1} + \frac{e}{1} = \varphi(d) + \varphi(e) \quad \text{and}$$

$$\varphi(de) = \frac{de}{1} = \frac{d}{1} \cdot \frac{e}{1} = \varphi(d)\varphi(e)$$

Hence φ is the alleged isomorphism.

8. Q is the smallest subfield of Q containing D^*. If T is a subfield containing D^* then T contains, for all $a, b \in D$, $a/1$ and $b/1$. If $b \neq 0$ then T must also contain $(b/1)^{-1} = (1/b)$ and so T contains $(a/1)(1/b) = a/b$ as well. Thus $T \supseteq Q$.

* * *

Of course, Q does not contain D so that we have not yet constructed a field containing D. However, because of the natural isomorphism φ, we shall "identify" D^* with D. By this we mean we shall simply give the elements of Q new names, in particular we shall give the elements of D^* the names of elements in D as prescribed by the isomorphism φ^{-1}. For example, if $d \in D$ we identify d and $d/1$. More formally we could construct the set $(Q - D^*) \cup D = \bar{Q}$ and define new operations $(\dotplus)$ and $(\circ)$ by a recipe involving φ, D, D^*, and Q:

$$a \dotplus b = \begin{cases} a + b & \text{if } a, b, \text{ and } a + b \in Q - D^*. \\ \varphi^{-1}(a + b) & \text{if } a, b \in Q, \text{ and } a + b \in D^*. \\ a + \varphi(b) & \text{if } a \in Q, b \in D, \text{ and } a + \varphi(b) \in Q - D^*. \\ \varphi(a) + b & \text{if } b \in Q, a \in D, \text{ and } \varphi(a) + b \in Q - D^*. \\ \varphi^{-1}(a + \varphi(b)) & \text{if } a \in Q - D^*, b \in D, \text{ and } a + \varphi(b) \in D^*. \\ \varphi^{-1}(\varphi(a) + b) & \text{if } a \in D, b \in Q - D^*, \text{ and } \varphi(a) + b \in D^*. \\ a + b & \text{if } a, b \in D. \end{cases}$$

The multiplication operation $(\circ)$ is defined similarly. We would still have to verify that $\bar{Q}$ was a field. This is tedious and tells us nothing we do not already know. We shall use the euphemism of "identification" and say that Q is a field containing D. There will be many other times when we shall apply a similar subterfuge. Incidentally, it is precisely this difficulty which troubles elementary school children in accepting 2/1 as 2.

Definition. The field Q constructed here will be called the field of quotients of D. If D is the integers, Q will be called the rational numbers, and we shall denote the rational numbers by Ra.

EXERCISE 1

1. Give a description of the field of quotients of the integral domain $\{a + b\sqrt{2} : a, b \in I\}$.

2. What rational numbers, if any, belong to the field of quotients of the rational numbers of the form a/b where $3 \nmid b$?

3. Is $\{x : x$ is real and x^2 is rational$\}$ a field under ordinary addition and multiplication?

4. Let D be an integral domain which is a subring of a field F. Show that the field, Q, of quotients of D is isomorphic to a subfield of F.

5. Let $\langle D, +, \cdot, \leq \rangle$ be an ordered integral domain. Show that its field of quotients, Q, may be ordered by a relation $(\leq)$. Show that if the following conditions hold, only one ordering of Q is possible: For all $a, b \in D$ then $a \leq b$ in D if and only if $a \leq b$ in Q. [*Hint:* How do you determine whether $31/163 \leq 33/164$?]

4.3. SUBFIELDS

Definition. A subset S of a field $\langle F, +, \cdot \rangle$ is called a *subfield* of F if S is a subring of F which is a field under $(+)$ and $(\cdot)$. Dually we say F is an *extension* of S if S is a subfield of F. If $S \neq F$, S is called a *proper subfield* of F.

The following lemma indicates the distinction between a subfield and a subring.

Lemma 4. If S is a subring of a field F containing at least two elements, then S is a subfield of F if and only if, whenever $0 \neq s \in S$, then $s^{-1} \in S$.

PROOF. The condition obviously holds if S is a subfield of F. Conversely if S is a subring of F it follows that $\langle S, + \rangle$ is a subgroup of $\langle F, + \rangle$. Moreover if $s, t \in S$ then $st \in S$, by Lemma 2.6; thus if $s \neq 0$, then $s^{-1} \in S$ by assumption and so $ts^{-1} \in S$. From Lemma 1.8 the nonzero elements of S (and there are some nonzero elements in S since S contains at least two elements) form a multiplicative subgroup of the nonzero elements of F. Thus $\langle S, +, \cdot \rangle$ is a field.

* * *

Corollary. If S is a subfield of F then $1 \in S$.

PROOF. Let $0 \neq s \in S$. We have $ss^{-1} = 1 \in S$.

* * *

This corollary holds for the more fundamental intrinsic property; in a field, 1 is the only nonzero solution of $x^2 = x$.

Theorem 2. If T is a set of subfields of a field F then the set intersection $\bigcap T$ is a subfield of F.

PROOF. This is almost a corollary of the corresponding result for rings. In view of Lemma 4, we need only check to see that if $t \in \bigcap T$ then $t^{-1} \in \bigcap T$ which, from Lemma 4, is the case.

* * *

Theorem 2 shows that if we take the set intersection of all subfields of a given field F, we obtain a subfield P. This field is a subfield of all other subfields of F, hence the smallest subfield in F. What is the nature of this field?

Definition. Let F be a field. P is called the *prime subfield* of F if P is a subfield of all subfields of F.

Lemma 5. For every field F, there is a unique prime subfield.

PROOF. This follows directly from the remarks preceding the definition $P = \bigcap \{T : T \text{ a subfield of } F\}$.

* * *

Theorem 3. Let F be any field. The prime subfield of F is isomorphic either to the rational numbers or to $I/\langle p \rangle$ where p is a prime.

PROOF. For this proof we need to distinguish between the integer 1 and the multiplicative identity of F. We shall use ϵ to denote the multiplicative identity of F in this proof only. We shall continue to use 0 to denote both the integer 0 and the additive identity of F.

The motivation for the proof stems from the observation that ϵ must belong to the prime subfield and hence $\epsilon + \epsilon = 2\epsilon$ and in general $n\epsilon$ belongs to the prime subfield for all integers n. This suggests that we consider the mapping $\Phi : I \to F$ given by $\Phi(n) = n\epsilon$. (Recall that $\epsilon \cdot 0 = 0$ and if $n \geq 0$ then $(n + 1)\epsilon = n\epsilon + \epsilon$ and $(-n)\epsilon = -(n\epsilon)$. This is merely adapting the definition of exponentiation in Chapter 1 to the additive notation.) Φ is clearly a ring homomorphism, and so we know its range, $\mathcal{R}_\Phi$ is a subring of F and from Theorem 2.2 we know its kernel is an ideal of I. From Theorem 2.3 we know this ideal is a principal ideal $\langle m \rangle$. From Theorem 2.4 we know $\mathcal{R}_\Phi \cong I/\langle m \rangle$. Since the range of Φ is a subring of a field it must, in particular, be an integral domain. Hence from Theorem 2.5, $m = 0$ or $m = p$, a prime.

We shall show that the prime subfield of F is

$$P = \{ab^{-1} : a, b \in \mathcal{R}_\Phi, b \neq 0\}.$$

First we note that since the prime subfield contains ϵ it must contain all of $\mathcal{R}_\Phi$ and indeed any element of P. On the other hand, routine arguments show that P is a subfield of F, hence P is the prime subfield of F. Moreover P is isomorphic to the field Q of quotients of $\mathcal{R}_\Phi$. This can be established by verifying that if a/b is the equivalence class in Q to which (b, a) belongs then the mapping θ defined by $\theta(ab^{-1}) = a/b$ is an isomorphism of P onto Q. (θ is a 1–1 function since the equalities $ab^{-1} = cd^{-1}$ in P, $ad = bc$ in P, $(b, a) = (d, c)$ in Q^*, and $a/b = c/d$ in Q, are all equivalent. Clearly θ maps P onto Q and by a routine argument θ is a field isomorphism.)

To complete the proof we must treat the two cases $m = 0$ and $m = p$ separately. If $m = p$ then it follows from the corollary to Theorem 2.5 that $I/\langle p \rangle \cong \mathcal{R}_\Phi$ is a field, and so $\mathcal{R}_\Phi$ is a subfield of F. By definition of the prime subfield it must be that $P \subseteq \mathcal{R}_\Phi$ while from the definition of P we have $\mathcal{R}_\Phi \subseteq P$. Thus $\mathcal{R}_\Phi = P$ and $P \cong I/\langle p \rangle$. If $m = 0$ then $\mathcal{R}_\Phi \cong I$ and so the field Q of quotients of $\mathcal{R}_\Phi$ is isomorphic to Ra. Since $P \cong Q$ we conclude that $P \cong$ Ra.

Corollary. If F is a finite field then its prime subfield is isomorphic with $I/\langle p \rangle$ for a prime p.

PROOF. Since F has a finite number of elements, its prime subfield cannot be isomorphic with Ra, which has an infinite number of elements.

$$* \quad * \quad *$$

Definition. The characteristic of a field F is an integer associated with F in the following manner.

> If the prime field of F is $I/\langle p \rangle$, the characteristic of F is p.
> If the prime field of F is Ra, the characteristic of F is 0.

We often write char(F) for the characteristic of F. If char$(F) = p \neq 0$ then $px = 0$ for all $x \in F$. We leave the proof of this remark as an exercise.

There is another useful notation in connection with the subfields of a field. If S is a subfield of a field F and if A is a set of elements in F we shall denote by $S(A)$ the smallest subfield of F containing $S \cup A$. We have of course that $S(A) = \bigcap \{T : S \subseteq T \subseteq F, A \subseteq T, \text{ and } T \text{ is a subfield of } F\}$. If $A = \varnothing$ then $S(\varnothing) = S$. In most of the applications we shall consider the set A will be a finite set, $\{a_1, \ldots, a_n\}$, and in this case we shall write $S(a_1, \ldots, a_n)$ for $S(A)$.

4.4. HOMOMORPHISMS OF FIELDS

The theory of field homomorphisms that are not isomorphisms is rather trivial, as the next theorem shows.

Theorem 4. If $\langle F, +, \cdot \rangle$ and $\langle \bar{F}, +, \cdot \rangle$ are fields and φ is a ring homomorphism of F into $\bar{F}$, then either $\varphi(a) = 0$ for all a or φ is 1–1 and is thus an isomorphism between F and a subfield F' of $\bar{F}$.

PROOF. As Problem 3 of Exercise 2.2 showed, F has only two ideals: $\{0\}$ and F itself. Hence φ is, respectively, 1–1 or $\varphi(a) = 0$ for all a. For the sake of completeness we recast the solution of this problem in terms of homomorphisms. We note first that if $\varphi(1) = \bar{0}$ then $\varphi(a) = \varphi(a1) = \varphi(a)\varphi(1) = \varphi(a)\bar{0} = \bar{0}$ for all $a \in F$. Hence if $\varphi(a) \neq \bar{0}$ for some a, we may assume that $\varphi(1) \neq 0$. But then if $b \neq 0$ we have $0 \neq \varphi(1) = \varphi(bb^{-1}) = \varphi(b)\varphi(b^{-1})$, and so $\varphi(b) \neq 0$. Thus if φ is not identically 0, we have that $\varphi(a) = 0$ if and only if $a = 0$. Now to show that φ is 1–1, suppose that $\varphi(a) = \varphi(b)$. Then $\bar{0} = \varphi(a) - \varphi(b) = \varphi(a - b)$. But this implies that $0 = a - b$, or that $a = b$.

* * *

In view of this theorem the only interesting endomorphisms of a field F are its automorphisms. A study of the automorphisms of a field is one of the most powerful tools in the study of the structure of fields.

Example 1. Let $F = \text{Ra}(\sqrt{2}) = \{a + b\sqrt{2} : a, b \in \text{Ra}\}$. Let φ be the mapping defined $\varphi(a + b\sqrt{2}) = a - b\sqrt{2}$. φ is easily verified to be an automorphism of F.

> **Theorem 5.** The set of all automorphisms of a field F forms a group under composition.

PROOF. We have only to verify that a composition of two automorphisms is again an automorphism and that the inverse mapping of an automorphism is an automorphism. These are routine details which we shall omit.

* * *

If $E \supseteq F$ we shall be interested in the automorphisms of E, which fix every element in F.

Corollary. The automorphisms σ of E such that $\sigma(a) = a$ for all $a \in F$ form a group called the group of automorphisms of E over F, which we denote by $\mathscr{G}(E/F)$.

EXERCISE 2

$a + b\sqrt{2} \quad a, b \in \text{Rat}.$

1. Describe the smallest subfield of the real numbers containing $\sqrt{2}$ and $\sqrt{3}$. Find three proper subfields of this field.
2. Find a subring S of the rational numbers such that $I \subset S \subset \text{Ra}$.
3. Prove or disprove: The integers are a homomorphic image of the integral domain D_3 of those rational numbers which in lowest terms have the form a/b where $3 \nmid b$.

4. Prove that if σ is an automorphism of a field, then $\{x : \sigma(x) = x\}$ forms a subfield.

5. Let F have characteristic p. Show that $px = 0$ for all $x \in F$.

6. Let F have characteristic p. Show that every subfield has characteristic p.

7. Prove that if F is a field with a finite number of elements n, then n is a power of a prime. [*Hint:* Use the fact that if a prime divides the order of an abelian group, then there is an element of that order.]

8. If F is a field of characteristic p, prove that $(x + y)^p = x^p + y^p$ for all $x, y \in F$. Generalize to $(\sum_{i=1}^{n} x_i)^{p^k}$.

9. Prove that if σ is an automorphism of a field F, then $\sigma(x) = x$ for all x in the prime subfield.

10. Show that if F is a finite field of characteristic p and $u \in F$, then there is exactly one element v such that $v^p = u$. In I_{13} find a thirteenth root of $\bar{3}$.

11. Let R be a commutative ring with identity 1. Let n be the smallest positive integer such that $n \cdot 1 = 0$. Show that $nx = 0$ for all $x \in R$. Show that if R is a field, either no such n exists or n is the characteristic of the field.

12. Let F be a field of characteristic p. Let $S = \{\alpha : \alpha \in F, \alpha^{p^n} - \alpha = 0\}$. Show that S is a subfield of F.

13. Let F be any field. Show that the affine transformations $x \to ax + b$, $a \neq 0$, $b \in F$ form a group G. Show that the translations $x \to x + b$ form a normal subgroup K of G under composition. What is the factor group G/K?

4.5. THE REAL NUMBERS

We do not intend to give a thorough development of the real numbers. Logically we should give a construction for the real numbers from the rational numbers. This program is carried out, for example, in the books of Landau, Fefferman, and van der Waerden mentioned in the reading lists; however, such a program takes us beyond the scope of this book as outlined in the Prologue. Our assumptions regarding the real numbers are collected in Theorem 8.

The need for a structure richer than the rational numbers stems from the inability to find rational numbers that express certain natural relationships. For example, we seek a number whose square is 2. Or, we seek a number which is the ratio of the circumference of a circle to its diameter. While it is easy, because of the algebraic nature of the question, to show that there is no rational number whose square is 2, it is more difficult to show that π is not a rational number. It is an impossible task to list *all* the situations that require new numbers. We shall therefore undertake to introduce the real numbers in another way—utilizing *order*. But first let us establish the first assertion about $\sqrt{2}$.

Lemma 6. There is no rational number whose square is 2.

PROOF. We prove this by showing that if a/b is a rational number such that $(a/b)^2 = 2$, then a contradiction arises. We pick from the equivalence class

a/b an ordered pair (a_1, b_1) where $\text{GCD}(a_1, b_1) = 1$. This is possible since if $a = a_1(a, b)$ and $b = b_1(a, b)$, then $(a_1, b_1) = 1$, while $a/b = a_1/b_1$. Now if $(a_1/b_1)^2 = 2$ then $(a_1/b_1)^2 = a_1{}^2/b_1{}^2 = 2$ and $a_1{}^2 = 2b_1{}^2$. Hence $2 \mid a_1{}^2$, or $2 \mid a_1 \cdot a_1$. Now 2 is a prime and thus $2 \mid a_1$, say $a_1 = 2c$. Hence $4c^2 = 2b_1{}^2$ or $2c^2 = b_1{}^2$. But, arguing as before, $2 \mid b_1$ contrary to $\text{GCD}(a_1, b_1) = 1$.

* * *

The order properties we use concern bounds, upper bounds, and least upper bounds.

Definition. Let S be any set on which a partial order relation ρ has been defined. A subset T of S is said to be _bounded from above_ if there is an element $b \in S$ such that $t \rho b$ for all $t \in T$.

Example 2. Let S be the integers and ρ the relation $(\leq)$. Let $T = \{a \in I : a^2 < 16\}$. Then T is bounded from above by 4 (or 5, or 6, or any integer b such that $b^2 \geq 16$).

Example 3. Again we take $S = I$ and $\rho = \leq$. Let $T = \{3 + 5a : a \in I\}$. T is not bounded from above.

Example 4. Let S be the rational numbers and $\rho = \leq$. Let $T = \{a$ is a rational number $: a^2 < 2\}$. Then T is bounded from above by 2.

Example 5. Let $T = \{a : a < 1\}$. Then T is bounded from above by 1 or any rational number larger than 1. (Take S to be the rational numbers.)

Definition. Let S be a set on which a partial order relation ρ has been defined. Let T be a subset of S. T is said to have a _least upper bound_ if there is an element $b \in S$ such that

1. b is an upper bound for T.
2. If c is any other upper bound, then $b \rho c$.

Lemma 7. If T has a _least upper bound_, then it is unique.

PROOF. If b and b_1 are least upper bounds for T, then, by 2, since b is a least upper bound, $b \rho b_1$. But similarly $b_1 \rho b$. Hence $b = b_1$.

* * *

The set in Example 2 has 4 as its least upper bound, the sets in Examples 3 and 4 have no least upper bound and the set in Example 5 has 1 as its least upper bound.

We should like to give an example to show that not every subset of rational numbers has a _least_ upper bound even though it may have many upper bounds. In particular we shall prove:

Theorem 6. The set of rational numbers $T = \{r : r^2 < 2\}$ has upper bounds but no least upper bound in the field of rational numbers.

While we can give a straightforward proof, it will be almost as easy to establish some intermediate results that are interesting in their own right.

Lemma 8. For any positive integer m, $m \geq 2$, and for all pairs of elements a, b in a ring R, if $a \neq b$ and if $ab = ba$ in R then

$$\frac{a^m - b^m}{a - b} = a^{m-1} + a^{m-2}b + \cdots + ab^{m-2} + b^{m-1} = \sum_{i=1}^{m} a^{m-i}b^{i-1}$$

PROOF. We simply compute

$$(a - b) \sum_{i=1}^{m} a^{m-i}b^{i-1} = \sum_{i=1}^{m} (a - b)a^{m-i}b^{i-1}$$

$$= \sum_{i=1}^{m} (a^{m-i+1}b^{i-1} - a^{m-i}b^i)$$

$$= \sum_{i=1}^{m} (a^{m-(i-1)}b^{i-1} - a^{m-i}b^i)$$

$$= \sum_{i=0}^{m-1} a^{m-i}b^i - \sum_{i=1}^{m} a^{m-i}b^i = a^m - b^m.$$

Lemma 9. For any positive integer $m \geq 2$, for all $a \in I_+$,

$$(a + 1)^m - a^m < m(a + 1)^{m-1}$$

PROOF. From the preceding lemma,

$$(a + 1)^m - a^m = \frac{(a + 1)^m - a^m}{(a + 1) - a}$$

$$= \sum_{i=1}^{m} (a + 1)^{m-i}a^{i-1} < \sum_{i=1}^{m} (a + 1)^{m-1} = m(a + 1)^{m-1}$$

* * *

Theorem 7. If r_1 and r_2 are rational numbers such that $0 < r_1 < r_2$ and if k is any positive integer, then there is a rational number t, depending on r_1, r_2, and k such that

$$r_1 < t^k < r_2.$$

PROOF. If $k = 1$, we take $t = (r_1 + r_2)/2$. Hence we suppose hereafter that $k \geq 2$. First choose an integer s such that

1. $s^k \leq r_1 < (s + 1)^k$.

We can make this choice because first of all $r_1 < n$ for some integer n, and $n \le n^k$ for all k. Hence using the well-ordering principle there is a least integer, call it $(s + 1)$, such that $r_1 < (s + 1)^k$.

Now if $(s + 1)^k < r_2$ the theorem holds. Hence we suppose

2. $s^k \le r_1 < r_2 \le (s + 1)^k$.

Thus $0 < r_2 - r_1 \le (s + 1)^k - s^k < k(s + 1)^{k-1}$ follows from 2 and Lemma 9, so that $1 < k(s + 1)^{k-1}/r_2 - r_1$. Now let m be the largest integer such that

3. $1 \le m \le 1 + \dfrac{k(s + 1)^{k-1}}{r_2 - r_1}$.

In fact $m \ge 2$. Again this is possible from an application of the well-ordering principle. Now from 3 and the choice of m we have

$$m > \frac{k(s + 1)^{k-1}}{r_2 - r_1} > 0 \quad \text{or} \quad \frac{k(s + 1)^{k-1}}{m(r_2 - r_1)} < 1,$$

or

4. $\dfrac{k(s + 1)^{k-1}}{m} < (r_2 - r_1)$.

Now that m has been chosen, we rewrite 2 as

5. $\left(\dfrac{ms}{m}\right)^k \le r_1 < r_2 < \left(\dfrac{ms + m}{m}\right)^k$.

Now let n be an integer such that $0 \le n \le m - 1$ and such that

6. $\left(\dfrac{ms + n}{m}\right)^k \le r_1 < \left(\dfrac{ms + n + 1}{m}\right)^k$.

Then, by using the inequality of the preceding lemma,

7. $\dfrac{(ms + n + 1)^k}{m^k} - \dfrac{(ms + n)^k}{m^k} < \dfrac{k(ms + n + 1)^{k-1}}{m^k} \le \dfrac{k(ms + m)^{k-1}}{m^k}$

$$= \frac{k}{m}(s + 1)^{k-1} < r_2 - r_1.$$

Let $t = (ms + n + 1)/m$. From 6 we have $r_1 < t^k$ and also $t^k - r_1 \le t^k - (ms + n/m)^k$. From 7 we have $t^k - (ms + n/m)^k < r_2 - r_1$. Hence $t^k - r_1 < r_2 - r_1$, or $t^k < r_2$. Thus $r_1 < t^k < r_2$ as was to be shown.

* * *

PROOF OF THEOREM 6. First we recall that there is no rational whose square is 2. Hence if $T = \{x : x^2 < 2\}$ has a least upper bound, b either $b^2 < 2$ or $2 < b^2$. If $b^2 < 2$, then there is a rational t, such that $b^2 < t^2 < 2$. Hence $t \in T$, but $b < t$—a contradiction of the allegation that b was an upper bound for T. Similarly, if $2 < b^2$, then there is a rational t such that $2 < t^2 < b^2$, and so t is an upper bound for T but $t < b$—a contradiction of the allegation that b was the least upper bound.

*   *   *

Thus it seems to be desirable to have a system of numbers containing the rational numbers with the property that every subset of numbers that has an upper bound, has a least upper bound. In the case in point, $\sqrt{2}$ is the desired least upper bound.

We may define the length of the circumference of a circle in a similar fashion. Let C be a circle of diameter 1. If P is an inscribed polygon, let $\lambda(P)$ be the length of its perimeter. Let $T = \{\lambda(P) : P \text{ any polygon inscribed in } C\}$. Then π is the least upper bound for T.

*   *   *

Our assumptions about the real numbers are contained in the next theorem.

Theorem 8. There exists a field $\langle \text{Re}, +, \cdot, \leq \rangle$ which is an ordered field and is an extension of the field of rational numbers Ra, in which every nonempty subset of Re possessing an upper bound has a least upper bound. Any two such fields are isomorphic.

One of the properties of the real numbers we shall assume is given in the next lemma.

Lemma 10. If x is a positive real number and n is any integer, there exists a unique positive real number $\sqrt[n]{x}$ such that $(\sqrt[n]{x})^n = x$.

EXERCISE 3

1. Show that if n is an integer not of the form $n = m^2$ for $m \in I$, then there is no rational number whose square is n.

2. Prove that the positive integers have no upper bound in the real numbers.

3. Prove that for every positive real number x there is a rational number r such that $0 < r < x$.

4. Prove that for all pairs of real numbers $u < v$ there is a rational number r such that $u < r < v$.

5. Let r be a positive real number and n a positive integer. Show that $\{u : u \in \text{Ra and } u^n \leq r\}$ has a least upper bound $z \in \text{Re}$ and $z^n = r$. Prove Lemma 10.

6. Show that any automorphism σ of the real numbers must be the identity. [*Hint:* $\sigma(a^2) = (\sigma(a))^2 \geq 0$.] Thus show that σ preserves order and hence that σ is continuous.

4.6. THE COMPLEX NUMBERS

Not all questions are answered by the construction of the real numbers. In particular, there are still some equations we cannot solve! For instance, $x^2 + 1 = 0$. In the real field, for all real numbers $x^2 \geq 0$ and so $x^2 + 1 > 0$. In this section we shall start with the real field and construct a larger field— the complex field—in which $x^2 + 1 = 0$ has a solution. The remarkable fact will then be that *every equation* of the form $a_n x^n + a_{n-1} x^{n-1} + \cdots + a_1 x + a_0 = 0$, where a_i is a complex number, will have all of its solutions in this field. The proof requires analytic tools which we shall not study here. In the references in the reading list at the end of this chapter there are various proofs of this theorem.

To motivate the construction of the complex numbers we shall employ the technique of supposing that there is a field T, containing the real field in which $x^2 + 1 = 0$ has a solution. Call the solution $\sqrt{-1}$. Then T must contain elements of the form $a + b\sqrt{-1}$, where a and b are real numbers. We should have $(a + b\sqrt{-1}) + (c + d\sqrt{-1}) = (a + c) + (b + d)\sqrt{-1}$, using the field axioms freely. Also $(a + b\sqrt{-1})(c + d\sqrt{-1}) = (ac - bd) + (ad + bc)\sqrt{-1}$.

We may formalize this treatment by associating $a + b\sqrt{-1}$ with the ordered pair of real numbers (a, b) and defining addition and multiplication appropriately. This we now do.

Definition. Let $C = \{(a, b) : a \text{ and } b \text{ are real numbers}\}$. Let

$$(a, b) + (c, d) = (a + c, b + d)$$

and

$$(a, b) \cdot (c, d) = (ac - bd, ad + bc).$$

Lemma 11. Under the above definitions of addition and multiplication, C becomes a field called the field of *complex numbers*.

PROOF 1. $\langle C, + \rangle$ is an abelian group, for it is just the direct product of two abelian groups both isomorphic to $\langle \text{Re}, + \rangle$. We leave the proof that multiplication is both associative and commutative to the student.

2. $(1, 0)$ is the multiplicative identity:

$$(a, b) \cdot (1, 0) = (a \cdot 1 - b \cdot 0, a \cdot 0 + b \cdot 1) = (a, b).$$

3. If $(a, b) \neq (0, 0)$ then $a^2 + b^2 \neq 0$, since a and b are real numbers. Hence $\left(\dfrac{a}{a^2 + b^2}, \dfrac{-b}{a^2 + b^2} \right)$ is in C, and

$$(a, b)\left(\frac{a}{a^2 + b^2}, \frac{-b}{a^2 + b^2} \right)$$

$$= \left(\frac{a^2}{a^2 + b^2} - \frac{-b^2}{a^2 + b^2}, \frac{a(-b)}{a^2 + b^2} + \frac{ba}{a^2 + b^2} \right) = (1, 0).$$

Thus if $(a, b) \neq (0, 0)$,

$$(a, b)^{-1} = \left(\frac{a}{a^2 + b^2}, \frac{-b}{a^2 + b^2} \right).$$

4. The distributive law holds: The proof is left to the student.

* * *

Lemma 12. C has a subfield isomorphic to the real numbers.

PROOF. The mapping $\varphi : a \to (a, 0)$ is easily seen to be a 1–1 correspondence.
$$\varphi(a + b) = (a + b, 0) = (a, 0) + (b, 0) = \varphi(a) + \varphi(b).$$
$$\varphi(ab) = (ab, 0) = (a, 0)(b, 0) = \varphi(a)\varphi(b).$$
Hence by Theorem 4 φ is an isomorphism of the real numbers onto a subfield of C.

* * *

Notation. It will be convenient to write a for $(a, 0)$ and i for $(0, 1)$. Thus if b is a real number we have $bi = (b, 0)(0, 1) = (0, b) = ib$. Moreover we can write $(a, b) = a + bi$.

Theorem 9. There is no order relation on C which will make C an ordered field.

PROOF. Suppose we could define an ordering on C. Then either $i > 0$ or $-i > 0$, and in any event $-1 = (i^2) = (-i)^2 > 0$. In addition, $1 = 1^2 > 0$. Hence $-1 + 1 > 0$—a contradiction.

* * *

Theorem 10. For every complex number $a + bi$ there is an equation $x^2 + Ax + B = 0$ where A, B are real numbers such that $(a + bi)$ and $(a - bi)$ are the only solutions.

PROOF. We have $(x - (a + bi))(x - (a - bi)) = x^2 - 2ax + (a^2 + b^2)$, for all complex numbers x. Hence if $x = a + bi$ or $x = a - bi$, $x^2 - 2ax + (a^2 + b^2) = 0$. On the other hand, if $x \neq a + bi$ and $x \neq a - bi$, neither factor on the left is zero, hence their product is not zero. Hence $x^2 - 2ax + (a^2 + b^2) = 0$ has precisely the two solutions $a + bi$ and $a - bi$.

* * *

Definition. Two complex numbers, α and β, are called (complex) conjugates if $\alpha = a + bi$ and $\beta = a - bi$. We shall denote the conjugate of α by $\bar{\alpha}$.

Lemma 13. The mapping $\varphi(\alpha) = \bar{\alpha}$ is an automorphism of C because $\overline{\alpha + \beta} = \bar{\alpha} + \bar{\beta}$ and $\overline{\alpha\beta} = \bar{\alpha}\bar{\beta}$.

PROOF. Let $\alpha = a + bi$; $\beta = c + di$. Then

$$\overline{\alpha + \beta} = \overline{(a + c) + (b + d)i}$$
$$= (a + c) - (b + d)i = (a - bi) + (c - di) = \bar{\alpha} + \bar{\beta}$$

$$\overline{\alpha\beta} = \overline{(ac - bd) + (ad + bc)i}$$
$$= (ac - bd) - (ad + bc)i = (a - bi)(c - di) = \bar{\alpha}\bar{\beta}.$$

    Theorem 11 (*Fundamental Theorem of Algebra*). Any equation of the form $a_0 + a_1x + \cdots + a_nx^n = 0$ where $a_i \in C$ (and $a_i \neq 0$ for some $i \geq 1$) has a solution in C.

While we will not prove this theorem we shall give in Chapter 8 an algebraic theorem that is sufficiently strong for our purposes.

We now consider a geometric representation of complex numbers which will be of help in obtaining some further information. The fact that a complex number is an ordered pair (a, b) of real numbers leads to the observation that we may associate a point in the plane or a vector with a complex number. The x-axis is traditionally taken as those numbers $(a, 0) = a$—the so-called axis of real numbers. The y-axis is taken as those numbers $(0, b) = bi$—the so-called axis of pure imaginaries.

We can use polar coordinates to designate any point in plane, and this alternative representation is useful. If α is a point in the plane, which is not the origin, draw the line from α to the origin 0, and let $\theta = \measuredangle(1, 0, \alpha)$. Analytically speaking we can define θ precisely

$$\theta = \begin{cases} \arctan \dfrac{b}{a} & \text{if } a > 0 \\[2mm] \pi + \arctan \dfrac{b}{a} & \text{if } a < 0. \\[2mm] \dfrac{\pi}{2} & \text{if } a = 0, b > 0 \\[2mm] -\dfrac{\pi}{2} & \text{if } a = 0, b < 0 \end{cases}$$

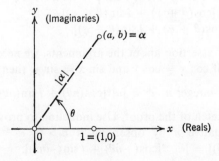

Figure 1

Here arctan x is taken as its principal value; $-\pi/2 < \arctan x \le \pi/2$. Let $|\alpha|$ be the distance from the origin to α. Thus $|\alpha| = \sqrt{a^2 + b^2}$ and $a = |\alpha| \cos \theta$; $b = |\alpha| \sin \theta$. Hence $\alpha = |\alpha| (\cos \theta + i \sin \theta)$. θ is called the *argument* of α, and $|\alpha|$ the *modulus* of α. The argument for 0 is not defined but $|0| = 0$. There is the usual trouble of multiple choice for the θ; clearly $\cos \theta + i \sin \theta = \cos(\theta + 2k\pi) + i \sin(\theta + 2k\pi)$. It is worth noting that $|(\cos \theta + i \sin \theta)| = 1$, so that every complex number is the product of a number representing a point of the unit circle (the circle with radius 1 centered at the origin) and a real number. Also it is easily verified that if $\alpha = |\alpha|(\cos \theta + i \sin \theta) \ne 0$ then $\alpha^{-1} = |\alpha|^{-1}(\cos \theta - i \sin \theta)$. In particular, the inverse of an element z on the unit circle is the element which is the reflection of z in the axis of reals.

Lemma 14. For all $\alpha \in C$, $|\alpha|^2 = \alpha\bar{\alpha}$; or $\sqrt{\alpha\bar{\alpha}} = |\alpha|$ since $|\alpha| \ge 0$. If $\alpha \ne 0$ then $\alpha^{-1} = \bar{\alpha}/|\alpha|^2$.

PROOF. $\alpha\bar{\alpha} = (a + bi)(a - bi) = a^2 + b^2 = |\alpha|^2$. The second half of the lemma is now immediate.

$$* \quad * \quad *$$

Lemma 15. $|\alpha\beta| = |\alpha| \, |\beta|$.

PROOF. It suffices to prove $|\alpha\beta|^2 = |\alpha|^2|\beta|^2$, but this is easy as $|\alpha\beta|^2 = \alpha\beta\overline{\alpha\beta} = \alpha\beta\bar{\alpha}\bar{\beta} = \alpha\bar{\alpha}\beta\bar{\beta} = |\alpha|^2|\beta|^2$.

$$* \quad * \quad *$$

Theorem 12. If α and β are two complex numbers then $|\alpha\beta| = |\alpha| \, |\beta|$ and if θ = argument of α, φ = argument of β, then $\alpha\beta = |\alpha| \, |\beta| (\cos(\theta + \varphi) + i \sin(\theta + \varphi)) = |\alpha\beta|(\cos(\theta + \varphi) + i \sin(\theta + \varphi))$.

Without worrying about the precise definition, we have from this theorem the fact that argument of $\alpha\beta$ = argument of α + argument of $\beta \pm 2\pi$.

PROOF. $\alpha\beta = |\alpha|(\cos \theta + i \sin \theta). |\beta|(\cos \varphi + i \sin \varphi)$
$\qquad |\alpha| \, |\beta| [\cos \theta \cos \varphi - \sin \theta \sin \varphi + i(\sin \theta \cos \varphi + \cos \theta \sin \varphi)]$
$\qquad = |\alpha| \, |\beta| [\cos(\theta + \varphi) + i \sin(\theta + \varphi)]$
$\qquad = |\alpha\beta| [\cos(\theta + \varphi) + i \sin(\theta + \varphi)]$.

To complete our assertion about the arguments, we need the lemma from trigonometry that if $\cos x = \cos y$ and $\sin x = \sin y$, then $x = y + 2k\pi$.

Corollary. For any integer n, $\alpha^n = |\alpha|^n[\cos(n\theta) + i \sin(n\theta)]$.

PROOF. Here is a sketch of the proof. Use induction to prove it for positive n. It follows for negative n by observing if $n > 0$, $\alpha^{-n} = (\alpha^n)^{-1} = |\alpha^n|^{-1} [\cos(n\theta) - i \sin(n\theta)] = |\alpha|^{-n}[\cos(-n\theta) + i \sin(-n\theta)]$.

$$* \quad * \quad *$$

Definition. Write $e^{i\theta} = \cos\theta + i\sin\theta$. It is proved in books on analysis that this definition, made formally here, is an actual theorem, when e^z is defined as

$$e^z = 1 + z + \frac{z^2}{2} + \frac{z^3}{3!} + \frac{z^4}{4!} + \cdots + \frac{z^n}{n!} + \cdots.$$

Using this notation we have $\alpha = |\alpha|e^{i\theta}$, and $\alpha\beta = |\alpha|e^{i\theta}|\beta|e^{i\varphi} = |\alpha|\,|\beta|e^{i(\theta+\varphi)}$ is an easy "proof"! It is also true that e^{x+iy} can be defined as the complex number $e^x e^{iy}$, where e^x is the real number z where

$$\int_1^z dt/t = \log_e z = x.$$

Using the representation of complex numbers as vectors, we clearly get the "parallelogram" law for addition or subtraction of vectors as shown in Figure 2.

The multiplication rule of Theorem 12 gives us an easy way to solve the equation $x^n = 1$ in C. That is, to find the nth roots of unity. Let $\alpha = \left(\cos\frac{2\pi}{n} + i\sin\frac{2\pi}{n}\right) = e^{i\frac{2\pi}{n}}$. Then $\alpha^k = \cos\frac{2k\pi}{n} + i\sin\frac{2k\pi}{n}$ and we see that if $1 \le k \le n$, then $\alpha^k = 1$ if and only if $k = n$. In other words α generates a cyclic group of order n and thus $\alpha, \alpha^2, \ldots, \alpha^n$ ($\alpha^n = 1$) are the elements of this group and each is a nth root of unity.

On the other hand these are the only solutions, for if $\beta = |\beta|(\cos\theta + i\sin\theta)$ is such that $\beta^n = 1$, then $1 = |\beta|^n(\cos n\theta + i\sin n\theta)$. Since $|\beta|$ is a positive real number, $|\beta|^n = 1$ implies $|\beta| = 1$. Next, $1 = \cos n\theta + i\sin n\theta$ implies $n\theta = 2m\pi$, or $\theta = 2m\pi/n$, and since cosine and sine have periods of 2π we may assume $1 \le m \le n$. Thus $\beta = \alpha^m$, where $1 \le m \le n$.

An nth root of unity is called *primitive* if it is a generator of the cyclic group of nth roots of unity. Thus α^k is primitive if and only if $(k, n) = 1$. In summary:

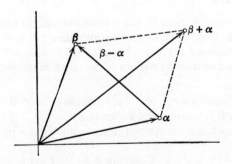

Figure 2

Theorem 13. The solutions to the equation $x^n = 1$ are precisely those complex numbers $\alpha^k = \cos \dfrac{2k\pi}{n} + i \sin \dfrac{2k\pi}{n}$ for $1 \le k \le n$. The primitive nth roots of unity are those with $(k, n) = 1$.

EXERCISE 4

1. Show that in C the equation $x^2 = a + bi$ always has a solution.

2. Show that the equation $ax^2 + bx + c = 0$ where a, b, c are real numbers always has a solution in C.

3. Show that the mapping $a + bi \rightarrow a - bi$ is an automorphism of C in which each real number is left invariant.

4. If $p(x) = a_n x^n + a_{n-1} x^{n-1} + \cdots + a_0$ has real coefficients and $z = z_1 + i z_2$ is a solution of $p(x) = 0$, then show that $\bar{z} = z_1 - i z_2$ is also a solution.

Hence, using the fundamental theorem of algebra, prove that $p(x)$ may be written as a product of linear factors and quadratic factors (with real coefficients) corresponding respectively to the real roots and the pairs of complex roots of $p(x)$.

5. Prove algebraically that the modulus of complex numbers has the following properties of "distance":

    (i) $|z - w| = 0$ if and only if $z = w$

    (ii) $|z - w| = |w - z|$

    (iii) $|z - w| + |w - u| \ge |z - u|$

    (iv) $|a + b| \le |a| + |b|$ and $|a - b| \ge |\,|a| - |b|\,|$

Illustrate geometrically.

6. Give geometrical interpretations of the following relations:

    (i) $|z - a| \le r$

    (ii) $|z - a| \le |z - b|$

    (iii) $|z - a| = r|z - b|$

    (iv) $|z - a| + |z - b| = 2r$

where a, b are complex constants and r is a real constant $(0 \le r)$.

7. Solve for z

    (i) $z^n = c$ (for n a positive integer)

    (ii) $z^2 + 2az + b = 0$

where a, b, c are complex. Note (i) has n solutions and (ii) has 2.

8. If p is a prime number show that the primitive pth roots of unity are just the roots of the equation $F_p(x) = x^{p-1} + x^{p-2} + \cdots + x + 1 = 0$.

9. Let G be the set of transformations of the complex numbers into themselves of the form

$$\varphi : x \rightarrow ax + b; \qquad a, b \text{ complex}, \quad a \ne 0.$$

    (i) Show that G is a group and compute φ^{-1}.

    (ii) Show that φ has order $n (n > 1)$ if and only if a is a primitive nth root of unity.

    (iii) Let $\theta : x \rightarrow cx + d \in G$. Compute $\varphi \, \theta \, \varphi^{-1}$. Find a proper normal subgroup of G.

10. Show that there is no real number x such that $p(x) = ix^3 + (1 + i)x^2 - (1 + 2i)x - (1 + i) = 0$. [*Hint:* Consider $p(x) - \overline{p(x)}$.]

11. For what positive integers n is -1 an nth root of unity?

12. Show that any nth root of unity is a primitive mth root of unity for precisely one m and for that m, $m \mid n$.

13. Evaluate the product of all the nth roots of unity.

14. Show that $\alpha^n = 1$ and $\alpha^m = 1$ if and only if $\alpha^d = 1$ where $d = (n, m)$.

SUPPLEMENTARY READING

T. M. Apostol, *Mathematical Analysis*, Reading, Mass.: Addison-Wesley (1957).

R. V. Churchill, *Complex Variables and Applications* (Second Edition), New York: McGraw Hill (1960).

S. Fefferman, *The Number Systems*, Reading, Mass: Addison-Wesley (1964).

N. Jacobson, *Lectures in Abstract Algebra*, vol. 1, Princeton, N.J.: Van Nostrand (1951).

I. Niven, *Irrational Numbers*, Carus Monograph, no. 11, Mathematical Association of America, Buffalo, N.Y., 1956.

R. M. Redheffer, What! Another note just on the fundamental theorem of algebra? *American Mathematical Monthly*, **71** (1964), 180–185.

B. L. van der Waerden, *Modern Algebra*, vol. 1 (F. Blum, translator), New York: Ungar (1949).

O. Zariski and P. Samuel, *Commutative Algebra*, vol. 1, Princeton, N.J.: Van Nostrand (1958).

5 | Euclidean Domains

5.1. INTRODUCTION

As we saw in the development of the field concept, a generalization of a class of abstract algebras to another class is accomplished by weakening the axiomatic structure of the algebras. To be a rewarding process there must almost always be a natural selection of the axioms which are isolated for special study. If we wish to generalize the integers many alternatives confront us. If we should decide to study the effect of a partial ordering of the elements we might develop the class of abstract algebras called lattices. If we should decide to study the effect of multiplication by an integer as an operator on the additive group we might develop the theory of modules and obtain theorems about ring representations. The course we take here is the selection of the division algorithm as the axiom for study. The main reason for selecting this theorem is its prominence in the proof of the unique factorization theorem. Because of it we could prove that every two integers possessed a GCD and hence that every irreducible was a prime. From this the unique factorization followed directly.

In Section 2.5 we could only draw some feeble statements about division—we could not even prove that every irreducible was a prime. The division algorithm made all this possible and it permitted us to determine all the ideals in I. Not only that, but the theorem turned out to be indispensable in the study of groups; in particular in studying the behavior of cyclic groups, and in the notion of the order of an element. As we shall see in Chapter 6 the set of polynomials with coefficients taken from a field forms a euclidean domain. This, aside from the integers, is perhaps the most important application of this chapter.

The statement of the generalization is a little tricky. Theorem 3.11 states that for all a, b ($b \neq 0$), there exist q and r such that $a = bq + r$ and $0 \leq r < |b|$. This latter condition speaks of *order*. If we assume very much about order we shall, in view of Theorem 3.10, have a system isomorphic with the integers and we do not want that! The trick is to postulate the existence of a function

v from an integral domain into the positive integers such that for all a and b ($b \neq 0$) there exist q and r such that $a = bq + r$ where $r = 0$ or $v(r) < v(b)$. This will give us many of the advantages of the ordering of the integers without assuming all the ordering properties for the elements of the integral domain. To prove any theorem, however, we need one more property for our function v—a property which in fact turns out to generalize Theorem 0.1.

Definition. A *euclidean domain* $\langle D, +, \cdot, v \rangle$ is an integral domain $\langle D, +, \cdot \rangle$ and a function v from the nonzero elements of D into the nonnegative integers such that

1. For all pairs a, b from D for which $b \neq 0$ there exist q and r in D such that

$$a = bq + r \text{ and either } 0 = r \text{ or } v(r) < v(b).$$

2. For all pairs a, b from D for which $a \neq 0$ and $b \neq 0$,

$$v(a) \leq v(ab).$$

Example 1. The integers may be viewed as a euclidean domain in which $v(a) = |a|$.

Example 2. The field of rational numbers may be viewed as a euclidean domain in which $v(a) = 1$ for all $a \neq 0$.

Example 3. The field of rational numbers may *not* be viewed as a euclidean domain in which $v(a) = |a|$ since otherwise we should infer $3/2 = |3/2| \leq |3/2 \cdot 2/3| = 1$.

Example 4. The Gaussian Integers

Definition. The set of gaussian integers G is the set of all complex numbers of the form $a + bi$ where a and b are integers.

> **Theorem 1.** The set G of gaussian integers is a subring of the complex numbers. The units of G are ± 1 and $\pm i$.

PROOF. We check to see that $G = \{a + bi : a, b \in I\}$ is closed under addition and multiplication. Hence G is a subring of the complex numbers and is an integral domain. If $\alpha = a + bi$ is a unit, we argue that $\bar{\alpha} = a - bi$ is also a unit, and from $1 = \alpha\beta$ we have $1 = \bar{\alpha}\bar{\beta}$ and hence if $\beta = c + di$, that $1 = (a^2 + b^2)(c^2 + d^2)$ or that $1 = a^2 + b^2$. Hence the only solutions are $a = \pm 1$, $b = 0$ or $a = 0$, $b = \pm 1$. These lead to the four units ± 1, $\pm i$.

* * *

This integral domain has been the source of much study. A most important fact is that G is a euclidean domain.

Theorem 2. The set of gaussian integers is a euclidean domain in which the function $N(\alpha) = \alpha\bar{\alpha}$ serves as the required function v.

PROOF. We certainly have that $N(\alpha) = 0$ if and only if $\alpha = 0$. Hence $N(\alpha) \geq 1$ for all $\alpha \neq 0$. From Lemma 4.13, $N(\alpha\beta) = N(\alpha)N(\beta)$ and so $N(\alpha\beta) \geq N(\alpha)$.

Given α and $\beta \neq 0$, we must find σ and ρ such that $\alpha = \beta \cdot \sigma + \rho$ where either $\rho = 0$ or $N(\rho) < N(\beta)$. Since $\beta \neq 0$ we would have to have $\rho = \alpha - \beta\sigma = \beta(\alpha/\beta - \sigma)$, and in the field of complex numbers, since $N(\rho) = \rho\bar{\rho} = |\rho|^2$, $|\rho|^2 = |\beta|^2|\alpha/\beta - \sigma|^2$. Thus $N(\rho) < N(\beta)$ if $|\alpha/\beta - \sigma|^2 < 1$. Hence our task is to choose $\sigma \in G$ so that $|\alpha/\beta - \sigma|^2 < 1$. Let $\alpha = a + bi$, $\beta = c + di$, and so, as a complex number, $(\alpha/\beta) = x + yi$ where x and y are rational numbers. Choose *integers e* and *f* such that $|x - e| \leq 1/2$ and $|y - f| \leq 1/2$ and let $\sigma = e + fi$. Then $\sigma \in G$ and $|\alpha/\beta - \sigma|^2 = |x + iy - (e + fi)|^2 = |(x - e) + (y - f)i|^2 = (x - e)^2 + (y - f)^2 \leq 1/4 + 1/4 = 1/2 < 1$. Consequently we have found the desired σ, and if we put $\rho = \alpha - \beta\sigma$ then our theorem is proved.

*   *   *

5.2. THE EUCLIDEAN ALGORITHM

We shall assume in this section that we are dealing with a euclidean domain $\langle D, +, \cdot, v \rangle$.

Lemma 1. If $a \in D$, $a \neq 0$, then $v(a) \geq v(1)$.

PROOF. From $1 \cdot a = a$ it follows that $v(1) \leq v(a)$.

*   *   *

Lemma 2. If $0 \neq a \in D$, then $v(a) = v(1)$ if and only if a is a unit.

PROOF. If a is a unit there exists, by definition, $c \in D$ such that $1 = ac$. Thus $v(a) \leq v(ac) = v(1) \leq v(a)$; hence $v(a) = v(1)$. Conversely, if $v(a) = v(1)$, we consider $1 = aq + r$ where $0 = r$ or $v(r) < v(a) = v(1)$. The latter inequality is impossible, so $0 = r$ and $a \mid 1$; that is, a is a unit.

Theorem 3. Every ideal in D is principal.

PROOF. Let A be an ideal in D. If $A = \{0\}$ then $A = \langle 0 \rangle$, so that we may assume A contains some nonzero elements. Let $T = \{v(x) : x \in A\}$. T is a nonempty subset of nonnegative integers and hence has a least member. Let $a \in A$ be chosen so that $v(a)$ is the minimal member of T. We shall prove that $A = \langle a \rangle$. Clearly $A \supseteq \langle a \rangle$. Let $x \in A$. We have $x = aq + r$ where $0 = r$ or $v(r) < v(a)$. Since $r = x - aq$ it follows that $r \in A$. The alternative $v(r) < v(a)$ contradicts the choice of a, hence $0 = r$ and so $x \in \langle a \rangle$. Thus $A = \langle a \rangle$.

*   *   *

The main theorem of this section is that every pair of elements from D has a greatest common divisor. There is a proof of this, which we leave as an exercise, based on Theorem 3. In brief, the argument is this: given a and b, form the ideal $S = \{ax + by : x \text{ and } y \text{ in } D\}$. By Theorem 3, $S = \langle s \rangle$, and now it is easy to show that s is a greatest common divisor of a and b. We prefer to give here another proof which is constructive in that it yields a process for determining the GCD and also two numbers u and t such that $\text{GCD}(a, b) = au + bt$. Careful reading will show that in fact the proof we give is but a longer and disguised form of the proof sketched above.

Lemma 3. Let a and $b \neq 0$ belong to an integral domain $\langle D, +, \cdot \rangle$. Let $a = bq + r$. If b and r possess a greatest common divisor d then d is a greatest common divisor for a and b.

PROOF. From $a = bq + r$ it is clear that every divisor of b and r is a divisor of a; in particular d must divide a. Thus d is a common divisor of a and b. On the other hand $r = a - bq$ and so any common divisor, c, of a and b divides r and so is a common divisor of b and r. Thus c must divide a greatest common divisor of b and r, in particular $c \mid d$. Thus d is a greatest common divisor of a and b.

*   *   *

Theorem 4 (*Existence of GCD*). Let $\langle D, +, \cdot, v \rangle$ be a euclidean domain. If $a, b \in D$ and one of them is nonzero then a and b have a greatest common divisor, and moreover there exist elements $u, t \in D$ such that if $d = \text{GCD}(a, b)$ then

$$d = au + bt.$$

PROOF. If $b \mid a$ or $a \mid b$ then the theorem is trivial; if, for example, $b \mid a$, then $\text{GCD}(a, b) = b = a \cdot 0 + b \cdot 1$. Thus, in particular, the theorem holds when one of a and b is a unit or when one, but not both, is zero. We now assume that $b \neq 0$ and proceed by induction on m, the minimum of $v(a)$ and $v(b)$. The induction begins at the minimal value for m, namely $v(1)$, which occurs when a or b is a unit, and then we know the theorem holds. Our induction hypothesis assumes the theorem for any two elements c, d when either c or d is zero or the minimum of $v(c)$ and $v(d)$ is less than m. Now suppose $a = 0$ or $m = v(b) < v(a)$. We have $a = bq + r$ with $0 = r$ or $v(r) < v(b)$. If $r = 0$ then $b \mid a$, and the theorem holds. If $v(r) < v(b) = m$, then by induction $\text{GCD}(b, r)$ exists, and for some $w, z \in D$ we have $\text{GCD}(b, r) = bw + rz$. By Lemma 3 we know that every $\text{GCD}(b, r)$ is a GCD for a, b and so we have $\text{GCD}(a, b) = \text{GCD}(b, r) = bw + rz = bw + (a - bq)z = az + b(w - qz)$.

*   *   *

The Euclidean Algorithm

The proof of Lemma 3 and Theorem 2 give a recursive procedure for determining $\text{GCD}(a, b)$ by generating a sequence $a, b, r_1, \ldots, r_n$ so that

$GCD(a, b) = GCD(b, r_1) = \cdots = GCD(r_{n-1}, r_n) = r_n$. The sequence is obtained by performing the division algorithm repeatedly. Let us illustrate this algorithm first with an example from the integers.

Example 5. Find $(84, 54)$.

$$84 = 54 \cdot 1 + 30 \qquad (84, 54) = (54, 30)$$
$$54 = 30 \cdot 1 + 24 \qquad (54, 30) = (30, 24)$$
$$30 = 24 \cdot 1 + 6 \qquad (30, 24) = (24, 6)$$
$$24 = 6 \cdot 4. \qquad\qquad (24, 6) = 6.$$

Thus 6 is the GCD of 84 and 54. Conversely we have

$$6 = 30 - 24$$
$$= 30 - (54 - 30) = 30 \cdot 2 - 54$$
$$= (84 - 54) \cdot 2 - 54 = 84 \cdot 2 - 54 \cdot 3$$

or

$$6 = 84 \cdot 2 + 54(-3).$$

In general the algorithm looks like this: Let us suppose that $v(b) \le v(a)$.

Step 1. $a = bq_1 + r_1$ where $0 = r_1$ or $v(r_1) < v(b)$. If $0 = r_1$ then $b \mid a$ and $(a, b) = b = a \cdot 0 + b \cdot 1$. If $0 \ne r_1$ then $v(r_1) < v(b)$ and a GCD of b and r_1 is a GCD of a and b. We continue:

Step 2. $b = r_1 q_2 + r_2$ where $0 = r_2$ or $v(r_2) < v(r_1)$. If $0 = r_2$ then $r_1 = (r_1, b) = (a, b) = a \cdot 1 + b(-q_1)$. If $0 \ne r_2$ then a GCD of r_1 and r_2 is a GCD of b and r_1, hence of a and b. We continue:

Step 3. $r_1 = r_2 q_3 + r_3$ where $0 = r_3$ or $v(r_3) < v(r_2)$. If $0 = r_3$ then $r_2 = (r_2, r_1) = (b, r_1) = (a, b) = b + r_1(-q_2) = b + [a + b(-q_1)](-q_2) = a(-q_2) + b(1 + q_1 q_2)$. If $0 \ne r_3$ then we continue....

Since the sequence of nonnegative integers $\{v(a), v(b), v(r_1), \ldots\}$ obtained in this way is a decreasing sequence, it is clear that in a finite number of steps we must obtain a remainder, r_n say, which divides r_{n-1} at the next step. Indeed $n \le v(b) + 1$.

Step (n). $r_{n-2} = r_{n-1} q_n + r_n$ where $GCD(r_n, r_{n-1}) = GCD(a, b)$, and
Step (n + 1). $r_{n-1} = r_n q_{n+1} + 0$, so that $r_n \mid r_{n-1}$ and $r_n = GCD(a, b)$.

Thus the last nonzero remainder in the algorithm is a GCD of a and b and, by stringing the equations together in reverse order, we obtain $r_n = au + bt$:

$$r_n = r_{n-2} + r_{n-1}(-q_n)$$
$$= r_{n-2} + [r_{n-3} + r_{n-2}(-q_{n-1})](-q_n)$$
$$= r_{n-3}(-q_n) + r_{n-2}(1 + q_{n-1}q_n)$$
$$\vdots$$
$$= au + bt.$$

For particular euclidean domains, special shortcuts are available. In our previous example in computing $(84, 54)$ in I, we could have written the shorter list of equations

$$84 = 54 \cdot 2 - 24$$
$$54 = 24 \cdot 2 + 6$$
$$24 = 6 \cdot 4$$

This comes about as $a = bq + r = b(q + 1) - (b - r)$ and it is clearly more efficient in the algorithm to select the alternative with the smaller value, r or $b - r$.

We can, of course, prove the existence and find the GCD of two integers by prime decomposition. If $p_1, \ldots, p_n$ are distinct primes and

$$a = p_1^{e_1} \ldots p_n^{e_n}, e_i \geq 0 \quad \text{and} \quad b = p_1^{f_1} \ldots p_n^{f_n}, f_i \geq 0,$$
$$\text{then } (a, b) = p_1^{g_1} \ldots p_n^{g_n} \text{ where } g_i = \min(e_i, f_i)$$
$$[a, b] = p_1^{h_1} \ldots p_n^{h_n} \text{ where } h_i = \max(e_i, f_i).$$

To prove this we need only know that all divisors of a have, to within unit factors, the form $p_1^{c_1} \ldots p_n^{c_n}$ with $0 \leq c_i \leq e_i$. This method works in any integral domain in which the unique factorization theorem holds. (See Theorems 3.13, and 5.13 and Section 6.6.) This method of determining (a, b) is quick if you know the factorization. If you do not, the euclidean algorithm is usually faster. This is particularly true for larger numbers. The reader is invited to find $(6711, 831)$. Since $[a, b] \sim ab/(a, b)$, these remarks hold for finding a LCM. Of course, this method gives no clue about the solution of $(a, b) = ax + by$.

EXERCISE 1

1. Let $\langle D, +, \cdot, v \rangle$ be a euclidean domain. Show that if a and b are associates then $v(a) = v(b)$.

2. Let g be an integer greater than 1. Show that every positive nonnegative integer a can be written uniquely in the form $a = c_0 + c_1 g + \cdots + c_n g^n$ where $c_n > 0$ and $0 \leq c_i < g$ for $0 \leq i < n$. Use this to show that the number of subsets of $S = \{1, \ldots, m\}$ is 2^m.

3. Find in the integers, $(6711, 831)$. Express this number as an integral combination of 6711 and 831.

4. Let $\alpha = 1 + 2i$ and $\beta = 3 + 4i$. In the gaussian integers find σ and ρ so that $\alpha = \beta\sigma + \rho$ with $N(\rho) < N(\beta)$.

5. In the domain of gaussian integers find a greatest common divisor of $3 + 4i$ and $7 - i$.

6. Show that $H = \{a + b\sqrt{-2} : a, b \in I\}$ is a euclidean domain with $g(\alpha) = a^2 + 2b^2$ if $\alpha = a + b\sqrt{-2}$.

7. Can the integral domain $\{a + b\sqrt{-2} : a, b \in I\}$ be ordered?

8. Let $\langle D, +, \cdot, v \rangle$ be a euclidean domain. Let k be an integer such that $v(1) + k \geq 0$. Define a new function v' on D by $v'(a) = v(a) + k$. Show that

$\langle D, +, \cdot, v' \rangle$ is a euclidean domain. If s is a positive integer and a function, v'' is defined by $v''(a) = sv(a)$; show that $\langle D, +, \cdot, v'' \rangle$ is a euclidean domain.

9. In defining the properties for the function v, what are some reasons for not defining $v(0)$ and for requiring $v(a) \geq 0$?

10. Extend the definition of greatest common divisor to an n-tuple of elements $(a_1, \ldots, a_n)$ and prove that if these belong to a euclidean domain a GCD exists and that there are elements $x_1, \ldots, x_n$ such that if d is a GCD, then $d = a_1 x_1 + \ldots + a_n x_n$.

11. Let p be a prime integer and let D_p be the integral domain of rational numbers defined in Problem 6 of Exercises 2.1. Show that for $r \in D_p$ there exist a unique pair of integers a and k such that $r = ap^k$ where $a \in I$, $p \nmid a$, and $k \in I$. Show that the function v defined by $v(r) = |a|$ makes D_p into a euclidean domain. In D_2 find an integer which is a GCD of $3/4$ and $7/2$.

12. A sequence of integers $L_0, L_1, \ldots, L_n$ are computed by the rule $L_0 = 0$, $L_1 = 1$, and $L_{n+2} = 4L_{n+1} - L_n$ for $n \geq 0$. It is known that L_{n+1} and L_{n-1} or L_{n+1} and $L_n + 1$ always have a common odd prime factor for $n \geq 2$. Use this fact to find the factorization of $L_{10} = 151{,}316$.

5.3. ARITHMETIC IN EUCLIDEAN DOMAINS

We are now able to prove analogues of the lemmas and theorems in Section 3.6. Our goal is to establish the results necessary to prove Theorem 13, the unique factorization theorem. Again we assume that we are in a euclidean domain $\langle D, +, \cdot, v \rangle$.

Definition. If $\mathrm{GCD}(a, b) = 1$ we say a and b are *coprime* or *relatively prime*.

Theorem 5. $\mathrm{GCD}(a, b) = 1$ if and only if there are elements x and y such that $ax + by = 1$.

PROOF. If $\mathrm{GCD}(a, b) = 1$, the result is a consequence of the euclidean algorithm. If $ax + by = 1$ and $d \mid a$ and $d \mid b$, then $d \mid 1$; that is, d is a unit and hence 1 is a GCD of a and b.

* * *

Theorem 6. If d is a common divisor of a and b, then $(a/d, b/d) = 1$ if and only if $(a, b) = d$.

PROOF. If $(a, b) = d$, then $d = ax + by$ and so $1 = (a/d)x + (b/d)y$. Hence $(a/d, b/d) = 1$. If $(a/d, b/d) = 1$ then $1 = (a/d)x + (b/d)y$ and so $d = ax + by$. Hence any common divisor of a and b divides d. But d, by assumption, is a common divisor of a and b, hence $d = (a, b)$.

* * *

Theorem 7. Let a and b be nonzero elements of a euclidean domain. Then $ax + by = d$ if and only if $(a, b) \mid d$. (This proof is left as an exercise.)

Theorem 8. If $a \mid bc$ and $(a, b) = 1$, then $a \mid c$.

PROOF. From $(a, b) = 1$ we have $1 = ax + by$, hence $c = acx + bcy$. But $a \mid a$ and $a \mid bc$, hence $a \mid c$.

*   *   *

Corollary. In a euclidean domain any irreducible is a prime.

PROOF. Let a be irreducible. Let $a \mid bc$ and suppose that $a \nmid b$. We are to show $a \mid c$. From the theorem we need only show that $(a, b) = 1$. Suppose that u is a common divisor of a and b. Since a is irreducible, $u \mid a$ implies that u is a unit or an associate of a. In the latter case, since $u \mid b$, it would follow that $a \mid b$, contrary to assumption. Thus we conclude that every common divisor of a and b is a unit, and so it must follow that $(a, b) = 1$.

*   *   *

Theorem 9. If $a \mid c$ and $b \mid c$ and $(a, b) = 1$, then $ab \mid c$.

PROOF. Let $c = ac_1 = bc_2$ and $1 = ax + by$. Then $c = acx + bcy = abc_2x + bac_1y$, or $ab \mid c$.

*   *   *

Theorem 10. If $a, b_1, b_2, \ldots, b_n$ are elements of a euclidean domain, and if $(a, b_i) = 1$ for all i, then $(a, (b_1 b_2 \cdots b_n)) = 1$.

PROOF (*Induction on n*). If $n = 1$ there is nothing to prove. By induction we have $(a, (b_2 \cdots b_n)) = 1$. Hence

$$ax + (b_2 \ldots b_n)y = 1 \quad \text{and} \quad au + b_1v = 1.$$

Multiplying, we have $1 = a(aux + (b_2 \ldots b_n)uy + b_1xv) + b_1b_2 \ldots b_n yv$, or $1 = ar + (b_1 \ldots b_n)s$.

*   *   *

Theorem 11. If $a_1, \ldots, a_n$ are elements of a euclidean domain which are mutually coprime, and if $a_i \mid c$ for all i, then $a_1 \ldots a_n \mid c$.

PROOF. The proof is by induction on n. For $n = 2$, this is Theorem 9. By induction we have $a_2 \ldots a_n \mid c$. By Theorem 10 $(a_1, (a_2 \ldots a_n)) = 1$, and thus, by Theorem 9, $a_1 a_2 \ldots a_n \mid c$.

*   *   *

Theorem 12. In a euclidean domain, if $a \mid b, b \neq 0$, and a is neither a unit nor an associate of b, then $v(a) < v(b)$.

PROOF. Since a is not an associate of b it follows that $b \nmid a$. Hence $a = bq + r$ where $v(r) < v(b)$. Now $b = ac$, so that $r = a - bq = a - acq = a(1 - cq)$ and so $v(r) \geq v(a)$. Thus $v(b) > v(a)$.

* * *

Theorem 13. In a euclidean domain each nonzero element is either a unit or can be written as a finite product of primes, which is unique in the following sense: If $a = p_1 \ldots p_n = q_1 \ldots q_m$ where each p_i and q_j is a prime, then $n = m$ and upon proper numbering p_i is an associate of q_i.

PROOF. The proof differs from the proof of Theorem 3.13 only in that we induct on $v(a)$ instead of a. We shall not repeat the details here.

* * *

Let us view the GCD from a slightly different point of view. Given elements c, a, b, when do elements x and y exist so that $c = ax + by$. Clearly any common divisor, in particular GCD(a, b), must divide c. Conversely, let $d = $ GCD(a, b) and $d \cdot r = c$. From Theorem 4 we have $d = au + bv$, hence $d \cdot r = a(ur) + b(ur)$.

Additional solutions to the equation $c = ax + by$ can be found easily if a solution exists. We have

$$c = ax + by = a(x - nb) + b(y + na),$$

since we have just added and subtracted anb. Not all solutions have this form, but one refinement of this trick does give all of them. Let $d = (a, b)$, $a = a_1d$ and $b = b_1d$. We may add and subtract $a_1b_1dn = ab_1n = ba_1n$ in this fashion:

$$c = a(x - b_1n) + b(y + a_1n).$$

Theorem 14. Let c, a, b belong to a euclidean domain D. The equation

$$c = ax + by$$

has solutions in D if and only if c is divisible by GCD(a, b). If $c = au + bv$ is a particular solution, then all solutions have the form $x = u - b_1n$; $y = v + a_1n$ where n is an arbitrary integer, and if $d = (a, b)$, then $b_1 = b/d$ and $a_1 = a/d$.

PROOF. We have shown that the first part of the theorem is valid. For the second, suppose

$$c = ax + by = au + bv.$$

Then $b(y - v) = a(u - x)$. We divide out $d = $ GCD(a, b):

$$b_1(y - v) = a_1(u - x).$$

Thus $a_1 \mid b_1(y - v)$, but $(a_1, b_1) = 1$. By Theorem 8 it must follow that $a_1 \mid y - v$. That is, $y - v = a_1n$; or $y = v + a_1n$. Similarly $b_1 \mid (u - x)$, or $u - x = b_1m$ or $x = u - b_1m$. It remains to show that $n = m$. To do this we check our solutions:

$$c = ax + by = a(u - b_1m) + b(v + a_1n) = au + bv - ab_1m + ba_1n.$$

Since $au + bv = c$, this gives $ab_1m = ba_1n$. Now divide out d to obtain $a_1b_1m = b_1a_1n$ from which it follows that $m = n$.

* * *

In euclidean domains we may solve certain congruences. Probably the two most useful results follow.

Theorem 15 (*Chinese Remainder Theorem*). Let D be a euclidean domain. If $m_1, \ldots, m_k$ are k elements of D which are coprime in pairs, $(m_i, m_j) = 1$ if $i \neq j$, then the system of congruences

$$x \equiv a_i \,(\text{mod } m_i) \qquad i = 1, \ldots, k$$

has a simultaneous solution.

PROOF. We induct on k. We might try to start our induction with $k = 1$, but more light is shed on the proof if we do it for $k = 2$, and indeed it will turn out that we must start our induction here. All solutions for $x \equiv a_1$ $(\text{mod } m_1)$ have the form $a_1 + um_1$ for $u \in D$. To solve $a_1 + um_1 \equiv a_2 \,(\text{mod } m_2)$ we must find u and v such that $a_1 + um_1 = a_2 + vm_2$, for then $x = a_1 + um_1 = a_2 + vm_2$ is a solution for both congruences. Now $(m_1, m_2) = 1$ and so $1 = m_1r + m_2s$, hence $(a_1 - a_2) = (a_1 - a_2)(m_1r + m_2s)$. If we let $u = -r(a_1 - a_2)$ and $v = s(a_1 - a_2)$ we have $a_1 + um_1 = a_2 + vm_2$ as desired.

Now let us suppose we can find a common solution for $x \equiv a_i \,(\text{mod } m_i)$ $i = 1, \ldots, k - 1$. Let us call the solution b. Consider

$$\begin{cases} x \equiv b \,(\text{mod } m_1m_2\ldots m_{k-1}) \\ x \equiv a_k \,(\text{mod } m_k). \end{cases}$$

From Theorem 10 $(m_k, (m_1m_2\ldots m_{k-1})) = 1$. Hence by what we have proved there is a common solution; we call it w. But if $w \equiv b \,(\text{mod } m_1m_2\ldots m_{k-1})$ surely $w \equiv b \,(\text{mod } m_i)$, and so $w \equiv a_i \,(\text{mod } m_i)$ for $i = 1, \ldots, k - 1$, and $w \equiv a_k \,(\text{mod } m_k)$ by the last construction.

* * *

Now that the proof is complete we see that it was necessary to give a straightforward proof for the case $k = 2$, otherwise we would not have been entitled to use the solution in the last step.

Theorem 16 In a euclidean domain the congruence $ax \equiv b \,(\text{mod } n)$ has a solution if and only if $(a, n) \mid b$.

PROOF. If there is an x such that $ax \equiv b \pmod{n}$, then $n \mid b - ax$ or $b - ax = mn$ or $b = ax + mn$ and hence any common divisor of a and n must divide b. On the other hand, if $(a, n) \mid b$, from Theorem 14, we have $b = ax + ny$, or $b \equiv ax \pmod{n}$.

$$* \quad * \quad *$$

Corollary. Let $\langle D, +, \cdot, v \rangle$ be a euclidean domain and let p be a prime in D. Then $D/\langle p \rangle$ is a field.

PROOF. From Theorem 2.12 we know that $D/\langle p \rangle$ is an integral domain. It remains to show that if $\bar{0} \neq \bar{a} \in D/\langle p \rangle$ then $(\bar{a})^{-1}$ exists. The condition $\bar{0} \neq \bar{a}$ means that $a \notin \langle p \rangle$ and so $p \nmid a$, hence $(p, a) = 1$. Thus we may solve the congruence $ax \equiv 1 \pmod{p}$. Let u be a solution so that $au - 1 \in \langle p \rangle$, or $p \mid au - 1$. Hence in the natural homomorphism $\varphi : D \to D/\langle p \rangle$, we have $\bar{0} = \varphi(au - 1) = \varphi(au) - \varphi(1) = \varphi(a)\varphi(u) - \varphi(1) = \bar{a}\bar{u} - \bar{1}$. Thus $\bar{u} = (\bar{a})^{-1}$.

$$* \quad * \quad *$$

Theorem 17. In a euclidean domain D, if $ax \equiv b \pmod{n}$ has a particular solution x_0, then all solutions have the form $x_0 + hn_1$ where $n_1 = n/(a, n)$. (In particular, if $(a, n) = 1$ then any two solutions are congruent, mod n.)

PROOF. If $ax_0 \equiv ax \equiv b \pmod{n}$ then $n \mid a(x - x_0)$. Writing $n = n_1(a, n)$ and $a = a_1(a, n)$, then $(n_1, a_1) = 1$ and $n_1 \mid a_1(x - x_0)$; hence $n_1 \mid (x - x_0)$, or $x - x_0 = hn_1$, or $x = x_0 + hn_1$. Conversely if $x = x_0 + hn_1$, then $ax = ax_0 + ahn_1 = ax_0 + a_1(a, n)hn_1 = ax_0 + a_1hn \equiv ax_0 \equiv b \pmod{n}$; that is, x satisfies the congruence.

If $D = I$ and if n and $d = (a, n)$ are positive, there are d distinct solutions, modulo n. If $x_0 + hn_1 \equiv x_0 + kn_1 \pmod{n}$, then $n \mid n_1(h - k)$, or $d \mid (h - k)$; that is, $h \equiv k \pmod{d}$. Hence if $h = 0, 1, \ldots, d - 1$, the d integers $(x_0 + hn_1)$ must be distinct mod n.

$$* \quad * \quad *$$

EXERCISE 2

1. Prove that every pair of non-zero elements in a euclidean domain has a LCM.
2. Find a solution in integers of $14x + 11y = 1$ and then find the most general solution. Find the least positive value of c for which $14x + 11y = c$ has exactly one solution in positive integers. Find the greatest value of c for which $14x + 11y = c$ has exactly five solutions in positive integers.
3. Solve the system of congruences $5x \equiv 20 \pmod{6}$, $6x \equiv 6 \pmod{5}$, $4x \equiv 5 \pmod{77}$.
4. Find necessary and sufficient conditions on a, b, n, and m for solving the pair of congruences $x \equiv a \pmod{n}$ and $x \equiv b \pmod{m}$.

5. Find all solutions for $(25/3)x \equiv 10/9 \bmod (5/27)$ in the integral domain D_3 in Problem 6 of Exercise 2.1.

6. A conjecture of Fermat stated that for all n the integer $2^{(2^n)} + 1$ is a prime. Euler found to the contrary that $641 \mid 2^{32} + 1$. Confirm this. [*Hint:* Use congruences; do not do the indicated division!]

7. Show that if D is a euclidean domain and p is a prime of D then $\langle p \rangle$ is a maximal ideal of D.

8. Let $\langle D, +, \cdot, v \rangle$ be a euclidean domain. We consider a subset of $D/\langle n \rangle$ defined

$$D^*_n = \{\bar{a} : (a, n) = 1\}.$$

Show that $\langle D^*_n, \cdot \rangle$ is the group of units in $D/\langle n \rangle$.

9. Show that if $D = I$, the integers, the order of I^*_n is $\varphi(n)$ where φ is the Euler φ-function.

10. If $(a, b) = 1$ in a euclidean domain D, show that $D^*_{ab} \cong D^*_a \times D^*_b$. [*Hint:* Show $S_a = \{\bar{x} : \bar{x} \in D^*_{ab}, x \equiv 1 \pmod{b}\}$ is isomorphic with D^*_a.] Conclude in the case $D = I$ that if $(a, b) = 1$ then $\varphi(ab) = \varphi(a)\varphi(b)$ where φ is the Euler φ-function. Show that if n is an integer and $n = p_1^{e_1} \ldots p_m^{e_m}$ is its factorization as a product of distinct positive prime powers then

$$\varphi(n) = n\left(1 - \frac{1}{p_1}\right) \cdots \left(1 - \frac{1}{p_m}\right).$$

Problems 11–16 deal with $I(\sqrt{-5}) = \{a + b\sqrt{-5} : a, b \in I\}$. Here $\sqrt{-5}$ is one of the solutions of $x^2 = -5$, which we may take to be $i\sqrt{5}$.

11. Prove that the only units of $I(\sqrt{-5})$ are $+1$ and -1.

12. Show that $(1 + 2\sqrt{-5})(1 - 2\sqrt{-5}) = 3 \cdot 7$.

13. Show that $(1 + 2\sqrt{-5})$ and 3 are irreducible in $I(-5)$. [*Hint:* If $3 = \alpha\beta$ then $9 = \bar{\alpha}\alpha\beta\bar{\beta}$.]

14. Show that 3 is not a prime in $I(\sqrt{-5})$.

15. Let $a = 3$, $b = 1 + 2\sqrt{-5}$ and $c = 7 \cdot (1 - 2\sqrt{-5})$. Prove that a and b are coprime but that ac and bc have no greatest common divisor.

16. Show in the notation of Problem 15 that a and b, while coprime, have no least common multiple in $I(\sqrt{-5})$.

5.4. APPLICATION TO GROUPS

As an exercise to recall some of our group concepts and to show the usefulness of Theorem 4 we shall establish an important decomposition theorem for abelian groups. The first lemma is the crux of the matter.

Lemma 4. Let $x \in G$ and let n be the order of x. If $n = rs$ where $(r, s) = 1$ then there exist a unique pair of elements $y, z \in G$ such that

    1. $x = yz = zy$, and
    2. y has order s and z has order r.

PROOF OF EXISTENCE. From $(r, s) = 1$ and Theorem 4 we know there exist integers u, v such that $ru + sv = 1$. Hence $x = x^{ru + sv} = x^{ru}x^{sv} = x^{sv}x^{ru}$. If we define $y = x^{ru}$ and $z = x^{sv}$ we have only to prove that the orders of y and z are s and r, respectively. Let us denote the order of y by d. In any event $y^s = (x^{ru})^s = (x^{rs})^u = 1$. Hence $d \mid s$. By definition, $1 = y^d = (x^{ru})^d$ and so $n \mid rud$ and as $n = rs$ we have that $s \mid ud$. But as $ru + sv = 1$ it follows from Theorem 5 that $(s, u) = 1$; then from Theorem 8 we have that $s \mid d$. Thus $s = d$. A similar argument shows that the order of z is r.

PROOF OF UNIQUENESS. Under the assumption of conditions 1 and 2 and $1 = ru + sv$, we shall show that $y = x^{ru}$ and $z = x^{sv}$. We have $x^{ru} = (yz)^{ru} = y^{ru}z^{ru}$ as y commutes with z. Since z is assumed to have order r we have $x^{ru} = y^{ru} = y^{(1 - sv)} = yy^{-sv} = y(y^s)^{-v} = y$ as y has order s.

*   *   *

By induction we can extend this to any number of coprime factors.

Corollary. Let $x \in G$ and let x have order n with $n = p_1^{e_1}\ldots p_k^{e_k}$ as its factorization into powers of distinct primes. There exist unique elements $y_1 \ldots y_k \in G$ such that

     1. $x = y_1 \ldots y_k$ and $y_i y_j = y_j y_i$ for all i, j, and
     2. each y_i has order $p_1^{e_1}$.

PROOF. If $k = 1$ there is nothing to prove. Proceeding by induction we apply the previous lemma with $r = p_1^{e_1}$ and $s = p_2^{e_2}\ldots p_k^{e_k}$ to obtain $x = y_1 z$. By induction we have $z = y_2 \ldots y_k$. $y_i y_j = y_j y_i$ since all the y's are powers of x; in fact, $y_i = x^{f_i}$ where $f_i = n/p_i^{e_i}$. The uniqueness follows by induction also.

*   *   *

Theorem 18. Let G be an abelian group in which every element has finite order. Let p be a prime and define

$$S_p = \{x : x \in G \text{ and } x^{p^k} = 1 \text{ for some integer } k\}.$$

Then for every prime p, S_p is a subgroup of G and every $x \in G$ has a unique representation

$$x = y_1 \ldots y_k \quad \text{where} \quad y_i \in S_{p_i}.$$

In particular, if G is finite and $|G| = m = p_1^{e_1}\ldots p_k^{e_k}$ is the factorization of m into distinct prime powers, then $G \cong S_{p_1} \times \ldots \times S_{p_k}$ and $|S_{p_i}| = p_i^{e_i}$.

PROOF. Here S_p is readily seen to be a subgroup. Lemma 4 and its corollary establish the existence and uniqueness of the decomposition. If G is finite these are the conditions of Theorem 1.36 that $G \cong S_{p_1} \times \ldots \times S_{p_k}$, and so

$|G| = |S_{p_1}| \ldots |S_{p_k}|$. Since the order of every element in S_{p_i} is a power of the prime p_i it follows from Theorem 1.31 that $|S_{p_i}|$ is some power of p_i. The unique factorization theorem shows that this power must be e_i.

* * *

Corollary. If A is a finite abelian group then there is an integer $m \le |A|$ such that (1) $a^m = 1$ for all $a \in A$, and (2) there exists an element $g \in A$ whose order is m.

PROOF. This theorem is easy if $|A| = p^e$ for a prime p. We simply choose m as the maximal order of the elements in A and let g be any element of order m. Since $m \mid p^e$, $m = p^f$ where $f \le e$. Then if $a \in A$ has order p^h, by the choice of f, it follows that $h \le f$ so that $a^{p^f} = (a^{p^h})^{p^{f-h}} = 1$.

In general $|A| = p_1^{e_1} \ldots p_n^{e_n}$ and $A = S_{p_1} \times \ldots \times S_{p_n}$. Let g_i be the element of maximal order $p_i^{f_i}$ in S_{p_i}. Clearly $m = p_1^{f_1} \ldots p_n^{f_n}$ is the desired integer, and $g = g_1 \ldots g_n$ is the desired element of A.

* * *

This corollary has a direct proof without recourse to the full statement of Theorem 18. This proof is outlined in Problems 1 and 2 of the next exercise set.

As a result of this corollary it seems appropriate to introduce some standard terminology.

Definition. Let G be a group. If there exists a positive integer m such that $g^m = 1$ for all $g \in G$, then the minimal such positive integer is called the *exponent* of G; otherwise we say that G has infinite exponent.

From the theorem of Lagrange we know that every finite group has an exponent. We have just proved that in *every finite abelian group there is an element whose order is the exponent of the group*. This is of course not true for all finite groups and an example is provided by the nonabelian group of order 6. Infinite groups may have a finite exponent; consider for example the group of all functions f from the integers I into $I/\langle 2 \rangle$ where the group operation is addition of functions. Here the exponent is 2. An infinite group may have no exponent and yet each element may have finite order. An example of such a group is provided by the factor group of the rational numbers under addition by the integers. The multiplicative group of complex numbers which are roots of unity is an isomorphic copy of this example.

The question of the relation between the finiteness of the exponent and the finiteness of the group was raised by Burnside. The Burnside problem is the following: Is every finitely generated group with finite exponent finite? (Recall that a group G is finitely generated if there is a finite set of elements

$S \subseteq G$ such that every element $x \in G$ can be expressed in the form $x = t_1 t_2 \ldots t_m$ where $t_i \in S$ or $t^{-1} \in S$. m depends on x, of course.) It is known that Burnside's problem has an affirmative answer if the exponent is 2, 3, 4, or 6. An unconfirmed announcement in 1959 by the Russian mathematician P. S. Novikov states that the answer is negative if the exponent is greater than or equal to 72.

EXERCISE 3

1. Let G be an abelian group. Let $y, z \in G$ have orders r and s, respectively. Show that there is an element whose order is the least common multiple of r and s. Prove this from the Corollary to Theorem 18 and then independently as follows: Prove first when $(r, s) = 1$; then, using prime factorization, reduce the general situation to several applications of this case.

2. Let G be a finite abelian group. Show that there is an integer m such that (1) $x^m = 1$ for all $x \in G$ and (2) there is an element in G whose order is m by employing Problem 1.

3. Show that if p and q are distinct primes the only abelian group of order pq is the cyclic group.

4. Show that if p is a prime there are exactly two nonisomorphic abelian groups of order p^2.

5. Find all abelian groups of order 12 and of order 1260. Generalize your answer to determine all abelian groups of an infinite class.

SUPPLEMENTARY READING

M. Hall, Jr., Generators and relations in groups—the Burnside problem, *Lectures on Modern Mathematics*, vol. II (edited by T. L. Saaty), New York: John Wiley & Sons (1964).

T. Motzkin, The euclidean algorithm, *Bulletin of the American Mathematical Society*, **55** (1949), 1142–1146.

W. Rudin, Unique factorization of Gaussian integers, *American Mathematical Monthly*, **68** (1961), 907–908.

B. L. van der Waerden, *Modern Algebra*, vol. 1 (F. Blum translator), New York: Ungar (1949).

O. Zariski and P. Samuel, *Commutative Algebra*, vol. 1, Princeton, N.J.: Van Nostrand (1958).

6 | Polynomials

6.1. INTRODUCTION

It is a convenient manner of speech, especially in high school algebra courses, to say that a polynomial is an expression of the form

$$x^3 - \tfrac{1}{2}x^2 + 1$$

or, more generally,

$$a_n x^n + a_{n-1} x^{n-1} + \cdots + a_1 x + a_0.$$

Usually we are told that the a_i's are called coefficients and are usually integers, rational numbers, real numbers, or complex numbers. Little is said about x. But surely this is a very pertinent question. What is "x"? From the definition, x is a polynomial, but what is "x"?

An answer suitable for most elementary situations is that it is an "unknown," that is, a number, coming from the same set as the coefficients, but, for the moment, unspecified.

This answer is good enough for us to prove basic identities like

$$\text{"}x^2 - 2ax + a^2 = (x - a)^2,\text{"}$$

which holds for all elements x in a commutative ring to which a belongs, or to solve equations like $x^2 + 2ax + a^2 = 0$.

$$\text{"If } x^2 + 2ax + a^2 = 0 \quad \text{then} \quad x = -a\text{"}$$

holds in any integral domain. But a different connotation is placed on $x^2 + 2ax + a^2$ when it is regarded as an "expression."

Another excellent reply to the question "What is x?" is given by pointing out that what is really meant is a function, f, whose value at x is

$$f(x) = x^2 + 2ax + a^2.$$

In this sense x is a generic name for an element in $\mathscr{D}_f$.

This is a perfectly valid idea, and while it *does not* represent what we shall

147

want to call a polynomial, it does represent a function, defined on a field F, with values in F. We require, of course, that a be a fixed element in F. We shall call such a function a *polynomial function*. We may define a polynomial function by a recursive scheme.

Let F be a commutative ring. The set of polynomial functions is the minimal set of functions $f: F \rightarrow F$ satisfying:

1. For each $k \in F$, the constant function, $f(x) = k$ for all $x \in F$, is a polynomial function.
2. The identity function, $f(x) = x$ for all $x \in F$, is a polynomial function.
3. If f and g are polynomial functions, then the functions $f \cdot g$ and $f + g$, defined as

$$(f \cdot g)(x) = f(x) \cdot g(x)$$
$$(f + g)(x) = f(x) + g(x),$$

are polynomial functions.

A little experimentation will convince you that we have included all functions of the type $f(x) = a_n x^n + \cdots + a_0$ and only such functions. If we knew what a polynomial is we could of course define a polynomial function more easily. This will be our approach later on in this chapter.

A word of caution. Polynomial functions may look different and yet be the same. Thus if F is the finite field of two elements, which is the integers modulo 2, $I/\langle 2 \rangle$, then it is easy to verify that the function defined by $f(x) = x^2 - x$ is the same as the constant function $g(x) = 0$. However, we do not wish to say that $x^2 - x$ and 0 are the same polynomial. We shall see in Theorem 13 that this identification of functions depends directly on the fact that the domain of the function is finite.

What, then, *is* x? Another convenient answer is that x is a new symbol, called an indeterminate. Such a definition makes clear the difference between $x^2 - x$ and 0. They are surely not the same symbol. It very well may raise such questions as "What is $1/x$?" but that can be circumvented by only discussing "proper expressions" in x. It is subject to the natural objection that x, as a *symbol*, is only a mark on paper. What does x stand for? Are polynomials merely such expressions written on paper? Perhaps there is a Platonic-ideal concept that mathematics in the twentieth century is missing. Anyway, a metaphysical question arises as to what happens when the mark is erased!

We shall avoid these pitfalls by defining polynomials in another way. For the time, our definition will seem cumbersome, but when we eventually use the symbol x we shall at least be able to state what it is a symbol for. We hope the pitfalls in this approach will at least be less obvious than the preceding ones! The precision we gain will make more complex situations easier to handle.

6.2. POLYNOMIAL RINGS

Definition. Let R be a ring. A *polynomial* f, over R, is a sequence $(a_0, a_1, a_2, \ldots)$ of elements from R in which only a finite number of terms are different from 0.

An immediate consequence of this definition is that for each polynomial f, there is an integer d, depending on f, such that for all $n > d$, $a_n = 0$. If $a_d \neq 0$, but $a_n = 0$ for all $n > d$, then d is called the *degree* of the polynomial f, and a_d is called the *leading coefficient* or *leading term* of f. In particular, the degree of the zero polynomial, $(0, 0, \ldots)$ is not defined. The usual terminology is to call the zero polynomial and the polynomials of degree 0, *scalar* polynomials; polynomials of degree 1, *linear* polynomials; polynomials of degree 2, *quadratic* polynomials; polynomials of degree 3, *cubic* polynomials; polynomials of degree 4, *quartic* polynomials; polynomials of degree 5, *quintic* polynomials, and so forth. If R is a ring with identity, a polynomial whose leading coefficient is 1 is called a *monic* polynomial.

As an aside to the reader, the polynomial $f = (a_0, a_1, \ldots)$ of degree d is meant to be the familiar polynomial $a_0 + a_1 x + \cdots + a_d x^d$. We shall make this identification in a moment.

We shall make the set of polynomials over R into a ring. Recall that as sequences $(a_0, a_1, \ldots) = (b_0, b_1, \ldots)$ if and only if $a_r = b_r$ for all r.

Definition.

Addition:
$$(a_0, a_1, \ldots) + (b_0, b_1, \ldots) = (a_0 + b_0, a_1 + b_1, \ldots, a_r + b_r, \ldots).$$

Multiplication:
$$(a_0, a_1, \ldots)(b_0, b_1, \ldots) = (c_0, c_1, \ldots, c_r, \ldots)$$

where c_r is defined to be $a_0 b_r + a_1 b_{r-1} + a_2 b_{r-2} + \cdots + a_{r-1} b_1 + a_r b_0$. In particular $c_0 = a_0 b_0$, $c_1 = a_0 b_1 + a_1 b_0$, $c_2 = a_0 b_2 + a_1 b_1 + a_2 b_0$. The general term c_r is given by $c_r = \sum_{i=0}^{r} a_i b_{r-i}$, or more informally $c_r = \sum_{i+j=r} a_i b_j$, where it is understood that the summation runs over all pairs $0 \leq i \leq r$, $0 \leq j \leq r$, subject to the condition that $i + j = r$. The careful reader will realize that this latter form of a sum does not fit the definition of page 102. However, assuming the result of Problem 7 in Exercise 3.3, this form is equivalent to the former.

Lemma 1. The set of polynomials is closed under the addition and multiplication operations defined above; moreover

1. If $\hat{0}$ is the zero polynomial, then $f + \hat{0} = \hat{0} + f = f$ and $\hat{0} = f \cdot \hat{0} = \hat{0} \cdot f$ for all polynomials f.
2. If $f \neq \hat{0}$ and $g \neq \hat{0}$ then degree $(f + g) \leq \max[$degree $(f),$ degree $(g)]$. (Equality holds if $\deg(f) \neq \deg(g)$.)

3. If $f \neq \hat{0}$ and $g \neq \hat{0}$, then either (i) $f \cdot g = \hat{0}$, or (ii) degree$(f \cdot g) \leq$ degree(f) + degree(g). If R is an integral domain, then (ii) holds with equality.

PROOF. (1) is established easily by inspecting the definitions. Let us suppose for the remainder of this proof that none of the polynomials under consideration is the zero polynomial. Let $f = (a_0, a_1, \ldots)$, $g = (b_0, b_1, \ldots)$, and $fg = (c_0, c_1, \ldots)$. Let the degree of f be p and the degree of g be q. Then for $n > \max(p, q)$, we have $a_n + b_n = 0 + 0 = 0$, thus proving (2) and showing that the set of polynomials is closed under addition. Finally, if $n > p + q$, we have that $c_n = \sum_{i+j=r} a_i b_j$. But if j is larger than q, then b_j is 0, while if i is larger than p, a_i is zero. Thus to get a nonzero term in the sum, $i \leq p$ while $j \leq q$. But then $i + j \leq p + q < n$, or $i + j \neq n$. Hence $c_n = 0$. This proves (3), except for the case where R is an integral domain, and shows that the polynomials are closed under multiplication. Specializing the above argument about c_n to the case where $n = p + q$, we see that $c_{p+q} = a_p b_q$, since there can be at most one nonzero term in the sum. If R is an integral domain, then $a_p \neq 0$ and $b_q \neq 0$ and so $a_p b_q \neq 0$. This completes the proof of this lemma.

* * *

Theorem 1. If R is a ring then the set of polynomials over R is a ring under the definitions for $(+)$ and $(\cdot)$ given above. The set of scalar polynomials forms a subring, which is isomorphic to R. If R is commutative then the polynomial ring is commutative. If R is an integral domain then the ring of polynomials is an integral domain, and the units of R are the scalar polynomials $(a, 0, \ldots)$ where a is a unit of R.

PROOF. Since addition of polynomials is done term-wise on the sequences, it is easy to see that under addition the polynomials form an additive abelian group. Let $f = (a_0, a_1, \ldots)$, $g = (b_0, b_1, \ldots)$, and $h = (c_0, c_1, \ldots)$. If the multiplication in R is commutative, then so is multiplication in the set of polynomials. The rth term of $f \cdot g$ is $\sum_{i+j=r} a_i b_j = \sum_{i+j=r} b_j a_i$. In the final form this is the rth term of $g \cdot f$, and so $f \cdot g = g \cdot f$.

To prove the distributive law note that the rth term of $f(g + h)$ is $\sum_{i+j=r} a_i(b_j + c_j)$, while the rth term of $fg + fh$ is $\sum_{i+j=r} a_i b_j + \sum_{i+j=r} a_i c_j$. Hence $f(g + h) = fg + fh$ holds by virtue of the distributivity in R.

Associativity follows similarly, but the details are messy. We are to prove $f(gh) = (fg)h$. We calculate the rth term of each and compare answers. Let the pth term of (gh) be $d_p = \sum_{i+j=p} b_i c_j$. Then the rth term of $f(gh)$ is

$$\sum_{p+q=r} a_q d_p = \sum_{p+q=r} a_q \left(\sum_{i+j=p} b_i c_j \right) = \sum_{i+j+q=r} a_q(b_i c_j)$$

where the last sum is understood to run over all triples of integers $0 \leq i, j,$

$q \leq r$ subject to the condition $i + j + q = r$. In a perfectly analogous way we have that the rth term of $(fg)h$ is

$$\sum_{j+t=r} (\sum_{i+q=t} a_q b_i) c_j = \sum_{q+i+j=r} (a_q b_i) c_j.$$

These final forms differ only by an application of the associative law in R. Hence multiplication of polynomials is associative. If the reader is not convinced by these manipulations with the $\sum$-notation an easy induction proof is outlined in the next exercise set.

If R is an integral domain, then by the first lemma, there are no proper zero divisors, and so the polynomial domain is again an integral domain.

The scalar polynomials clearly form a subring which is isomorphic to the ring R itself under the mapping $(a, 0, \ldots) \rightarrow a$. Hereafter we shall identify R with this subring.

It is clear that $(1, 0, \ldots)$ is an identity of the polynomial ring. Now if $f \cdot g = (1, 0, \ldots)$ from Lemma 1, it follows that $\deg(f) + \deg(g) = 0$ and hence f and g are scalar polynomials; $f = (a, 0, \ldots)$ and $g = (b, 0, \ldots)$ and $ab = 1$. Thus a is a unit of R. Conversely it is easy to see that if a is a unit of R then $(a, 0, \ldots)$ is a unit of the polynomial ring.

* * *

Now we are ready to introduce some notations that will enable us to view polynomials in their usual form. Let us choose a *new symbol*, say x, and use the symbol ax^r to denote the polynomial $(0, \ldots, a, 0, \ldots)$ where a is the $(r + 1)$st term in the polynomial. Thus

$$ax^0 = (a, 0, \ldots)$$
$$ax^1 = (0, a, 0, \ldots)$$
$$ax^2 = (0, 0, a, 0, \ldots), \text{ etc.}$$

Now we may denote a polynomial of degree at most d, $(a_0, a_1, \ldots, a_d, 0, \ldots)$, by the form $a_0 x^0 + a_1 x^1 + a_2 x^2 + \cdots + a_d x^d$. If we go further and follow standard convention, as we do wish to do, and simply write a for the polynomial ax^0 and ax for the polynomial ax^1, then any polynomial $f = (a_0, a_1, \ldots)$ can be written as

$$a_0 + a_1 x + a_2 x^2 + \cdots + a_d x^d$$

where the ambiguity between a, as an element of R and a, as a polynomial is intentional and causes little trouble. Hereafter 0 shall denote either or both the zero polynomial and/or the zero of R.

Note, as one would hope and expect, that $(ax^r)(bx^s) = (ab)x^{r+s}$. If R has a multiplicative identity, then we shall write x for the polynomial $1x^1$. In this case we have that $1x^0 = 1$, and indeed 1 serves as an identity for the ring of polynomials.

Using the above notations it is convenient to use the symbol $R[x]$ to denote the ring of polynomials over R. We may think of this as a symbolic adjunction of a new symbol, x, to R and calculate with it as though it were an element of R under the further assumption that x commutes with all elements of R. The elements of $R[x]$ we usually denote by a single letter, f, or, for emphasis we use the customary notation, $f(x)$. We call the symbol x an *indeterminate*. Indeed this is the very approach of which we were so critical. We are loath to surrender the convenience of this point of view! However, we are now able to replace any mystical metaphysical arguments with the more concrete representation in terms of sequences.

Definition. A function $\varphi : R \to R$ is called a *polynomial function* if there is a polynomial $\sum_i^n a_i x^i$ in $R[x]$ such that for all $b \in R$

$$\varphi(b) = a_0 + a_1 b + a_2 b^2 + \cdots + a_n b^n.$$

Every polynomial $f = a_0 + a_1 x + \cdots + a_n x^n$ can clearly be associated with the function from R into R whose value at $b \in R$ is $a_0 + a_1 b + \cdots + a_n b^n$. We shall use f for this function as well as for the polynomial and write

$$f(b) = a_0 + a_1 b + \cdots + a_n b^n.$$

If $f(b) = 0$, b is called a *zero* of the polynomial f or a *root* of the function equation $f(x) = 0$. In particular if f is the zero polynomial then every element of R is a zero of f.

If the ring R is not commutative, then in general it is false, for polynomials and polynomial functions, that if $f = g \cdot h$ as polynomials, it follows that $f(a) = g(a) \cdot h(a)$ for all a in R. This anomaly occurs because of the way multiplication was defined. Thus

$$(x - b)(x - c) = x^2 - (b + c)x + bc \quad \text{in } R[x],$$

while $\quad (a - b)(a - c) = a^2 - ac - ba + bc \quad$ in the ring R.

If $ca \neq ac$, then $-ac - ba \neq -(c + b)a$, in general (for example, in the ring of Example 2.7 take $c = b$). Situations in which this extra care must be exercised are commonplace in the theory of matrices. It is always true that if $f = g + h$ then $f(a) = g(a) + h(a)$, since addition is commutative and the distributive law holds. Another reason for this state of affairs is that the symbol $(\cdot)$ denotes one operation in $R[x]$ and another in R, as does $(+)$. The two denotations, however, coincide in the subring of scalar polynomials.

Theorem 2. Let R be a ring and suppose that for some $u \in R$, $au = ua$ for all $a \in R$. Then ux^r commutes with all polynomials of $R[x]$.

PROOF. Because of the distributive laws, it suffices to prove $(ux^r)(ax^s) = (ax^s)(ux^r)$ for all s. However, we have $(ux^r)(ax^s) = (ua)x^{r+s} = (au)x^{r+s} = (ax^s)(ux^r)$.

Theorem 3. Let R be a ring and suppose that for some $u \in R$, $au = ua$ for all $a \in R$. Then the mapping

$$\sum_{i=0}^{n} a_i x^i \to \sum_{i=0}^{n} a_i u^i$$

is a homomorphism of $R[x]$ into R.

PROOF. The mapping is clearly well defined and since we add polynomials term-wise and have the distributive law in R,

$$\sum a_i x^i + \sum b_i x^i = \sum (a_i + b_i)x^i \to \sum (a_i + b_i)u^i = \sum a_i u^i + \sum b_i u^i.$$

Thus addition is preserved. (The careful student may express concern that the polynomials may not have the same degree. However, we may add terms to the polynomial of lower degree, each with zero coefficient to make the pseudo degrees equal.)

Since u commutes with all ring elements, preservation of multiplication follows similarly.

$$\left(\sum a_i x^i\right)\left(\sum b_j x^j\right) = \sum_r \left(\sum_{i+j=r} a_i b_j\right)x^r \to \sum_r \left(\sum_{i+j=r} a_i b_j\right)u^r$$

while

$$\left(\sum a_i u^i\right)\left(\sum b_j u^j\right) = \sum_j \left(\sum_i a_i u^i\right)b_j u^j = \sum_j \left(\sum_i a_i b_j u^{i+j}\right) = \sum_p \left(\sum_{i+j=p} a_i b_j\right)u^p.$$

* * *

Corollary. If R is a commutative ring and if f and g are two polynomials over R, then for all $a \in R$.

$$(f + g)(a) = f(a) + g(a)$$
$$fg(a) = f(a) \cdot g(a),$$

hold when f and g are considered as polynomial functions.

PROOF. The mapping $h(x) \to h(a)$ is a homomorphism of $R[x]$ into R and thus preserves multiplication and addition—which is all that the corollary claims!

* * *

Usually we shall be talking about the case in which R is a field or an integral domain. However, for applications in the theory of matrices, Theorem 3 is an important tool, where the a_i are scalar matrices and u is a fixed matrix.

We close this section with some rather obvious but useful remarks which we should have on record. If S is a subring of a ring R then $S[x]$ is a subring of $R[x]$. In particular, if $f(x)$ and $g(x) \in S[x]$ and $f(x) \mid g(x)$ in $S[x]$ then $f(x) \mid g(x)$ in $R[x]$. If σ is an homomorphism from a ring R into a ring $\bar{R}$

then σ can be extended to a homomorphism σ^* of $R[x]$ into $\bar{R}[x]$. If σ is an isomorphism then σ^* is an isomorphism. In later chapters this will be most useful when $R = \bar{R}$ and σ is an automorphism of R.

EXERCISE 1

1. Prove, from the formal definitions, that if $a \in F$, then the polynomial product $a \cdot x^n$ is the polynomial denoted ax^n.

2. Let F be the finite field of two elements, I_2. Find all functions from I_2 into I_2. Which of these are polynomial functions?

3. Find the coefficient of x^{20} in the products

    (i) $(2x^{100} + 3x^{20} + x^{18} + 2)(x^3 - 5x^2 + 1)$,
    (ii) $(x^{18} + x^7 + 1)(x^3 + 1)$.

4. Prove the remarks at the end of the section.

5. Let R be a commutative ring and $G = \{\sigma_1, \ldots, \sigma_n\}$ be a finite group of automorphisms of R. Show that $T = \{r \in R : \sigma(r) = r \text{ for all } \sigma \in G\}$ is a subring of R. Show that for any $a \in R$, $[(x - \sigma_1(a))\ldots(x - \sigma_n(a))] \in T[x]$.

6. Prove the associativity of polynomial multiplication by induction as follows: Let $\tau(f)$ be the number of nonzero coefficients in f. Prove $f(gh) = (fg)h$ if $\tau(f) = \tau(g) = \tau(h) = 1$. Now proceed by induction on $\tau = \tau(f) + \tau(g) + \tau(h)$ by considering three cases corresponding to the situations where f, g, and h, in turn, have more than one nonzero coefficient. Use the distributive law.

6.3. POLYNOMIALS OVER A FIELD

We shall now establish that if F is a field then $F[x]$ is a euclidean domain in which the degree of a polynomial is a suitable euclidean function v. This is probably the most important result in this chapter. First we shall prove a lemma of interest in its own right which facilitates some of the technical details.

Lemma 2 (*Division Algorithm*). Let R be a ring with identity, 1. If $a(x) \in R[x]$ and $b(x) \in R[x]$ is a monic polynomial then there exist polynomials $q(x)$ and $r(x)$ in $R[x]$ such that

    $a(x) = b(x)q(x) + r(x)$ where $0 = r(x)$ or $\deg(r) < \deg(b)$.

We shall in effect show that the familiar high school algorithm for dividing one polynomial by another actually works! Thus, for example,

$$
\begin{array}{r}
x^2 \\
x - 2 \overline{\smash{\big)}\ x^3 + x + 1} \\
\underline{x^3 - 2x^2} \\
2x^2 + x + 1
\end{array}
$$

$\left.\begin{array}{c} \cdot \\ \cdot \\ \cdot \end{array}\right\}$ Induction takes over!

We note first that if $\deg(b) > \deg(a)$, we may choose $q = 0$ and $r(x) = a(x)$. Hereafter we suppose that $\deg(a) \geq \deg(b)$. We shall proceed by induction on $d = \deg(a) - \deg(b)$. Let $a(x) = a_0 + \cdots + a_m x^m$ and $b(x) = b_0 + \cdots + b_{n-1}x^{n-1} + x^n$. We have $d = m - n$. Suppose that $d = 0$, or $n = m$. Then we have

$$a(x) = b(x) \cdot a_n + [(a_{n-1} - b_{n-1}a_n)x^{n-1} + \cdots + (a_0 - b_0 a_n)]$$

and we are done. So we may start our induction with $d = 0$. We assume the theorem for all polynomials $f(x)$ such that $\deg(f) - \deg(b) < d$. We have $a(x) = b(x) \cdot a_m x^{m-n} + f(x)$, where

$$f(x) = (a_{m-1} - b_{n-1}a_m)x^{m-1} + \cdots + (a_0 - b_0 a_m).$$

Clearly $\deg(f) \leq m - 1$. If $\deg(f) < n$ we are done; if $\deg(f) \geq n$ then $\deg(f) - \deg(b) \leq n - 1$; thus by induction $f(x) = b(x)g(x) + r(x)$, where $0 = r(x)$ or $\deg(r) < \deg(b)$. Hence

$$\begin{aligned} a(x) &= b(x) \cdot a_m x^{m-n} + b(x)g(x) + r(x) \\ &= b(x)[a_m x^{m-n} + g(x)] + r(x) \end{aligned}$$

and we are done.

Theorem 4. If F is a field then $F[x]$ is a euclidean domain.

PROOF. As a consequence of Lemma 1 and Theorem 1 we know $F[x]$ is an integral domain. We shall prove that $\deg(f)$ has the requisite properties of a function v to satisfy the definition of a euclidean domain. Clearly $\deg(f) \geq 0$ and since F has no zero divisors if f and g are nonzero polynomials, $\deg(f) \leq \deg(f \cdot g)$. Now let $b(x)$ be a nonzero polynomial and let $a(x) \in F[x]$. If the leading coefficient of $b(x)$ is b_n, we have, as $b_n \neq 0$, that $b'(x) = b_n^{-1}(bx)$ is a monic polynomial and $\deg(b) = \deg(b')$. Hence, from Lemma 2, there exist polynomials $q'(x)$ and $r(x)$ such that

$$a(x) = b'(x)q'(x) + r(x) \text{ where } 0 = r(x) \text{ or } \deg(r) < \deg(b'),$$

and so $a(x) = [b_n b'(x)][b_n^{-1}q'(x)] + r(x)$, or

$$a(x) = b(x)q(x) + r(x) \text{ where } 0 = r(x) \text{ or } \deg(r) < \deg(b)$$

as desired. This completes the proof that the degree of a polynomial is an acceptable euclidean function, and thus $F[x]$ is a euclidean domain.

Here, $F[x]$ cannot be a field, for consider the question of finding a polynomial that would be a multiplicative inverse for x. We should have $x \cdot f = 1$. Now, $f \neq 0$ and so a look at the degrees yields the contradiction:

$$0 = \deg(1) = \deg(x) + \deg(f) = 1 + \deg(f) \neq 0,$$

since $\deg(f) \geq 0$. Thus we have proved that not only does $\frac{1}{x}$ not "look like" a polynomial, it *is not* a polynomial!

In the case of the polynomial domain $F[x]$, where F is a field, we can prove the uniqueness of the q and r of Theorem 4. The proof is similar to that given for the integers in Theorem 3.11. The analogous theorem is stated here for completeness.

* * *

Theorem 5. Let F be a field. Let $a, b \in F[x]$. If $b \neq 0$, then there exist *unique* polynomials $q, r \in F[x]$ such that

1. $a = bq + r$.
2. $r = 0$ or degree (r) < degree (b).

In view of Theorem 4 we may apply all the theory of Chapter 5. We list these results in the next theorem.

Theorem 6. 1. All pairs of polynomials, $a, b \in F[x]$ possess a $GCD(a, b) = d$, and there exist polynomials u and v such that $au + bv = d$.

2. $(a, b) = 1$ if and only if there exist polynomials u and v such that $au + bv = 1$.

3. Every irreducible polynomial is a prime element in $F[x]$.

4. If $f, g \in F[x]$ and $f \mid g$, then either f is a unit, or f is an associate of g, or $\deg(f) < \deg(g)$.

5. Let $f \in F[x]$ and $\deg(f) \geq 1$. f can be written as a finite product $p_1 p_2 \ldots p_n$ of irreducible polynomials in $F[x]$. This representation of f is unique except for unit factors and the order in which the irreducible polynomials appear in the product.

6. Every ideal in $F[x]$ is principal.

7. If $p \in F[x]$ is an irreducible polynomial then $F[x]/\langle p \rangle$ is a field.

PROOF. (1) is Theorem 5.4. (2) is Theorem 5.5. (3) is the corollary to Theorem 5.8. (4) is Theorem 5.12. (5) is Theorem 5.13. (6) is Theorem 5.3. (7) is the corollary to Theorem 5.16.

* * *

Item (7) is perhaps the most important result for our future work, although (1) is probably the most effective tool in many situations.

It is conventional to refer to the prime elements of $F[x]$ as irreducible polynomials. In view of (3) there is no harm in this and it helps the vocabulary problem since almost always "prime" denotes a prime integer.

From Theorem 1 it follows that the units of $F[x]$ are the nonzero scalar polynomials. Thus, if a polynomial f is reducible, then $f = gh$ where g and h are polynomials of degree at least 1. As a consequence we see that any linear polynomial is irreducible in $F[x]$.

The dependence of the ring of polynomials on the field of coefficients is of course crucial. The polynomial $x^2 - 2$ in Ra[x] is irreducible, but regarded as a polynomial in Re[x] it is reducible: $x^2 - 2 = (x - \sqrt{2})(x + \sqrt{2})$. However a striking feature of a GCD of a pair of polynomials is that it is uneffected by the field.

> **Theorem 7.** Let F be a subfield of a field E. Let f and $g \in F[x]$. If d is a GCD of the polynomials f and g in $F[x]$ then $d = (f, g)$ in $E[x]$.

PROOF. We note that as $F \subseteq E$, it follows that $F[x]$ is a subring of $E[x]$. (Figure 1 indicates these relations.) In particular this means that since d divides f and g in $F[x]$ it follows that d divides f and g in $E[x]$. Moreover, in $F[x]$ we have $d = fu + gv$ for polynomials $u, v \in F[x]$. This equation holds in $E[x]$ so that any polynomial in $E[x]$ dividing both f and g must also divide d. Thus d is a GCD for (f, g) in $E[x]$.

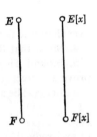

> **Corollary.** If $F \subseteq E$, f and $g \in F[x]$ then $f \mid g$ in $E[x]$ if and only if $f \mid g$ in $F[x]$.

PROOF. The "if part" is trivial. On the other hand, if $f \mid g$ in $E[x]$ then $(f, g) = f$ in $E[x]$; hence $(f, g) = f$ in $F[x]$ for otherwise a contradiction would ensue.

Figure 1

* * *

It is of some importance in many applications to utilize the variety of solutions for $d = rf + sg$. Recall Theorem 5.14. One such application is given in the next theorem.

> **Theorem 8.** Let F be a field and suppose that f and g are coprime, nonunit polynomials in $F[x]$. There exist $a, b \in F[x]$ such that $1 = af + bg$, and
>
> $$\deg(a) < \deg(g) \quad \text{and} \quad \deg(b) < \deg(f).$$

PROOF. We can find one solution, say $1 = rf + sg$. From Theorem 5.14 we have other solutions of the form $1 = (r + ug)f + (s - uf)g$, where $u \in F[x]$ is arbitrary. By the division algorithm we have $s = f \cdot q + b$ where $b = 0$ or $\deg(b) < \deg(f)$. Thus $1 = (r + q \cdot g)f + bg$. If $b = 0$, then f is a unit contrary to hypothesis, hence $b \neq 0$ and $\deg(b) < \deg(f)$. Now it must follow that $\deg(r + q \cdot g) < \deg(g)$, because otherwise a contradiction to

$$0 = \deg(1) = \deg[(r + q \cdot g)f + bg]$$

arises as follows:
   If $\deg(r + q \cdot g) \geq \deg(g)$, then $\deg[(r + q \cdot g) \cdot f] = \deg(r + q \cdot g) +$

$\deg(f) \geq \deg(g) + \deg(f)$. Since neither g nor f is a unit, this sum is strictly positive and cannot be zero.

* * *

EXERCISE 2

1. Find the GCD of polynomials $x^4 + x^3 + 2x^2 + 3x + 1$ and $x^4 + x^3 - 2x^2 - x + 1$ over the rationals.

2. Solve the congruence

$$(x^2 + 1) \cdot f \equiv 1 \ (\mathrm{mod}\ x^3 + 1)$$

over the rationals.

3. Solve the congruence, if possible,

$$(x^4 + x^3 + x^2 + 1) \cdot f \equiv (x^2 + 1)(\mathrm{mod}\ x^3 + 1)$$

over the finite field $I/\langle 2\rangle = \{0, 1\}$.

4. Show that $Ra[x]/(x^2 - 1)$ is not a field. Why?

5. Extend Theorem 8 to deal with the case $d = (a, b) \neq 1$. Formulate and prove a correct theorem.

6. Let $g(x)$ be any polynomial in $F[x]$. In the field of quotients of $F[x]$ show that $\dfrac{1}{g(x)} = \dfrac{f_1(x)}{p_1(x)} + \cdots + \dfrac{f_i(x)}{p_i(x)}$ where $\deg f_i(x) < \deg p_i(x)$ and each $p_i(x)$ is a power of an irreducible polynomial.

7. Apply Problem 6 to integrate

$$\int \frac{dx}{(x + 1)(x^2 + x + 1)(x^2 - 2x + 1)}$$

8. Let R be a ring. Determine the units in $R[x]$. Show that if $r \in R$ and r is irreducible then r is irreducible in $R[x]$.

9. Let T be the set of functions f from the nonnegative *integers* into the rational numbers such that $f(n) = 0$ for all but a finite number of values of n. Define addition and multiplication ($\cdot$) as follows:

$$(f + g)(n) = f(n) + g(n)$$

$$(f \cdot g)(n) = \sum_{0 \leq x \leq n} f(n - x)g(x).$$

Show that this is a ring by showing $\langle T, +, 0\rangle$ is isomorphic with $Ra[x]$.

10. In the example of Problem 9, modify T to T^* dropping the condition "nonnegative" and defining

$$(f \cdot g)(n) = \sum_{-\infty < x < \infty} f(n - x)g(x).$$

Does a ring result? An integral domain?

11. Let a relation $\langle\leq\rangle$ be defined on $I[x]$ as follows:

$$f \leq g \quad \text{if and only if} \quad f(0) \leq g(0).$$

Does ($\leq$) make $F[x]$ into a totally ordered domain?

12. Let a relation ($\leq$) be defined on $I[x]$ as follows: $f \leq g$ if and only if $g - f = a_0 + a_1x + \cdots + a_nx^n$ and either all $a_i = 0$ or the *first non-zero* coefficient is positive. Show that ($\leq$) makes $I[x]$ into a totally ordered domain. Which axioms for the integers are not satisfied by $\langle I[x], +, \cdot, \leq \rangle$?

6.4. THE COMPLEX NUMBERS

In this section we shall construct the complex numbers in a new way, which utilizes (7) of Theorem 6. This will yield a sharper insight to the nature of the complex numbers and at the same time give an example of how this theorem works to produce new fields. We begin with a lemma.

Lemma 3. In $\text{Re}[x]$, the polynomial $x^2 + 1$ is irreducible.

PROOF. Suppose $x^2 + 1 = f \cdot g$. If f and g are not units, both must have degree 1. By multiplying f and g by a unit factor we may suppose that $f = (x - a)$ and $g = (x - b)$ where $a, b \in \text{Re}$. Thus for some unit e, $x^2 + 1 = e(x - a)(x - b) = e[x^2 - (a + b)(x + ab)]$. It follows that $e = 1$, $a + b = 0$, and $ab = 1$. So $a = -b$ and $ab = a(-a) = -a^2$. But $-a^2 = 1$ implies $a^2 = -1$, contrary to $a^2 \geq 0$.

$$* \quad * \quad *$$

Thus Theorem 6 says that $\text{Re}[x]/\langle (x^2 + 1) \rangle$ is a field. The elements are residue classes of the form $\bar{f} = \{g : g \equiv f \bmod x^2 + 1)\}$. In each nonzero residue class there is a unique polynomial of degree at most 1 since there is a unique polynomial r such that

$$g = (x^2 + 1)q + r; \quad r = 0 \text{ or } \deg(r) < 2,$$

and so $g \equiv r \pmod{x^2 + 1}$. The zero residue class contains 0 and multiples of $x^2 + 1$. In particular, different polynomials of degree at most 1 cannot be congruent mod $x^2 + 1$.

The result of these observations is that we can, in a 1–1 fashion, associate a unique polynomial of the form $ax + b$ with each residue class. Thus, for example, the residue class to which $2x^3 + x + 1$ belongs contains $-x + 1$ and each and every polynomial of the form $(-x + 1) + (x^2 + 1)f$ where f is *any* polynomial of $\text{Re}[x]$.

Now let j denote the residue class to which x belongs. Addition and multiplication of residue classes have already been defined for us in Chapter 2. Thus $j + j$ is the residue class to which $x + x$ belongs; j^2 is the residue class to which x^2 belongs. Since x^2 is not of the form $ax + b$, we may find an element in that residue class of the form $ax + b$, and indeed $x^2 \equiv -1 \pmod{x^2 + 1}$, or j^2 is the residue class to which -1 belongs. If r is a real number, and if we let $\bar{r}$ denote the residue class to which the real number r belongs, then each residue class in $\text{Re}[x]/(x^2 + 1)$ can be written as $\bar{a} + \bar{b}j$

where a and b are real numbers. (Caution: the bar on a, ($\bar{a}$), does not mean complex conjugate as it did in Section 4.6.) This suggests the next theorem.

Theorem 9. The field of complex numbers is isomorphic to $\text{Re}[x]/\langle(x^2 + 1)\rangle$.

PROOF. The idea of the proof should be clear. We shall prove that the mapping $\Phi : C \to \text{Re}[x]/\langle(x^2 + 1)\rangle$ defined by

$$\Phi(a + bi) = \bar{a} + \bar{b}j$$

is a field isomorphism. Since each element of $\text{Re}[x]/\langle x^2 + 1\rangle$ has a representative in the form $\bar{a} + \bar{b}j$, the mapping is *onto*. Since a field can have only trivial homomorphisms (Theorem 4.4) and since φ is onto, all we need to prove is that φ preserves addition and multiplication. Since

$$(a + bi) + (c + di) = (a + c) + (b + d)i$$

while

$$(\bar{a} + \bar{b}j) + (\bar{c} + \bar{d}j) = (\bar{a} + \bar{c}) + (\bar{b} + \bar{d})j$$

it is clear that addition is preserved. In a similar way φ preserves multiplication once it is seen that $j^2 = -\bar{1}$, and we have already observed that -1 belongs to the residue class j^2.

The realization of the complex numbers we have just presented shows directly the justification for calling i a "number" such that $i^2 = -1$ and then operating formally with expressions of the form $a + bi$, where a and b are real numbers.

Finally, three remarks: First, we drop the convention of using a special symbol $\bar{r}$ to denote the residue class to which the field element r belongs. In other words we identify the real number r with the residue class $\bar{r}$. We shall use the usual notation i for j, the residue class to which x belongs, and we shall denote the field of complex numbers in whatever guise it appears by C.

Second, we may consider $C[y]$—polynomials in the indeterminate y with coefficients in C. We want to point out, *with great force*, that the polynomial $y^2 + 1$ now has a zero in C. Indeed C was constructed to the end that this polynomial have a zero. The complex number i is a zero of this polynomial because $i^2 + 1 = 0$. This equation asserts that the residue class to which $x^2 + 1$ belongs is the zero residue class of $\text{Re}[x]/\langle x^2 + 1\rangle$, which is the statement $x^2 + 1 \equiv 0 \,(\text{mod}\,(x^2 + 1))$.

Third, it should be clear that this process may be done much more generally. Let F be any field. Let $p(x)$ be an irreducible polynomial over F. To construct a field E in which a corresponding polynomial $p(y)$ has a root we simply let $E = F[x]/\langle p(x)\rangle$. Then, if θ is the residue class to which x belongs, $p(\theta) = 0$, since $p(x) \equiv 0 \,(\text{mod}\,p(x))$. This remark is intended as a glance ahead to Chapter 8 where this construction will play the major role in treating the theory of field extensions. To utilize this result we state it in the form of the next theorem, which will be proved in Chapter 8.

Theorem 10. Let F be a field. If $p(x)$ is a nonscalar polynomial of $F[x]$ then there exists a field $E \supseteq F$, in which $p(x)$ has a zero.

EXERCISE 3

1. Carry out the procedure of the proof of this section when the field Re is replaced by I_3. Find a representative for each residue class and write out the multiplication table. Show that the multiplicative group of the resulting field is cyclic.

6.5. SPECIAL PROPERTIES OF $F[x]$

In this section we shall continue to suppose that F is a field and proceed to develop some of the special features of the euclidean domain $F[x]$.

Theorem 11 (*Remainder Theorem*). Let R be a commutative ring with identity. If f is any polynomial in $R[x]$, then for all polynomials $(x - a)$ in $R[x]$ it is true that

$$f = (x - a)q + f(a).$$

PROOF. By the division algorithm $f = (x - a)a + r$, where either $r = 0$ or has degree < 1. In any event r is a scalar polynomial. By Theorem 3 and its corollary we obtain $f(a) = (a - a)q(a) + r(a)$, or $f(a) = r(a)$.

However, since r has at most degree 0, r is an element of R, hence $r(a)$ *is the polynomial r under our notation convention of identifying the polynomial $(r, 0, 0, \ldots)$ with r.*

* * *

Corollary 1 (*Factor Theorem*). If F is a field, the polynomial $f \in F[x]$ is divisible by $(x - a)$ if and only if a is a zero of f.

PROOF. Since the quotient and the remainder are determined uniquely (Theorem 5), we have $f = (x - a)q$ if and only if $f(a) = 0$.

* * *

Corollary 2. Let f be a quadratic or cubic polynomial in $F[x]$. Then f is reducible if and only if f has a zero in F.

PROOF. By the factor theorem, if f has a zero, a, in F, then f is divisible by $(x - a)$. Conversely if f is reducible and has degree 2 or 3, it must have a factor which is of degree 1. Because F is a field it has a monic factor of degree 1, call it $x - a$. Then, by the factor theorem, a is a zero of f.

* * *

Theorem 12. Let F be a field. A nonzero polynomial in $F[x]$ which has degree n has at most n distinct zeros.

PROOF. Let $a_1, \ldots, a_m$ be m distinct zeros of f. Then $(x - a_1), \ldots, (x - a_m)$ are m distinct divisors of f. Since each is linear, each is irreducible and so they are mutually coprime. By Theorem 5.11, we have

$$f = (x - a_1) \ldots (x - a_m) f_1.$$

If $m > n$, we should have higher degree on the right than on the left. Hence $m \leq n$ and the proof is complete.

* * *

Remark. The contrapositive form of this theorem is often of more immediate usefulness:

Theorem 13. If f is a polynomial of degree at most n but possessing more than n distinct zeros, then $f = 0$, the zero polynomial.

Corollary. If F is a field with an infinite number of elements, then each polynomial function has a unique representation as a polynomial.

PROOF. If f and g are two polynomials such that $f(a) = g(a)$ for all $a \in F$, then the polynomial $h = f - g$ has an infinite number of zeros but finite degree. From Theorem 13, it follows that $h = f - g = 0$, or that $f = g$.

* * *

Theorem 14 (*Lagrange Interpolation Formula*). If $a_1, \ldots, a_n$ are n distinct elements of a field F and if $b_1, \ldots, b_n$ are any n elements of F, there is a unique polynomial f in $F[x]$ such that $f(a_i) = b_i$ for $i = 1, \ldots, n$ and such that $\deg(f) \leq n - 1$.

PROOF. As is usual, the unicity of the polynomial is the easier to prove. Suppose that f and g are two polynomials satisfying the conditions required. Then $h = f - g$ has zeros $a_1, \ldots, a_n$, more than its degree. Hence $h = 0$.

The existence is proved by explicitly constructing f. The following polynomial works!

$$f = \sum_{i=1}^{n} b_i \cdot \frac{(x - a_1) \ldots (x - a_{i-1})(x - a_{i+1}) \ldots (x - a_n)}{(a_i - a_1) \ldots (a_i - a_{i-1})(a_i - a_{i+1}) \ldots (a_i - a_n)}.$$

* * *

While this completes the proof, the question of how one guesses what f should be needs some illumination unless one has seen this trick before. Geometrically, the theorem asks for a polynomial which passes through n distinct coplanar points. As an example, let us discuss the case $n = 3$, which is illustrated in Figure 2. Now it is easy to construct a (polynomial) function which is 0 at a_2 and a_3, but not at a_1: $(x - a_2)(x - a_3)$ works. Now its value at a_1 is $(a_1 - a_2)(a_1 - a_3)$; thus to make it have the value b_1 we simply multiply it by a "fudge" factor. Then,

$$g_1 = \frac{b_1}{(a_1 - a_2)(a_1 - a_3)} (x - a_2)(x - a_3)$$

has the value b_1 at a_1, 0 at a_2, and 0 at a_3. Now do a similar stunt at points a_2 and a_3, getting functions g_2 and g_3. Then $f = g_1 + g_2 + g_3$ has *all* the desired properties.

We have not said much about "multiple zeros." If $(x - a)$ divides f, when does $(x - a)^2$ divide f? It would seem that one could divide out $(x - a)$ and then ask whether $(x - a)$ divides the quotient. This might be difficult to do in practice as a may not belong to F. The problem then is to determine, without having to construct the field guaranteed by Theorem 10, whether a polynomial has a "multiple" root. First we define "multiplicity."

Definition. Let $f \in F[x]$. Let f have a zero a in some extension field E of F $(E \supseteq F)$; a is said to be a zero of *multiplicity* k if, in $E[x]$, $(x - a)^k \mid f$ but $(x - a)^{k+1} \nmid f$. A zero of multiplicity 1 is called a *simple* zero of f.

Next we prove a lemma of considerable interest.

Lemma 4. Let f and g be two polynomials in $F[x]$. f and g have a common zero in some field extension E over F if and only if $(f, g) \neq 1$. In particular, if f is irreducible in $F[x]$, $g \neq 0$ and $\deg(g) < \deg(f)$ then f and g can have no common zero in any field containing F.

The reader is urged to note that the existence of a common zero in some unspecified field is apparently a much more difficult problem than the decision $[(f, g) \neq 1?]$, which is done by the euclidean algorithm in $F[x]$.

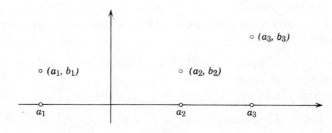

Figure 2

PROOF. If $(f, g) = d \neq 1$, then any zero of d is a zero of f and of g, for we have $d \mid f$ or $f = d \cdot q$. By Theorem 10, there is a field extension E over F in which d has a zero, a. Thus in E we must have $f(a) = d(a) \cdot q(a) = 0$. Similarly $g(a) = 0$.

Conversely suppose that $(f, g) = 1$. Then $1 = f \cdot r + g \cdot s$ in $F[x]$ and in $E[x]$, as well, for any field extension E over F. If f and g had a common zero a in E then we should have $1 = f(a)r(a) + g(a)s(a) = 0$—a contradiction.

Finally, suppose that f is irreducible. Then $(f, g) = 1$ or $(f, g) = f$. The latter condition implies that $f \mid g$. Hence if $g \neq 0$ and $\deg(g) < \deg(f)$ it follows that $(f, g) = 1$. Thus f and g can have no common zero in any field containing F.

*   *   *

To settle the multiple zero question, the concept of a formal derivative turns out to be useful. The idea, of course, comes from our experience from the calculus. Suppose a is a zero of multiplicity k. Pretending we are discussing functions of real numbers we have

$$f(x) = (x - a)^k g(x)$$
$$f'(x) = k(x - a)^{k-1} g(x) + (x - a)^k g'(x)$$

and so, if $k > 1$, $(x - a)$ is a zero of $f'(x)$ of multiplicity at least $k - 1$. It is not of multiplicity k since

$$f'(x) = (x - a)^{k-1}[kg(x) + (x - a)g'(x)]$$

so that if $(x - a)^k$ divided $f'(x)$, then $(x - a)$ divides $g(x) + (x - a)g'(x)$, or $(x - a)$ divides $g(x)$, contrary to the assumption that a was a zero of multiplicity k of $f(x)$.

Now the virtue of this fact is that if $f(x) = \sum_{i=0}^{n} a_i x^i$, then $f'(x) = \sum_{i=1}^{n} i a_i x^{i-1}$, and so belongs to $F[x]$. Thus if $f(x)$ has a multiple zero then $f(x)$ and $f'(x)$ have a common zero, and since f and f' belong to $F[x]$, the question whether f and f' have a common zero can be settled by using Lemma 4. The converse also holds.

Now adapting this much of the calculus is not difficult since we can define derivatives *formally* without recourse to limits and prove the basic algebra of derivatives for polynomials. (Why is this not a satisfactory procedure in the calculus?)

Definition. Let $f = \sum_{i=0}^{n} a_i x^i \in F[x]$. The derivative of f is defined to be the polynomial $f' = \sum_{i=1}^{n} i a_i x^{i-1}$.

We note that $f' \in F[x]$.

Lemma 5. If $f, g \in F[x]$, then $(f + g)' = f' + g'$.

PROOF. Easy!

Lemma 6. If $f, g \in F[x]$ then $(f \cdot g)' = f'g + fg'$.

PROOF. We shall prove this by an induction on the number of nonzero terms in f. If f has only one nonzero term, say $f = ax^n$, while $g = \sum_{j=0}^{m} b_j x^j$, then $fg = \sum_{j=0}^{n} ab_j x^{n+j}$. Thus, $(fg)' = \sum_{j=0}^{m} ab_j(n+j)x^{n+j-1}$ while $f'g = \sum_{j=0}^{m} a \cdot n \cdot b_j x^{j+n-1}$, and $fg' = \sum_{j=0}^{m} ab_j \cdot jx^{n+j-1}$ and so $f'g + fg' = \sum_{j=0}^{m} ab_j \cdot (n+j)x^{n+j-1} = (fg)'$. (The careful reader will realize that these summation limits are wrong if either term is zero, but these are really trivial cases we leave for him to verify.) Now suppose that f has k nonzero terms and that the lemma holds for polynomials with fewer than k terms. Then $f = f_1 + f_2$ where f_1 and f_2 have fewer than k terms. Hence $(fg)' = ((f_1 + f_2)g)' = (f_1 \cdot g + f_2 \cdot g)' = (f_1g)' + (f_2g)'$ by Lemma 5. By induction $(f_1g)' = f_1'g + f_1g'$, similarly for $(f_2g)'$. Thus $(fg)' = f_1'g + f_1g' + f_2'g + f_2g' = (f_1' + f_2')g + (f_1 + f_2)g' = (f_1 + f_2)'g + (f_1 + f_2)g' = f'g + fg'$.

*   *   *

Lemma 7. If $f = (x - a)^k$ then $f' = \begin{cases} 1 & \text{if } k = 1 \\ k(x - a)^{k-1} & \text{if } k \neq 1. \end{cases}$

PROOF. This is a simple induction on k. If $k = 1$ this is trivial. We have, in the general case, $f = (x - a)^{k-1}(x - a)$, then $f' = (k - 1)(x - a)^{k-2}(x - a) + (x - a)^{k-1} = k(x - a)^{k-1}$. Now we can prove more formally our criterion for f to have a multiple zero.

*   *   *

Theorem 15. Let $f \in F[x]$. f has a multiple zero if and only if $(f, f') \neq 1$.

PROOF. In view of Lemma 4 we need only prove that f has a multiple zero if and only if f and f' have a common zero in some extension field E over F. Let us suppose that f has a zero, a, of multiplicity $k(k \geq 2)$ in a field E. Then $f = (x - a)^k g$ in $E[x]$, and $f' = k(x - a)^{k-1}g + (x - a)^k g' = (x - a)^{k-1}[kg + (x - a)g']$. Hence a is a zero of multiplicity $k - 1$ of f'; thus f and f' have a common zero. Conversely if a is not a multiple root of f, then $f' = g + (x - a)g'$, and since a is not a zero of g, a cannot be a zero of f'. Thus, if f has no multiple zeros in any field, then no zero of f is a zero of f', that is, f and f' have no common zeros.

*   *   *

Corollary. If F is a field of characteristic 0 then every irreducible polynomial in $F[x]$ has only simple zeros.

PROOF. Let $p(x) = a_0 + a_1x + \cdots + a_nx^n$ where $a_n \neq 0$ and $n \geq 1$. Then its derivative $p'(x) \neq 0$ and $\deg(p') = n - 1$. If $p(x)$ had a multiple zero then

$(p, p') \neq 1$ and so there would exist a nonunit divisor of p and p'. As p is irreducible, this contradicts Lemma 4.

* * *

EXERCISE 4

1. Let F be a field, $f \in F[x]$, and $a, b \in F$. If $f = (x - a)(x - b)q + r$, what can you say about the form of r? (Be sure to treat the case $a = b$.)

2. Of the following polynomials in $Ra[x]$, which pairs have common zeros? Of those pairs that do, state how many: $(x - 1)$, $(x^3 + 2x^2 + 2x + 1)$, $(x^3 + x^2 + x + 1)$, $(x^2 - x + 1)$.

3. Which of the following polynomials in $Ra[x]$ have multiple zeros? $(x^4 - x^3 + 2x^2 - x + 1)$, $(x^4 - 2x^3 + 2x^2 - 2x + 1)$.

4. Let $f(x)$ be irreducible in $F[x]$ where F is a field of characteristic $p > 0$. Describe the form that $f(x)$ must have if it is irreducible in $F[x]$ and has multiple zeros.

5. Show that $(x - a) \mid f(x) - f(a)$ for all $a \in F$, a field, and all $f \in F[x]$.

6. Show that any two irreducible polynomials in $F[x]$ having a common zero are associates.

6.6. FACTORIZATION IN $R[x]$

For a general ring R it is a difficult question to decide whether a given polynomial is irreducible in $R[x]$. While certain general methods exist in special situations, these are often not practical. On the other hand there are a number of special theorems which are very helpful, and in this section we shall prove a few of them. They concern the case where R is a quotient field of an integral domain D. (In standard cases, R is taken to be the rational numbers.) These theorems give information about irreducibility in $R[x]$ when something is known about irreducibility in $D[x]$.

It will be useful to prove these theorems when the integral domain D is not a euclidean domain. It turns out that for these theorems we require only the property of unique factorization in D, not a division algorithm. The ring $D = I[x]$ is a classic example of what we have in mind. It turns out (Theorem 18) that the unique factorization theorem holds in $I[x]$, but $I[x]$ is not a euclidean domain. For example, the elements 2 and x in $I[x]$ have only 1 and -1 as common divisors; yet we cannot find polynomials u and v in $I[x]$ such that $1 = 2 \cdot u + x \cdot v$.

Definition. An integral domain $\langle D, +, \cdot \rangle$ is called a *unique factorization domain* (UFD) if every nonzero element r is either a unit or can be written as a finite product of irreducibles; moreover, if

$$r = p_1 \ldots p_n = q_1 \ldots q_m,$$

where p_i and q_j are irreducibles in D, then $n = m$ and, on proper numbering, p_i is an associate of q_i.

In this section D shall denote a unique factorization domain.

Let us remark that from Theorem 5.13 every euclidean domain is a UFD. Soon we shall prove (Theorem 18) that if D is a UFD; then $D[x]$ is a UFD, and so in particular $I[x]$ is a UFD.

A word of reassurance. We shall make most use of the theorems in this section under the assumption that D is the ring of integers. The reader who would like to visualize his proofs may do so by taking D to be the ring of integers.

Lemma 8. Let D be a UFD. Every irreducible element of D is a prime.

PROOF. Let r be irreducible. Let $r \mid ab$ while $r \nmid a$. We are to show that $r \mid b$. Let $a = p_1 \ldots p_n$ and $b = q_1 \ldots q_m$ be the unique factorizations of a and b. Thus $p_1 \ldots p_n q_1 \ldots q_m$ becomes a factorization of ab into irreducibles, which is by hypothesis unique—up to unit factors and the ordering of irreducible elements. Now we also have $ab = rc$. Let us suppose that c has a factorization $t_1 \ldots t_u$ into irreducibles. Thus $ab = p_1 \ldots p_n q_1 \ldots q_m = rt_1 \ldots t_u$. Since the factorization is unique, re, an associate of r, must *appear* among $p_1, \ldots, p_n, q_1, \ldots, q_m$. Since $r \nmid a$, no associate of r can appear among $p_1, \ldots, p_n$. Thus re must appear among $q_1, \ldots, q_m$. Thus $r \mid b$.

* * *

Lemma 9. Let D be a UFD. Any two elements, a, b in D, have a GCD(a, b).

PROOF. By hypothesis a is a product of primes and b is a product of primes. By collecting primes that are associated and compensating by unit factors we may write $a = e p_1^{a_1} \ldots p_n^{a_n}$ where e is a unit and a_i is a positive integer. We can obtain a similar expression for b. By permitting the exponents on the primes to be 0 and adjusting for unit factors we may assume that $b = f p_1^{b_1} \ldots {}_n^{b_n}$. (For example, $-12 = (-1)2^2 \cdot 3 \cdot 5^0$; $15 = 2^0 \cdot 3 \cdot 5$.) Then clearly $p_1^{c_1} \ldots p_n^{c_n}$, where c_i is the minimum of a_i, b_i is a GCD of a and b.

* * *

Lemma 10. If $d = $ GCD(a, b) then GCD$(a/d, b/d) = 1$.

PROOF. We continue the notation of Lemma 9. It is clear from the proof of Lemma 9 that $a/d = e p_1^{a_1 - c_1} \ldots p_n^{a_n - c_n}$ and $b/d = f p_1^{b_1 - c_1} \ldots p_n^{b_n - c_n}$ can have no common prime factor, since for all i, either $a_i - c_i = 0$ or $b_i - c_i = 0$. Thus any common factor must be a unit.

* * *

A straightforward proof by induction shows that we may extend these results to n-tuples.

Lemma 11. Any n-tuple $(a_1, \ldots, a_n)$ from D has a GCD. If $d = \text{GCD}(a_1, \ldots, a_n)$ then $1 = \text{GCD}(a_1/d, \ldots, a_n/d)$.

Lemma 12. Let D be a UFD. If $u \mid ab$ and $\text{GCD}(u, a) = 1$ then $u \mid b$.

PROOF. Compare the factorization of ab with that of u. Since $(u, a) = 1$, no prime dividing u can appear in the prime factorization of a; hence each prime dividing u must occur, and at least as often, in the prime factorization of b.

* * *

Theorem 16. Let D be a UFD. Let Q be its quotient field. Let $f = a_0 + \cdots + a_n x^n \in D[x]$. If f has a nonzero root $u/v \in Q$ where $(u, v) = 1$, then $u \mid a_0$ and $v \mid a_n$.

PROOF. Suppose $f(u/v) = 0$. Then
$$0 = v^n f(u/v) = a_0 v^n + a_1 u v^{n-1} + \cdots + a_n u^n.$$
Hence
$$0 \equiv a_0 v^n \ (\text{mod } u)$$
and
$$0 \equiv a_n u^n \ (\text{mod } v).$$

Since $(u, v) = 1$, it follows that $u \mid a_0$ and $v \mid a_n$.

Example 1. The polynomial $x^3 + 4x + 3$ is irreducible over the rational numbers. First, if it is reducible it must have a rational zero by Corollary 2 of Theorem 11. Clearly, 0 is not a zero of the polynomial. By Theorem 16 the possibilities are ± 1 and ± 3. We test these; none are zeros.

The question of factorization in $D[x]$ when D is not a field is somewhat complicated because not every nonzero element of D is a unit. Thus, for example, $2x + 4$ is an irreducible polynomial in $\text{Ra}[x]$, but in $I[x]$ $2x + 4 = 2(x + 2)$ is reducible. The factors of a polynomial in $D[x]$, which belong to D, should intuitively cause no trouble in factoring a polynomial; and they do not. They do require, however, that the theorems be stated with care. To that end we introduce a few definitions.

Definition. Let D be a UFD. A polynomial $a_0 + a_1 x + \cdots + a_n x^n$ in $D[x]$ is called *primitive* if it is not a unit and if $a_0, a_1, \ldots, a_n$ have no common divisor other than units in D. We should notice that if f is irreducible in $D[x]$ then f is primitive.

Lemma 13. Let $f \in D[x]$. Then there exist $d \in D$ and a primitive polynomial $g \in D[x]$ such that $f = dg$. Moreover, if $f = dg = bh$, where g and h are primitive and d and b belong to D, then d and b are associates in D and g and h are associates in $D[x]$.

PROOF OF EXISTENCE. Let $a_0 + a_1 x + \cdots + a_n x^n$ and let $d = \text{GCD}(a_0, \ldots, a_n)$. Then $f = dg$ where $g = (a_0/d + \cdots + (a_n/d)x^n$ is primitive from Lemma 11.

PROOF OF UNIQUENESS. Suppose $f = dg = bh$ where $g = g_0 + g_1 x + \cdots + g_n x^n$ and $h = h_0 + h_1 x + \cdots + h_n x^n$ are primitive. Let $c = \text{GCD}(d, b)$. It follows that $dg_i = bh_i$ for all i and so $(d/c)g_i = (b/c)h_i$ for all i. Since $(d/c, b/c) = 1$ it follows from Lemma 12 that $(d/c) \mid h_i$ and $(b/c) \mid g_i$ for all i. Since g and h are primitive, however, it follows that $d/c = u$ and $b/c = v$ are units, so $d = cu$ and $b = cv$ are associates. It now follows that $ug = vh$; thus g and h are associates.

*   *   *

In view of the lemma all interesting factorization problems in $D[x]$ occur with primitive polynomials. In particular, note that if $f \in D[x]$ is primitive and reducible then $f = gh$, where both g and h are nonscalar polynomials.

Our next theorem is an extremely useful one. Consider the following problem similar to those seen in high school algebra texts: "Factor, if possible, $x^2 - 6x + 6$." It is not clear over what field the factorization is to be carried out, but usually the intended field is the rational numbers. The argument runs as follows: If $x^2 - 6x + 6 = (x - a)(x - b)$, then a and b must be positive, $ab = 6$ and $a + b = 6$. Hence a, b must be 1, 6 or 2, 3. Since $1 + 6 \neq 6 \neq 2 + 3$, the conclusion is that $x^2 - 6x + 6$ cannot be factored. We have really shown that $x^2 - 6x + 6$ is irreducible in $I[x]$, not in $\text{Ra}[x]$. Why limit ourselves to integers? There are many other rational numbers whose product is 6. Our next theorem tells us that considering integers for a and b suffices; if $x^2 - 6x + 6$ were reducible over the rationals, it would be reducible over the integers.

> **Theorem 17.** (*Gauss*). Let D be a UFD and let Q be its field of quotients. Let f be a nonscalar primitive polynomial in $D[x]$. f is reducible in $D[x]$ if and only if f is reducible in $Q[x]$.

PROOF. We identify D with the subring of Q under the natural mapping $d \to d/1$ of Theorem 4.1. Then $D[x]$ appears naturally as a subring of $Q[x]$. Thus if f is reducible in $D[x]$ it is, *a fortiori*, reducible in $Q[x]$.

Now let us suppose that f factors in $Q[x]$. We have then $f = gh$, where g and h are nonscalar polynomials. Now the coefficients in g have the form b/c where $b, c \in D$. Thus we may replace each coefficient in g with an equivalent one so that all coefficients have a common denominator. We can then factor out the common denominator and write $g = (1/s)g_1$ where g_1 is a polynomial in $D[x]$. Similarly, we write $h = (1/t)h_1$; $h_1 \in D[x]$. Next we factor out the GCD (in D) of all the coefficients of g_1 (call it u) and of h_1 (call it v). Then we have $gh = (uv/st)g_2 h_2$ where $g_2 \in D[x]$ and *there is no prime dividing each coefficient of g_2*. A similar statement holds for h_2. Finally we write $uv/st = y/z$ where $(y, z) = 1$; thus $f = gh = (y/z)g_2 h_2$, where f, g_2, and h_2 are all primitive polynomials in $D[x]$. It now suffices to prove that z is a unit, hence that $y/z \in D$ and so f is reducible in $D[x]$.

Suppose, to the contrary, that z is not a unit. There must be a prime dividing z, call it p. Since $(y, z) = 1$, in particular $p \nmid y$. We have

(1) $$zf = y g_2 h_2 \text{ with } z \equiv 0 \pmod{p}.$$

We now choose to consider the integral domain $D/\langle p \rangle = D^*$ and $D^*[x]$. The natural homomorphism $D \to D/\langle p \rangle = D^*$ induces a natural homomorphism $D[x] \to D^*[x]$. Equation (1) then becomes

(2) $$\bar{z}\bar{f} = \bar{y}\bar{g}_2\bar{h}_2.$$

Since $z \equiv 0 \pmod{p}$, it follows that $\bar{z} = \bar{0} \in D^*$. Thus (2) yields $\bar{0} = \bar{y}\bar{g}_2\bar{h}_2$. Now by Theorem 2.12, D^* is an integral domain and so, by Theorem 1, $D^*[x]$ is an integral domain. Since $p \nmid y$ we know $\bar{0} \neq \bar{y}$, hence $\bar{g}_2 = \bar{0}$ or $\bar{h}_2 = \bar{0}$ in $D^*[x]$. Let us suppose that $\bar{g}_2 = \bar{0}$ in $D^*[x]$. Since $\bar{g}_2$ is a polynomial with coefficients in D^*, $\bar{g}_2 = \bar{0}$ means that every coefficient is $\bar{0}$ in D^*, or that every coefficient of g_2, considered in $D[x]$, is divisible by p—contrary to the condition that g_2 is primitive. Hence no such p can exist, and z is a unit. The proof is complete.

*   *   *

Example 2. $x^4 + 3x + 1$ is irreducible over the rational numbers. First it has no linear factor since it has no rational zero (± 1 are the only possibilities). Thus if it factors, it must factor into the product of two quadratics with rational coefficients. By Theorem 17, it must then have quadratic factors with integral coefficients. Moreover, since the leading coefficient of $x^4 + 3x + 1$ is 1 and since it equals the product of the leading coefficients of the quadratic factors, they may be chosen to be 1. Hence

$$\begin{aligned}
x^4 + 3x + 1 &= (x^2 + ax + b)(x^2 + cx + d) \\
&= x^4 + (a + c)x^3 + (b + d + ac)x^2 + (bc + ad)x + bd.
\end{aligned}$$

Thus we must solve a system of equations *in integers*:

$$\begin{aligned}
a + c &= 0, \\
b + d + ac &= 0, \\
bc + ad &= 3, \\
bd &= 1.
\end{aligned}$$

Thus $b = d = 1$ or $b = d = -1$, while $a = -c$; so $ac = -a^2 = -(b + d) = \pm 2$. No integral solution exists.

Corollary 1. Let D be a UFD. If f is an irreducible polynomial of $D[x]$, then f is a prime in $D[x]$.

PROOF. We can assume $\deg(f) \geq 1$, else Lemma 8 applies. Let $f \mid gh$ in $D[x]$. We are to show $f \mid g$ or $f \mid h$ in $D[x]$. Let Q be the field of quotients of D; clearly $f \mid gh$ in $Q[x]$. As f is irreducible in $D[x]$, f is also irreducible in $Q[x]$, by Theorem 17. Hence f is a prime in $Q[x]$ and so $f \mid g$ or $f \mid h$ in $Q[x]$.

Suppose $f \mid g$. In $Q[x]$ we have $g = fr$ and, as in the proof of Theorem 17 and since f is primitive in $D[x]$, we must have $g = f \cdot (t/u)r_1$ where $t \in D$, $u \in D$, $(t, u) = 1$, and r_1 is a primitive polynomial of $D[x]$. It then follows from the proof of Theorem 17 that u is a unit and so $f \mid g$ in $D[x]$.

*   *   *

Theorem 18. If D is a UFD, then $D[x]$ is a UFD.

PROOF. Let $0 \neq f \in D[x]$ and suppose that f is not a unit of $D[x]$. We must prove both the existence and uniqueness of a factorization of f into irreducibles.

Existence. The proof is by induction on $\deg(f)$. If $\deg(f) = 0$ then $f \in D$ and so has a factorization. If $\deg(f) > 0$, by Lemma 13, we have $f = dg$ where $d \in D$ and g is a primitive polynomial of $D[x]$. Since $d \in D$, d has a factorization. If g is irreducible we have nothing more to prove. If g is reducible, since g is primitive, both its factors must be polynomials of lower degree, and so by induction these polynomials must have factorizations.

Uniqueness. Since Corollary 1 has shown that every irreducible of $D[x]$ is a prime, the proof may proceed just like the proof of unique factorization in the integers (Theorem 3.13) except that the induction is on the degree of the polynomial. We shall not repeat the details here.

Theorem 19 (*Eisenstein's Irreducibility Criterion*). Let D be a UFD and Q its field of quotients. Let $f = a_0 + a_1 x + \cdots + a_n x^n$ in $D[x]$. If there is a prime $p \in D$ such that p divides every coefficient except a_n and such that $p^2 \nmid a_0$, then f is irreducible in $Q[x]$.

PROOF. *Case* 1: f is a primitive polynomial of $D[x]$. By Theorem 17 it suffices to show that f is irreducible in $D[x]$. Let us suppose that $f = g \cdot h$ in $D[x]$ with

$$g = b_0 + b_1 x + \cdots + b_r x^r$$
and
$$h = c_0 + c_1 x + \cdots + c_s x^s.$$

Then $a_0 = b_0 c_0$ and, since p is a prime such that $p \mid a_0$ but $p^2 \nmid a_0$, we may suppose that $p \mid b_0$ and $p \nmid c_0$. Now, without loss of generality, we may suppose that $p \mid b_0, p \mid b_1, \ldots, p \mid b_{m-1}$ but $p \nmid b_m$. (It is conceivable that $m = r$.) Now consider the coefficient of x^m in f as it must arise in the product $g \cdot h$. We have $a_m = b_0 c_m + b_1 c_{m-1} + \cdots + b_{m-1} c_1 + b_m c_0$. Since $m \le r < r + s = n$, we have $p \mid a_m$. On the other side $p \mid b_0, \ldots, b_{m-1}$, and so $p \mid b_m c_0$. Since p is a prime, $p \mid b_m$ or $p \mid c_0$; either alternative is a contradiction.

Case 2: f is not a primitive polynomial of $D[x]$. By Lemma 13 we may write $f = dk$ where $d \in D$ and k is a primitive polynomial of $D[x]$. Let $k = k(x) = k_0 + k_1 x + \cdots + k_n x^n$. We have in D that $a_i = dk_i$ for all i and since $p \nmid a_n$ it follows that $p \nmid d$ and $p \nmid k_n$. However, since p is a prime,

$p \nmid d$, and $p \mid a_i$ for $0 \leq i < n$, we have $p \mid k_i$ for $0 \leq i < n$. Similarly $p^2 \nmid k_0$. Thus, by Case 1, $k = k(x)$ is an irreducible polynomial of $D[x]$, hence of $Q[x]$. Clearly, then, f is irreducible in $Q[x]$ for any proper factor of f must divide k (d is a unit in $Q[x]$)—a contradiction.

Example 3. $x^4 + 9x + 3$ is irreducible over the rationals. In view of the Gauss theorem it suffices to prove that $x^4 + 9x + 3$ is irreducible over the integers, a well-known UFD! Here 3 is a prime satisfying the conditions of Theorem 19. (On the other hand, note that while neither $9x^2 + 27$ nor $x^2 + 2x + 3$ satisfies the conditions of Theorem 19, each is irreducible over the rationals!)

Example 4. For any prime integer $p, f = (x^p - 1)/(x - 1) = x^{p-1} + \cdots + 1$ is irreducible over the rationals.

Eisenstein's criterion is not immediately applicable, but a simple trick makes it so. Consider the polynomial

$$g(x) = f(x + 1) = \frac{(x + 1)^p - 1}{(x + 1) - 1} = \frac{(x + 1)^p - 1}{x} = x^{p-1} + \cdots + p.$$

As a consequence of the binomial theorem it is easily seen that $g(x)$ satisfies the conditions for Theorem 19 with p in the role of the prime. (Again we must appeal to Theorem 17 to permit consideration of $I[x]$ instead of $Ra[x]$.) Now it remains to argue that any factorization of $f(x)$ would entail a factorization of $f(x + 1) = g(x)$. This is obvious, and so the irreducibility of $g(x)$ entails the irreducibility of $f(x)$.

It is not always an easy task to decide whether a given polynomial in $F[x]$ is irreducible. When F is the field of rational numbers, an algorithm of not too much practical value but still an interesting result is the object of Problem 5 in the next Exercise.

EXERCISE 5

1. Find all the irreducible polynomials of degree ≤ 3 over I_2.

2. Show that if $f(x) \in F[x]$ has degree n, then $x^n f(1/x)$ is a polynomial! (This polynomial is often called the *reverse* of $f(x)$. Why?) Show that $f(x)$ is reducible if and only if $g(x) = x^n f(1/x)$ is reducible. Is the mapping $f(x) \to x^n f(1/x)$ (where $n = \deg f$) an automorphism of $F[x]$?

3. Use Problem 2 to write another "Eisenstein's irreducibility criterion theorem."

4. Show that the trick employed in showing $(x^p - 1)/(x - 1)$ is irreducible is essentially the observation that $f(x) \to f(x + 1)$ is an automorphism of $F[x]$. Find as many automorphisms of $F[x]$ as you can. Contrast the cases where F is a field and where it is merely an integral domain.

5. Prove that in $R[x]$, where R is a commutative ring, $f(x) \mid g(x)$ implies $f(a) \mid g(a)$ for all $a \in R$. Formulate an algorithm for finding all factors of $f(x) \in I[x]$ using the observation above and the Lagrange interpolation theorem.

6. Let $f \in I[x]$. Show that if f is monic and irreducible in $I_p[x]$, f is irreducible in $I[x]$. Use this to show that $x^4 + 3x + 1$ is irreducible in $Ra[x]$.

7. Let G denote the Gaussian integers. Show that $x^4 - 2$ is irreducible in $G[x]$.

6.7. THE FIELD OF QUOTIENTS OF $R[x]$

If R is an integral domain, then so is $R[x]$, as we have seen. An important concept is the field of quotients of $R[x]$. A typical element is an equivalence class whose typical representative we may write as

$$\frac{f}{g} = \frac{a_0 + a_1 x + \cdots + a_n x^n}{b_0 + b_1 x + \cdots + b_m x^m}.$$

We shall refer to this field as the field of rational functions over R and denote it by $R(x)$. Note, however, that if R is a finite field this terminology for $R(x)$ is really inappropriate, since the polynomials differ from the polynomial functions of R into R.

Theorem 20. If R is an integral domain and Q_R is its field of quotients, then $Q_R(x) \cong R(x)$.

PROOF. Recall that $Q_R(x)$ is the field of quotients of $Q_R[x]$—the ring of polynomials with coefficients in Q_R—whereas $R(x)$ is the field of quotients of $R[x]$—the ring of polynomials in x with coefficients in R. The essential part of the proof is an identification of the elements in $Q_R(x)$ and $R(x)$. The identification begins with the identification which has already been made with R and a subring of Q_R and which identifies $a/1$ with a if $a \in R$. If $f \in Q_R(x)$ then $f = g(x)/h(x)$ where $g(x) = \sum r_i x^i$ and $h(x) = \sum s_j x^j$. Now $r_i = a_i/b_i$ and $s_j = c_j/d_j$ where a_i, b_i, c_j, $d_j \in R$. If $B = \prod b_i$ and $D = \prod d_j$ then $f = BDg(x)/BDh(x)$. But $BDg(x) = \sum \bar{r}_i x^i$ and $BDh(x) = \sum \bar{s}_j x^j$ where now $\bar{r}_i$ and $\bar{s}_j$ belong to R under the identification of R with the subring of Q_R. Thus every class of quotients in $Q_R(x)$ has a member which is a quotient of two polynomials in $R[x]$. Since equality of quotients $u(x)/v(x)$ and $u_1(x)/v_1(x)$ means $u(x)v_1(x) = u_1(x)v(x)$ in $Q_R(x)$ (or $R(x)$), it is clear that if $u(x)$, $v(x)$, $u_1(x)$, $v_1(x) \in R[x]$, then $u/v = u_1/v_1$ in $R(x)$ if and only if they are equal in $Q_R[x]$. Once again this makes use of the identification of $a/1$ and a. From this it follows that if we choose, as we may, from the class of quotients represented by f, an ordered pair $(\bar{h}, \bar{g})$, where $\bar{g}$ and $\bar{h} \in R[x]$, then a mapping $\varphi(f) = \bar{g}/\bar{h}$ is defined which is 1–1 and is clearly an isomorphism of $Q_R(x)$ onto $R(x)$.

* * *

6.8. POLYNOMIALS IN SEVERAL VARIABLES

It is an easy matter of applying our theorems about $R[x]$ to study polynomials of the form $x^2 + xy + y^2$ or $z^2 x + 2(x + y)x - 4zy^3$. The first may be regarded as a polynomial in y with coefficients in $R[x]$. This makes good sense, since $R_1 = R[x]$ is a ring and we are simply considering $R_1[y] = R[x, y]$. Similarly, the second polynomial is a polynomial in z with coefficients in $R[x, y]$. All such polynomials we denote by $R[x, y, z]$. More formally we can define these domains as follows. The definition is an inductive one.

Definition. Let R be an integral domain. Let $R^{(0)} = R$ and define inductively $R^{(n)} = R^{(n-1)}[x]$.

This definition says that an element f of $R^{(n)}$ is a sequence $f = (\hat{a}_0, \hat{a}_1, \dots)$ where $\hat{a}_i \in R^{(n-1)}$; so, if $n > 1$, $\hat{a}_i$ is yet another sequence. Our notational convention permits us to write $f = \sum \hat{a}_i x^i$ where $\hat{a}_i \in R^{(n-1)}$. "x" is an overworked symbol, for we might be tempted to write, since $R^{(n-1)} = R^{(n-2)}[x]$, that $\hat{a}_i = \sum \bar{a}_{ij} x^j$ where $\bar{a}_{ij} \in R^{(n-2)}$ and it would certainly be incorrect to identify these two uses of the symbol "x." The situation is relieved by the next theorem.

Theorem 21. In $R^{(n)}$ there exists a chain of subrings $R_n = R^{(n)} \supset R_{n-1} \supset R_{n-2} \supset \cdots \supset R_1 \supset R_0$ such that $R_i \cong R^{(i)}$, and there exist elements $x_i \in R_i$, $1 \le i \le n$ such that every $f \in R^{(n)}$ has a unique representation in the form

$$f = \sum a_{i_1 \dots i_n} x_1^{i_1} \dots x_n^{i_n} \text{ where } a_{i_1 \dots i_n} \in R_0.$$

PROOF. Naturally the proof is by an induction on n. There is nothing to prove for $n = 0$, while for $n = 1$ this is an old result; $x_1 = (0, 1, 0, \dots)$.

Since $R^{(n)} = R^{(n-1)}[x]$ we know that in $R^{(n)}$ the subring of "scalar" polynomials $(\hat{a}, \hat{0}, \dots)$ is isomorphic with $R^{(n-1)}$ under the isomorphism $\varphi(\hat{a}, \hat{0}, \dots) = \hat{a}$. We define $R_{n-1} \cong R^{(n-1)}$ and we define $x_n = (\hat{0}, \hat{1}, \hat{0}, \dots)$ where of course $\hat{0}$ and $\hat{1}$ are the additive and multiplicative identities of $R^{(n-1)}$. We know that we may write

$$(*) \qquad f = \sum \hat{a}_i x_n^i \text{ where } \hat{a}_i = (\hat{a}_i, \hat{0}, \dots) \in R_{n-1}$$

and indeed we employed the symbol "$\hat{a}_i$" in two different roles to emphasize the identification of R_{n-1} and $R^{(n-1)}$. Now by induction $R^{(n-1)}$ has subrings $\hat{R}_{n-2}, \dots, \hat{R}_1, \hat{R}_0$ with $\hat{R}_i \cong R^{(i)}$ and so R_{n-1} will have isomorphic copies of these rings. Let R_i be the image of $\hat{R}_i$ in the isomorphism φ^{-1}. (Figure 3 pictures these relations.) Moreover, there exist $\hat{x}_1, \dots, \hat{x}_{n-1}$ in $R^{(n-1)}$ such that for $\hat{a} \in R^{(n-1)}$ we have $\hat{a} = \sum \hat{a}_{i_1 \dots i_{n-1}} \hat{x}_1^{i_1} \dots \hat{x}_{n-1}^{i_{n-1}}$ with $\hat{a}_{i_1 \dots i_{n-1}} \in \hat{R}_0 \cong R$. Define $x_i = \varphi^{-1}(\hat{x}_i)$ and $a = \varphi^{-1}(\hat{a})$ if $\hat{a} \in \hat{R}_0$. Thus if we replace the dummy index i in $(*)$ by the index i_n we may write $f = \sum \hat{a}_{i_n} x_n^{i_n}$ with $\hat{a}_{i_n} \in R_{n-1}$; thus, by induction and the isomorphism φ^{-1}, we have $\hat{a}_{i_n} = \sum a_{i_1 \dots i_{n-1} i_n} x_1^{i_1} \dots x_n^{i_n}$, where $a_{i_1 \dots i_n} \in R_0$ and $x_i \in R_i$. So much for the existence.

The uniqueness is proved in much the same way. If $\bar{0} = \sum a_{i_1 \dots i_n} x_1^{i_1} \dots x_n^{i_n}$

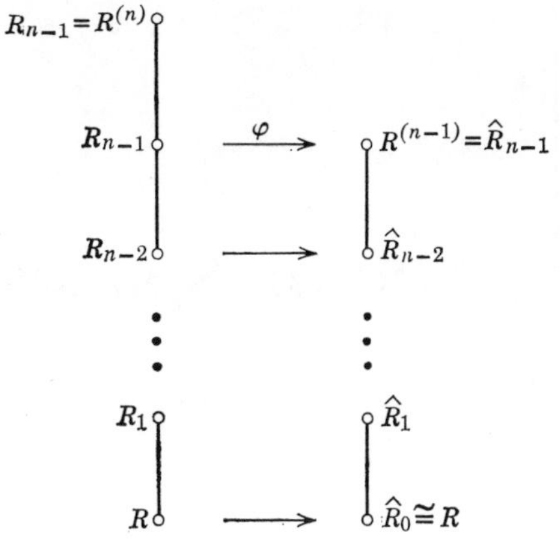

Figure 3

is the zero polynomial in $R^{(n)}$, then for each i_n we just have that $\hat{0} = \hat{a}_{i_n} = \sum \hat{a}_{i_1 \ldots i_n} \hat{x}_{n-1}^{i_{n-1}} \ldots \hat{x}_{n-1}^{i_{n-1}}$ is the zero polynomial in $R^{(n-1)}$. Hence by induction $a_{i_1 \ldots i_n} = 0$ for all coefficients.

$$* \quad * \quad *$$

In view of this theorem it is common terminology to say that the elements $x_1, \ldots, x_n$ are n distinct indeterminates over R, and to write $R^{(n)} = R[x_1, \ldots, x_n]$. We say that $R[x_1, \ldots, x_n]$ is the result of adjoining n distinct indeterminates to R. We understand that $x_1, \ldots, x_n$ are symbols that have not been used to denote elements in R. We have proved that $R[x_1, \ldots, x_n] = R[x_1, \ldots, x_{n-1}][x_n]$. Hereafter we shall adopt this informal terminology.

From repeated applications of Theorem 18 we see that if R is a UFD, then so are $R[x_1]$, $R[x_1, x_2]$, and so on, to include $R[x_1, \ldots, x_n]$. In particular the theorems of Gauss and Eisenstein hold.

EXERCISE 6

1. Show that the mapping $x \to (ax + b)/(cx + d)$ where $ad - bc \neq 0$ generates an automorphism of $F(x)$.

2. In $Ra[x, y]$, factor $x^3 - y^3$ into irreducible factors. Be sure to prove the factors *are* irreducible.

3. Show that $R[x, y]$ and $R[y, x]$ are isomorphic.

SUPPLEMENTARY READING

B. L. van der Waerden, *Modern Algebra*, vol. 1 (F. Blum translator), New York: Ungar (1949).

J. H. Wahab, Irreducibility of polynomials, *American Mathematical Monthly*, **68** (1961), 366–367.

7 | Vector Spaces

7.1. INTRODUCTION

With this chapter the introduction of the basic algebraic systems, groups, rings, fields, and vector spaces will be complete. The subsequent chapters will develop special features of these theories of particular importance in many areas of mathematics and its applications.

The nature of a vector space differs from those of the previous systems we have discussed in that an auxiliary system is present—a field, which is a set of operators on the vector space. (It would be well to review this definition in Chapter 0.) It is important to appreciate at the outset that the idea of a vector space is the algebraic abstraction and generalization of the cartesian coordinate system introduced into the euclidean plane—that is, a generalization of analytic geometry. In analytic geometry ordered pairs of real numbers are used to represent points. In this way geometric questions may be studied algebraically and conversely. In a similar manner such physical concepts as force at a point, velocity, and acceleration may be interpreted as ordered sets of numbers. These quantities, or "vectors" are "added" or "subtracted" by adding or subtracting the corresponding numbers in the ordered sets. Thus Figure 1 is a common one in many physics texts. In addition a "scalar multiplication" is introduced whereby a vector $\vec{v}$ is multiplied by a number c to form $c\vec{v}$. If $\vec{v}$ is represented by (v_1, v_2) then $c\vec{v}$ is represented by (cv_1, cv_2); physically the vector has changed only by a factor in its magnitude, if $c \geq 0$.

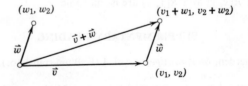

Figure 1

The features important to an algebraic generalization of these notions are the operation of adding vectors (vector addition) and multiplying a vector by a number (scalar multiplication).

7.2. DEFINITIONS AND EXAMPLES

Definition An abelian group $\langle V, \dot{+} \rangle$ is called a vector space over a field $\langle F, +, \cdot \rangle$ by a scalar multiplication (∗) if and only if F is a set of operators for V by (∗) such that for all $a, b \in F$ and $v, w \in V$ the following conditions hold:

$$\begin{cases} V1. & a * (v \dot{+} w) = (a * v) \dot{+} (a * w), \\ V2. & (a + b) * v = (a * v) \dot{+} (b * v), \\ V3. & (a \cdot b) * v = a * (b * v), \\ V4. & 1 * v = v. \end{cases}$$

[handwritten annotations:] $a(v+w)=av+aw$; $(a+b)v = av+bv$; $(a\cdot b)v = a(bv)$; $1\cdot v = 1$

A vector space consists of a set of elements V and an operation ($\dot{+}$) such that $\langle V, \dot{+} \rangle$ is an abelian group, a field $\langle F, +, \cdot \rangle$, and a mapping (∗): $F \times V \to V$. The conditions $V1$–$V4$ relate the operations ($\dot{+}$), ($+$), ($\cdot$), and (∗). For emphasis we shall sometimes write $\langle V, \dot{+}, F, * \rangle$ to indicate that V is a vector space over F by (∗).

Note that two vector spaces $\langle V, \dot{+}, F, * \rangle$ and $\langle W, \oplus, G, \circledast \rangle$ are the same if and only if V and W are the same sets, F and G are the same fields, the operations ($\dot{+}$) and ($\oplus$) are the same, and the scalar multiplications (∗) and ($\circledast$) are the same. In the following examples we shall see that a change in any one of these components results in a change in the vector space.

We shall usually refer to the elements of V as *vectors*, and here in the first section we shall often put an arrow above a symbol to emphasize that the symbol denotes a vector. In particular we use $\vec{0}$ to denote the identity of V. We shall usually refer to the elements of F as *scalars*. It is common usage to employ the symbol ($+$) both for addition in F and for the group operation in V. You will probably never confuse the two operations! We shall drop the symbol (∗) in favor of juxtaposition to denote scalar multiplication. Thus axiom $V1$ becomes $a(\vec{v} + \vec{w}) = a\vec{v} + a\vec{w}$.

One of the implications of condition $V4$ is to exclude the trivial definition of scalar multiplication $a\vec{v} = \vec{0}$ for all $a \in F$ and $\vec{v} \in V$, which would make any abelian group a vector space over every field.

Example 1 (*Classic Example*). For $\langle V, \dot{+} \rangle$ we take the direct product of the additive group of real numbers with itself; $V = \text{Re} \times \text{Re}$. For F we take Re. Scalar multiplication is defined

$$r(a, b) = (ra, rb) \qquad (r \in \text{Re}).$$

Conditions $V1$–$V4$ are easily verified.

Example 2. For $\langle V, + \rangle$ we take the same group Re $\times$ Re as in Example 1. For F we take Ra, the rational numbers. Scalar multiplication is defined just as in Example 1 except that $r \in$ Ra. Conditions $V1$–$V4$ hold by the same reasoning as in Example 1. Note that $\langle V, +, \text{Re}, * \rangle \neq \langle V, +, \text{Ra}, * \rangle$.

Example 3. For $\langle V, + \rangle$ we take the direct product of the additive group of complex numbers with itself: $V = C \times C$. For F we take C. Scalar multiplication is defined, as in Example 1, $c(a, b) = (ca, cb)$ for $c \in C$. As in Example 1, $V1$–$V4$ are readily verified.

Example 4. We take for $\langle V, + \rangle$ the same group as in Example 3 and again let $F = C$. However scalar multiplication is now defined $c(a, b) = (\bar{c}a, \bar{c}b)$ where $c \in C$, and $\bar{c}$ denotes the complex conjugate of c.

Now we had better verify the conditions $V1$–$V4$. Let $\vec{v} = (a, b)$ $\vec{w} = (c, d)$ and $r, s \in C$.

$V1$. $r(\vec{v} + \vec{w}) = r(a + c, b + d) = (\bar{r}(a + c), \bar{r}(b + d))$ while
 $r\vec{v} + r\vec{w} = (\bar{r}a, \bar{r}b) + (\bar{r}c, \bar{r}d) = (\bar{r}a + \bar{r}c, \bar{r}b + \bar{r}d)$;

thus $V1$ holds by the distributive law in C. Axiom $V2$ has a similar verification, which we can omit. Axiom $V4$ holds since $\bar{1} = 1$.

$V3$. $(rs)\vec{v} = rs(a, b) = (\overline{rs}a, \overline{rs}b)$ while
 $r(s\vec{v}) = r(\bar{s}a, \bar{s}b) = (\bar{r}(\bar{s}a), \bar{r}(\bar{s}b))$;

thus $V3$ holds since $\overline{rs} = \bar{r}\bar{s}$ and multiplication is associative in C.

Note that the vector spaces of Examples 3 and 4 are different because of the scalar multiplication, even though the vector group and the field are the same.

Example 5 (*Generalization of Example 1*). For F take any field. For V take the set of all ordered n-tuples of elements in F. Here, n may be any positive integer which is, of course, held fixed. Thus $V = \{(a_1, \ldots, a_n) : a_i \in F\}$.

Vector addition: $(a_1, \ldots, a_n) + (b_1, \ldots, b_n) = (a_1 + b_1, \ldots, a_n + b_n)$.

Scalar multiplication: $a(b_1, \ldots, b_n) = (ab_1, \ldots, ab_n)$.

The verification of the axioms is handled just as in the previous example. This vector space shall be denoted $V_n(F)$.

Example 5 is, of course, a whole class of examples. Just how important is this class of examples is the content of Theorem 8, which says that under a fairly general hypothesis, any vector space may be represented by (is isomorphic to) a member of this class of examples.

Example 6 (*Generalization of Example 5*). For F, take any field. For V, take the set of all infinite sequences from F. $\vec{v} = (a_1, a_2, \ldots)$. Vector addition and scalar multiplication are to be performed componentwise. This vector space shall be denoted $V_\infty(F)$.

Example 7 (*Generalization of Example 6*). For F, take any field. For V, take the set of functions f from F into F.

Vector addition: $f + g$ is the function whose value at $a \in F$ is $f(a) + g(a)$. In brief $(f + g)(a) = f(a) + g(a)$.

Scalar multiplication: af is the function whose value at $b \in F$ is $a(f(b))$. In brief $(af)(b) = a(f(b))$.

Example 8. Let F be any field and let E be an extension of F; that is, F is a subfield of E. E is a vector space over F if we use F as the field of scalars and define vector addition just as addition in E and scalar multiplication as multiplication in E. The identities in axioms $V3$ and $V4$ are now simply statements of identities holding in any field.

While the class of spaces mentioned in Example 8 may seem puny in comparison to those of Example 7, nevertheless this example is the chief reason for including a chapter on vector spaces in this book! The vector space concept is a powerful tool in later chapters.

As members of this class we have the complex numbers over the reals, the complex numbers over the rationals, the reals over the rationals, and in general any field over its prime subfield. As a particular example consider $\{a + b\sqrt{2} : a, b \in \text{Ra}\}$ as a field extension of the rationals.

Example 9. Let $\langle D, +, \cdot \rangle$ be a division ring and F a subring that is a field. D is a vector space, $\langle D, +, F, \cdot \rangle$ over F by the scalar multiplication which is the multiplication in D. As in Example 8, vector addition is the addition in D. These vector spaces and those of Example 8 are very much alike because the commutativity of the multiplication of elements in D or E plays no role in the vector space concepts; hence the verification of the axioms will be the same.

Some elementary properties must be established early:

> **Theorem 1.** Let V be a vector space over F. For all $a \in F$ and $\vec{v} \in V$, $\vec{0} = 0 \cdot \vec{v} = a\vec{0}$. Conversely, if $a \neq 0$ and $a\vec{v} = \vec{0}$, then $\vec{v} = \vec{0}$. Moreover, $-\vec{v} = (-1)\vec{v}$.

PROOF. We calculate using $V2$:

$$0\vec{v} + 0\vec{v} = (0 + 0)\vec{v} = 0\vec{v}$$

and

$$a\vec{0} + a\vec{0} = a(\vec{0} + \vec{0}) = a\vec{0}.$$

By cancellation $0\vec{v}$ and $a\vec{0}$ are $\vec{0}$. If $a \neq 0$ and $a\vec{v} = \vec{0}$, then $\vec{0} = (1/a)\vec{0} = (1/a)(a\vec{v}) = (a/a)\vec{v} = 1\vec{v} = \vec{v}$. Finally we calculate $\vec{0} = 0\vec{v} = [1 + (-1)]\vec{v} = 1\vec{v} + (-1)\vec{v} = \vec{v} + (-1)\vec{v}$. Hence the inverse of $\vec{v}$ must be $(-1)\vec{v}$.

EXERCISE 1

1. Show that the complex numbers are members of the class of vector spaces given in Examples 1 and 8.

2. If F is a finite field with q elements, how many elements are there in $V_n(F)$? Construct a vector space of exactly four elements. Explicitly give the addition and scalar multiplication tables.

3. Show that the example constructed in Problem 2 can be made into a field by constructing a multiplication table for the vectors.

4. Using a natural definition for vector addition and scalar multiplication, which of the following are vector spaces?

  (a) The ring of polynomials $F[x]$ in a single indeterminate over a field F.

  (b) The set of all ordered pairs of integers.

  (c) The set of all sequences $(a_1, a_2, \ldots)$ of rational numbers in which at least one of the a_i is zero.

  (d) Let S be any subset of the interval $[0, 1]$. Let V be the set of all the real valued continuous functions defined on $[0, 1]$ such that whenever $x_1, x_2 \in S$ then $f(x_1) = f(x_2)$.

  (e) Let V be the set of ordered pairs of real numbers (b, c). Define addition componentwise, and scalar multiplication by $a(b, c) = (0, ac)$.

  (f) Let V be the set of ordered pairs of real numbers (b, c). Define addition and scalar multiplication by

$$(b, c) + (e, f) = (0, c + f)$$
$$a(b, c) = (ab, ac).$$

5. Let V be a vector space over a field F. Let λ be an automorphism of F. Let (*) be the operation defined by $a * v = \lambda(a)v$ for all $a \in F$ and all $v \in V$. Show that V is a vector space over F by (*).

7.3. SUBSPACES

As in any algebraic system, the subsets that have the same algebraic structure as the parent system are important. For vector spaces these subsets, naturally called subspaces, are a powerful tool for the study of the whole space.

Definition. Let V be a vector space over F by a scalar multiplication (*). A subgroup S of V is called a subspace of V if S is a vector space over F by the scalar multiplication defined by restricting (*) to $F \times S$.

It is useful to note that all that is required to verify that a subset S is a subspace is to show that S is closed under addition and that if $a \in F$ and $w \in S$ then $aw \in S$ (we say that S is closed under scalar multiplication). Thus, under these closure properties, we have that conditions V1–V3 hold in S since they hold in V. Theorem 1 shows that if S is closed under scalar multiplication and if $v \in S$, then $(-1)v = -v \in S$, thus if v and $w \in S$ it follows that $v - w \in S$, hence $\langle S, + \rangle$ is a subgroup of $\langle V, + \rangle$. Finally F is an operator set for S since S is closed under scalar multiplication.

Example 10. The set $\{0\}$ and V are subspaces of any vector space V.

Example 11. As a subspace of $V_\infty(F)$ consider the set of all sequences $(a_1, a_2, \ldots)$ where $a_i \in F$ and all but a finite number of the a_i are equal to 0. Clearly this is closed under addition and scalar multiplication.

Example 12. Let S be the set of continuous functions from Re into Re. S is a subspace of the vector space of all functions from Re into Re described in Example 7.

Example 13. Let T be the set of polynomial functions from Re into Re. T is a subspace of the vector space S of Example 12.

Example 14. Let $P = \{v_1, \ldots, v_n, \ldots\}$ be any collection of vectors in a vector space V over a field F. Let S be the set of all *finite* linear combinations of the form $\sum_{i=1}^m a_i v_i$ where $a_i \in F$. S is a subspace of V, which we say is generated or spanned by P. Closure under addition and scalar multiplication is built into the definition.

The subspaces described in this example constitutes an extremely important class. The concept of a generating set is very useful—so useful that it rates a formal definition.

Definition. Let S be a subspace of V, a vector space over F. A set P of vectors $\{v_1, \ldots\} = P$ is said to *span* S if $P \subseteq S$, and for all $w \in S$ there is a finite number, say $v_1, \ldots, v_m$, of vectors in P and scalars $a_1, \ldots, a_m \in F$ such that

$$w = \sum_{i=1}^m a_i v_i.$$

The space S is said to be spanned by P. Example 14 shows that any set of vectors span some subspace—indeed the very subspace they generate, which is equivalently the smallest subspace containing the set.

> **Theorem 2.** If S and T are subspaces of a vector space V over a field F, then the set intersection $S \cap T$ is a subspace of V. More generally, if $\mathcal{S}$ is any set of subspaces S of V then the set intersection $\bigcap \mathcal{S}$ is a subspace of V.

PROOF. The closure properties are preserved under set intersection.

> **Theorem 3.** Let S and T be two subspaces of a vector space V over a field F. Let R be the subspace spanned by the set union of S and T. Then R is contained in any subspace containing both S and T. Moreover, any vector in R may be expressed as a sum of a vector in S and in T.

PROOF. Since any subspace containing the set union $S \cup T$ must be closed under addition and scalar multiplication it must contain any finite sum of vectors from S and T. This means that R is a subset of any subspace containing both S and T. Now since any vector in R is the sum of vectors in S and T, we may use the commutative and associative laws to group together the summands from S and from T.

* * *

Notation. In analogy with our notation from groups and rings we shall denote the subspace spanned by two subspaces S and T by $S \vee T$, called the *join of* S and T. Note that in general $S \vee T \neq S \cup T$. Many authors write $S + T$ for $S \vee T$ since $S \vee T = \{s + t : s \in S \text{ and } t \in T\}$ as we have shown.

EXERCISE 2

1. Give a different proof for Theorem 3 by showing first that $Q = \{s + t : s \in S, t \in T\}$ is a subspace of V and then that $Q = R$.

2. Show that if S and T are subspaces then $S \cup T = S \vee T$ is a subspace if and only if $S \subseteq T$ or $T \subseteq S$.

3. If S is a subspace of T and T is a subspace of V, show that S is a subspace of V.

4. Describe the subspace spanned by a single vector.

5. Let S and T be subspaces of V. Show that the representation of vector in $S \vee T$ in the form $s + t$ where $s \in S$ and $t \in T$ is unique if and only if $S \cap T = \{0\}$.

7.4. DEPENDENCE AND BASIS

The purpose of this section is to show that vector spaces can be catalogued by the least cardinal number of a set of vectors which span the vector space. This cardinal number is called the dimension of the vector space, and any two vector spaces over the same field with the same dimension are isomorphic. We shall prove this theorem only in the finite dimensional case.

The notion of *independence* transcends the role it plays in the proof of this property of the cardinality of a minimal spanning subset of vectors. We shall use the "independence" of a set of vectors more often then we use the numerical properties of dimension of a vector space.

Definition. Let V be a vector space over a field F. A finite set of vectors $\{v_1, \ldots, v_m\}$ is said to be (linearly) *dependent over* F if there exist elements $a_1, \ldots, a_m \in F$ such that $\sum_{i=1}^{m} a_i v_i = 0 \in V$ and for some i, $a_i \neq 0 \in F$.

An infinite set of vectors shall be called dependent if some finite subset of them is dependent.

A set of vectors $\{v_1, \ldots\}$ will be called (linearly) *independent over* F if they are not dependent.

Some remarks are in order. If we did not specify that some $a_i \neq 0$, then any set of vectors would be dependent. If a set S is dependent, then any set of vectors containing S is dependent; $\{\vec{0}\}$ is a dependent set and so any set containing $\vec{0}$ is dependent. Finally, it is but an exercise of logic to see that if $S = (v_1, \ldots)$ is independent, then for every finite subset of S, say $(w_1, \ldots, w_n) \subseteq S$, it is true that $\sum a_i w_i \neq 0$ if some $a_i \neq 0$.

Definition. A subset $U = \{u_1, \ldots\}$ of a vector space V over a field F is called a *basis* for V over F if V is spanned by U and U is independent.

Example 15. Consider $V_n(F)$. Let $\varepsilon_1 = (1, 0, \ldots, 0)$, $\varepsilon_2 = (0, 1, 0, \ldots, 0)$; in general ε_i is the vector with 1 in coordinate position i and 0 elsewhere. $U = \{\varepsilon_1, \ldots, \varepsilon_n\}$ is a basis. First, if $v = (v_1, \ldots, v_n)$, then clearly $v = v_1 \varepsilon_1 + \cdots + v_n \varepsilon_n$ so that U spans V. Similarly $\sum a_i \varepsilon_i = (a_1, \ldots, a_n)$, so that if $\sum a_i \varepsilon_i = 0$, then $a_i = 0$ for all i. Thus U is independent.

Example 16. Consider $V_2(F)$. Let $u_1 = (1, 1)$, $u_2 = (1, 0)$. Then $U = \{u_1, u_2\}$ is a basis for $V_2(F)$. To show that U spans the space we need only show that $(0, 1)$ belongs to the space spanned by U since we know that $\{(0, 1), (1, 0)\}$ spans the space. Now $(0, 1) = u_1 - u_2$. Furthermore, $a_1 u_1 + a_2 u_2 = (a_1 + a_2, a_2)$. Thus, if $a_1 u_1 + a_2 u_2 = 0$, then $a_2 = 0$ and hence $a_1 = 0$. For these reasons $\{u_1, u_2\}$ is a basis.

The next theorem that should be proved is one which asserts the existence of a basis for every vector space. We could give a proof that would seem plausible, however, to make it completely correct, we should have to rely on a strong axiom of set theory. For this reason we shall presently introduce an additional axiom for the vector spaces we study. Before doing so, we shall prove a theorem about bases that will give some insight to the problem of the existence of a basis.

> **Theorem 4.** Let V be a vector space over a field F. Let $U = \{u_1, u_2, \ldots\}$ be an independent set of vectors in V which is *maximal* in the sense that if S is any subset of V that properly contains U, then S is dependent. Under this condition U is a basis for V.

PROOF. We need only prove that U spans V. Let $v \in V$. If $v \in U$ we need do no more. If $v \notin U$, consider the set $S = U \cup \{v\}$. Since this set properly contains U it is dependent and hence there is a finite subset of S, which we may suppose includes v, say, $\{v, u_1, \ldots, u_n\}$, and scalars $a_0, a_1, \ldots, a_n \in F$ not all zero such that $a_0 v + a_1 u_1 + \cdots + a_n u_n = 0$. If $a_0 = 0$, then a dependence exists within U, contrary to hypothesis. Thus $v = -1/a_0(a_1 u_1 + \ldots + a_n u_n)$, and so the proof is complete.

* * *

In light of this theorem, to show the existence of a basis, we need "only" show that such a maximal independent set of vectors exists. To do so we may form the set of all independent subsets of vectors in V and partially order this set by set inclusion. From this partially ordered set we then "select" an element, that is, an independent set, at the "top" of this partially ordered set. The trouble is that not every partially ordered set has a maximal element and if it has one, it need not be unique. As an example of a partial ordered set without a maximal element consider the set of all finite subsets of the integers. To show that the partially ordered set we are now considering has a maximal element we need a principle from set theory. A form of this principle guarantees the existence of maximal elements under rather weak conditions.

Maximal Principle. If P is a partially ordered set in which every totally ordered subset has an upper bound, then P has a maximal element.

It is not difficult to show that the partially ordered set we are considering satisfies the hypothesis of the maximal principle. We argue as follows: Let $\mathscr{C}$ be a chain in the partially ordered set. Remember that an element of $\mathscr{C}$ is an independent subset of vectors in V. Let C be the set union of all the subsets that are elements in $\mathscr{C}$; $C = \bigcup \{S : S \in \mathscr{C}\}$. C is easily seen to be an independent set, hence it is upper bound for the chain $\mathscr{C}$. The maximal principle then assures us that there is a maximal independent set of vectors which, by Theorem 4, is a basis.

Under some circumstances we need not appeal to this maximal principle. It may be possible in a particular case to prove that the partially ordered set of independent sets of vectors has a maximal element; or, it may be possible to construct a basis in the following way:

Select a nonzero vector, u_1. If u_1 spans V, then $\{u_1\}$ is a basis. If not, select another vector u_2 not in the space spanned by $\{u_1\}$. Then $\{u_1, u_2\}$ is independent and either it spans all of V or it does not. If it does not, select any vector, u_3 in V but not in the space spanned by $\{u_1, u_2\}$. If V is spanned by $\{u_1, u_2, u_3\}$ we have a basis. Continue in this way; if the process stops in a finite number of steps we have our basis. Even if the process does not end in a finite number of steps it may be possible to show that the infinite set $\{u_1, u_2, \ldots\}$ formed in this way spans V, in which case we have a basis. If neither of these fortuitous events obtains a basis then we must proceed in another way.

We shall dodge the whole problem by assuming another axiom for vector spaces.

$V5$. Every vector space over a field possesses a basis over that field.

Now we continue with our task of defining the dimension of a vector space. The next theorem attributed to E. Steinitz (1871–1928) is an extremely useful one.

> **Theorem 5.** (*Steinitz Replacement Theorem*). Let $W = \{w_1, w_2, \ldots\}$
> be a subset of a vector space V. Let S be the space spanned by W. If
> $\{v_1, \ldots, v_k\}$ is an independent set of vectors in S then there exist k of

the w's, say $w_1, \ldots, w_k$ which may be replaced by $v_1, \ldots, v_k$ such that the v's and the remaining w's, if any, span S. In particular the set W contains at least k vectors.

PROOF (*Induction on* k). If $k = 1$, then we must have $v_1 = a_1 w_1 + \cdots + a_n w_n$ for some n and coefficients $a_1, \ldots, a_n$. Not all the a_i are zero, or else $v_1 = 0$, contrary to the independence hypothesis. Let us suppose for ease of notation that $a_1 \neq 0$. Thus $w_1 = 1/a_1[v_1 - (a_2 w_2 + \cdots + a_n w_n)]$, and so w_1 belongs to the space spanned by $\{v, w_2, \ldots\}$. Clearly then $\{w_1, w_2, \ldots\}$ and $\{v, w_2, \ldots\}$ span the same space.

The induction hypothesis is to assume the theorem for any set of fewer than k independent vectors. Thus we may assume that $\{w_1, \ldots\}$ has more than $k - 1$ vectors and that $\{v_1, \ldots, v_{k-1}, w_k, \ldots\}$ span S. Now, since $v_k \in S$, we have

$$v_k = a_1 v_1 + \cdots + a_{k-1} v_{k-1} + b_k w_k + \cdots + b_m w_m.$$

If all the b_i are zero, we would have to conclude that $\{v_1, \ldots, v_k\}$ were linearly dependent. Thus it must be that for some i, $b_i \neq 0$. Again for ease of notation, suppose that $b_k w_k \neq 0$, and so

$$w_k = 1/b_k[v_k - (a_1 v_1 + \cdots + a_{k-1} v_{k-1} + b_{k+1} w_{k+1} + \cdots + b_m w_m)].$$

Consequently $\{v_1, \ldots, v_{k-1}, w_k, w_{k+1}, \ldots\}$ and $\{v_1, \ldots, v_k, w_{k+1}, \ldots\}$ span the same space.

Corollary 1. Let $s_1, \ldots, s_n$ be n linearly independent vectors and let S be the space they span. Let $t_1, \ldots, t_p$ also span S. Then

1. $n \leq p$.
2. $n = p$ if and only if $t_1, \ldots, t_p$ are independent.
3. Any basis for S has exactly n elements.

PROOF. 1. By the Steinitz replacement theorem, with s_i in the role of v_i and t_i in the role of w_i, $n \leq p$ follows.

2. If $t_1, \ldots, t_p$ are linearly independent then we may interchange the role of the vectors s_i and t_i and by 1 conclude $p \leq n$. Conversely if $n = p$ and if $t_1, \ldots, t_p$ are dependent we could express some t_j as a linear combination of the remaining $(p - 1)$ vectors and so we would have shown that some $(p - 1)$ vectors span S. But now, from the Steinitz theorem, using s_i in the role of v_i we would have that $n \leq p - 1$—a contradiction of $n = p$.

3. This follows from definition of a basis and 2.

* * *

The important corollary of the Steinitz theorem for those vector spaces possessing a finite basis is (3) that any two bases have the same cardinality. This is true in general for any vector space, but the proof requires more set theory than is at our disposal. Granting this we can make the following definition.

Definition. The *dimension* of a vector space V over a field F is the cardinal number of a basis for V over F. We shall denote this number by dim (V). We agree to define dim $(\vec{0}) = 0$ and we note that dim $V = 0$ if and only if $V = \{0\}$.

Another important corollary of Theorem 4 and the maximal principle is that any linearly independent set of vectors is either a basis or vectors may be added to it to form a basis. We say that we *extend* the independent set to a basis. From our axiom $V5$ and the Steinitz theorem we prove the finite version.

Theorem 6. Let $\{v_1, \ldots, v_k\}$ be a linearly independent set of vectors in V. There exist vectors $w_{k+1}, \ldots$ so that $\{v_1, \ldots, v_k, w_{k+1}, \ldots\}$ is a basis for V.

PROOF. By axiom $V5$ a basis exists $\{u_1, \ldots\}$. Now apply the Steinitz theorem.

* * *

Corollary. If S is a subspace of a finite dimensional vector space T then dim $(S) \leq$ dim (T).

PROOF. Since any basis for S may be extended to a basis for T, it is clear that the number of elements in a basis for S is at most as large as the number of elements in the basis for T.

* * *

This corollary is true even if dim (T) is not finite, but we shall not prove this.

Theorem 7. Let $\{u_1, u_2, \ldots\}$ be a basis for a vector space V over a field F. Then every element v in V can be expressed in a unique way:

$$v = \sum_{i=1}^{m} c_i u_i \qquad (c_i \in F; \quad m \text{ depends on } v).$$

PROOF. The existence of such a sum for v is a part of the definition of a basis. The unicity follows from the independence of the basis vectors, for suppose $\sum_{i=1}^{m} c_i u_i = \sum_{i=1}^{n} d_i u_i$. Since only a finite number of basis vectors are involved we may suppose that $m = n$, by adding some terms with 0 coefficients. But then $0 = \sum_{i=1}^{m} (c_i - d_i) u_i$ and from the independence we conclude that $c_i = d_i$ for all i. The coefficients c_i are called the *coordinates* of v with respect to the basis $\{u_1, u_2, \ldots\}$.

* * *

When V has a finite basis, a result of this theorem is the important representation we promised earlier.

Theorem 8. Let V be a vector space of dimension n over a field F. V is isomorphic with $V_n(F)$.

PROOF. Let $\{u_1, \ldots, u_n\}$ be a basis for V. Each element $v \in V$ has a unique form, $v = \sum_{i=1}^{n} c_i u_0$. Thus the mapping $\Phi : V \to V_n(F)$ defined by $\Phi(v) = \Phi(\sum c_i u_i) = (c_1, \ldots, c_n) \in V_n(F)$ is 1–1 and onto. It is easy to show that Φ is the desired isomorphism, by verifying that $\Phi(v + w) = \Phi(v) + \Phi(w)$, and $\Phi(av) = a\Phi(v)$.

*   *   *

Theorem 9. A finite field F has p^n elements where p is the characteristic of F.

PROOF. We note that F is a vector space of finite dimension over the prime subfield P. Suppose that the dimension is n. Then $F \cong V_n(P)$ and the latter has p^n elements, there being p choices for each of n coordinates.

*   *   *

Theorem 10. Let S and T be finite dimensional subspaces of a vector space V. Then

$$\dim (S) + \dim (T) = \dim (S \vee T) + \dim (S \cap T).$$

PROOF. Since S has finite dimension, so has any subspace, in particular $S \cap T$. The relationships are shown in Figure 2. Let $\dim (S \cap T) = k$ and let $\{v_1, \ldots, v_k\}$ be a basis for $S \cap T$. From Theorem 6 we may add vectors $s_1, \ldots, s_n$ so that $\{v_1, \ldots, v_k, s_1, \ldots, s_n\}$ is a basis for S, and we may add vectors $t_1, \ldots, t_m$ so that $\{v_1, \ldots, v_k, t_1, \ldots, t_m\}$ is a basis for T. Thus $\dim (S) = k + n$ and $\dim (T) = k + m$. Our theorem states $\dim (S \vee T) = \dim (S) + \dim (T) - \dim (S \cap T)$, hence our proof would be complete if we could prove that $\{v_1, \ldots, v_k, s_1, \ldots, s_n, t_1, \ldots, t_m\}$ is a basis for $S \vee T$. Clearly these vectors must span $S \vee T$ and so we need only show them to be linearly independent.

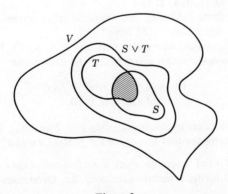

Figure 2

We point out first of all that if S' denotes the subspace of S spanned by $\{s_1, \ldots, s_n\}$ then $S' \cap (S \cap T) = S' \cap T = \{0\}$. For if $s \in S'$ then $s = \sum d_i s_i$ and if $s \in S \cap T$ then $s = \sum e_j v_j$. Thus $0 = \sum d_i s_i - \sum e_j v_j$ and from the independence of $\{v_1, \ldots, v_k, s_1, \ldots, s_n\}$ it follows that for all i, $d_i = 0$. Thus $s = 0$. Similarly if T' is the space spanned by $\{t_1, \ldots, t_m\}$ then $T' \cap S = \{0\}$.

Now suppose that $\sum a_i v_i + \sum b_j s_j + \sum c_h t_h = 0$. Let $v = \sum a_i v_i$, $s = \sum b_j s_j \in S'$, and $t = \sum c_h t_h \in T'$. From $0 = v + s + t$ we have $s = -(v + t)$ and so $s \in T$, hence $s \in S' \cap T$ from which we conclude $s = 0$. Similarly $t = 0$ and consequently $v = 0$. Now from the independence of $\{v_1, \ldots, v_k\}$, $\{s_1, \ldots, s_n\}$, and $\{t_1, \ldots, t_m\}$ it follows that all coefficients, a_i, b_j, and c_h are 0. Thus we have shown that $\{v_1, \ldots, v_k, s_1, \ldots, s_n, t_1, \ldots, t_m\}$ is independent and so this set is a basis for $S \vee T$.

*   *   *

Theorem 11. If S and T are finite dimensional subspaces of V such that $S \subseteq T$ and dim $(S) =$ dim (T) then $S = T$.

PROOF. Consider a basis for S. From Theorem 6 we may add vectors to this basis to form a basis for T. However, since dim $(S) =$ dim $(T) =$ the number of elements in a basis for T, no vectors can be added. Thus the basis for S must indeed be a basis for T.

*   *   *

EXERCISE 3

1. Show that if w does not belong to the subspace with basis $\{v_1, \ldots\}$ then $\{w, v_1, \ldots\}$ is independent.

2. Let S be spanned by $w_1, \ldots, w_n$. Show that there is a subset of $\{w_1, \ldots, w_n\}$ which is a basis.

3. Find a basis for the subspace of $V_5(\text{Ra})$ spanned by $(0, 1, -1, 2, 3)$, $(-6, -1, -11, 4, 9)$, $(1, 1, 1, 1, 1)$.

4. Let F be the finite field with two elements. How many *distinct* bases does $V_3(F)$ have? How many does $V_n(F)$ have?

5. Let F be the finite field with q elements. Let $V = V_n(F)$. The set of functions from V into F becomes a vector space under the definitions

$$(f_1 + f_2)(x) = f_1(x) + f_2(x)$$
$$(af)(x) = a(f(x)).$$

(i) Exhibit all elements in this space when $q = 2$ and $n = 2$.
(ii) What is the dimension of this space for general n and q?

6. Show that the set of functions which are solutions of the differential equation $y'' - 3y' + 2y = 0$ forms a vector space over Re. Determine its dimension and find a basis for it.

7. Show that if T is a finite dimensional vector space, and if S is a proper subspace of $T (S \neq T)$, then dim $S <$ dim T. Show, by example, that this is not true for infinite dimensional vector spaces.

8. Let $\{w_1, \ldots, w_m\}$ span a subspace W of V. Let k be the number of vectors in a maximal independent subset of $\{w_1, \ldots, w_m\}$. Prove that dim $(W) = k$.

9. Let $S = \{v_1, \ldots\}$ be a sequence of vectors in a vector space V. Suppose that for all $k \geq 2$, $v_k \notin \langle v_1, \ldots, v_{k-1} \rangle$. Show that S is an independent set.

7.5. LINEAR TRANSFORMATIONS

The analogue of the homomorphism concept for groups and rings is developed for vector spaces in a perfectly natural way. We consider a function λ, from one vector space V into another W, which is a group homomorphism of $\langle V, + \rangle$ into $\langle W, + \rangle$ and which also preserves the scalar multiplication. For the latter to make sense V and W must be vector spaces over the same field.

Definition. Let V and W be vector spaces over a field F. A mapping λ from V into W is called a *linear transformation* (homomorphism) if

1. λ is a group homomorphism from $\langle V, + \rangle$ into $\langle W, + \rangle$.
2. For all $a \in F$ and $v \in W$, $\lambda(av) = a\lambda(v)$.

If λ is a 1–1 mapping of V onto W, V and W are called isomorphic and λ is called a *nonsingular* linear transformation otherwise λ is called *singular*.

Example 17. Let $V = V_n(F)$, $W = V_m(F)$ where $n > m$. Define $\lambda(v) = \lambda(v_1, \ldots, v_n) = (v_1, \ldots, v_m)$.

The next three examples are so important that we shall give them special designations:

Example 18 (E1: *Multiplication of a Coordinate by a Nonzero Scalar*). Let $V = W$, let $\{u_1, u_2, \ldots\}$ be a basis, let $0 \neq m \in F$ and let $1 \leq i$. If $v = \sum a_k u_k$ define $\lambda(v) = \sum_{k \neq i} a_k u_k + m a_i u_i$.

Example 19 (E2: *Interchange of Coordinates*).Using the notation of Example 18, select particular basis elements u_i and u_j. If $v = \sum a_k u_k$ define $\lambda(v) = (\sum_{k \neq i,j} a_k u_k) + a_i u_j + a_j u_i$.

Example 20 (E3: *Addition of One Coordinate to Another*). Using the notations of Example 18, select basis elements u_i and u_j. Define $\mu(v) = (\sum_{k \neq i,j} a_k u_k) + a_i u_i + (a_i + a_j)u_j$.

As with any homomorphism, the kernel (the set of vectors mapped onto 0) is an important object of study as is the set of images of the vectors under λ. The next theorem ties these two sets of vectors together.

Theorem 12. Let V and W be vector spaces over a field F and λ a linear transformation from V into W.

1. $K = \{v : \lambda(v) = 0\}$ is a subspace of V. (K is called the kernel or null space of λ.)
2. $R = \{\lambda(v) : v \in V\}$ is a subspace of W. (R is called the range space of λ.)
3. $\dim(V) = \dim(K) + \dim(R)$.

PROOF. 1 and 2 are easily established since closure under vector addition and scalar product is assured by the preservation of these operations under λ.

We can prove 3 only under the assumption that $\dim(K)$ is finite since we do not have an "infinite" Steinitz replacement theorem; however, the technique of our proof can be extended to infinite sets with theorems from set theory.

Let $\{v_1, \ldots, v_k\}$ be a basis for K. Extend this basis to a basis A for V; $\{v_1, \ldots, v_k, v_{k+1}, \ldots, v_n\} = A$. To prove 3 it suffices to show that $B = \{\lambda(v_{k+1}), \ldots, \lambda(v_n)\}$ is a basis for R. Surely B spans R for any vector $v \in V$ can be written

$$v = a_1 v_1 + \cdots + a_k v_k + a_{k+1} v_{k+1} + \cdots + a_n v_n$$

and so

$$\lambda(v) = \sum_{i=1}^{n} a_i \lambda(v_i) = \sum_{i=k+1}^{n} a_i \lambda(v_i)$$

since $\lambda(v_1) = \cdots = \lambda(v_k) = 0$. On the other hand $\{\lambda(v_{k+1}), \ldots, \lambda(v_n)\}$ is linearly independent, for suppose a finite combination of them is 0:

$$\sum_{i=k+1}^{n} b_i \lambda(v_i) = 0.$$

Then $\lambda(\sum_{i=k+1}^{n} b_i v_i) = 0$, so that $\sum_{i=k+1}^{n} b_i v_i \in K$ and so $\sum_{i=k+1}^{n} b_i v_i = \sum_{i=1}^{k} (-b_i) v_i$ for some coefficients $-b_1, -b_2, \ldots, -b_k$. Thus $\sum_{i=1}^{n} b_i v_i = 0$, and since A is an independent set it must follow that all the b_i's are 0, in particular $b_{k+1}, \ldots, b_n$ are zero.

* * *

An important property of a linear transformation on a vector space is that it is completely determined by its effect on a basis. Thus if $v = \sum a_i v_i$ then $\lambda(v) = \sum a_i \lambda(v_i)$, so that if the image of a basis is known, the image of any vector can be determined. Conversely, given V and W and a basis $\{v_1, \ldots\}$ for V we may choose arbitrarily any sequence of vectors in W (with the same cardinality), $\{w_1, \ldots\}$ and define $\lambda(v_i) = w_i$. Then we may extend this definition to all of V so that λ becomes a linear transformation from V by defining $\lambda(v)$ as follows:

If $v = \sum a_i v_i$, then define $\lambda(v) = \sum a_i w_i = \sum a_i \lambda(v_i)$.

This definition is possible since each vector of V has a unique expression in the form $\sum a_i v_i$. Moreover it should be clear that the mapping λ so defined is a linear transformation.

Theorem 13. Let V and W be vector spaces over a field F. The set of linear transformations $\mathscr{L}(V \to W)$ forms a vector space over F under the definitions of vector addition and scalar multiplication given by

$$(\varphi + \theta)(v) = \varphi(v) + \theta(v) \quad \text{for all } v \in V,$$

and

$$(a\varphi)(v) = a(\varphi(v)) \quad \text{for all } v \in V \quad \text{and} \quad a \in F.$$

If V and W are finite dimensional then $\dim(\mathscr{L}(V \to W) = \dim(V) \cdot \dim(W)$.

PROOF. It is a simple matter to verify that under these pointwise definitions for vector addition and scalar multiplication $\mathscr{L}(V \to W)$ is a vector space over F. For this theorem we shall denote the zero linear transformation by $\hat{0}$. We have $\hat{0}(v) = 0$ for all $v \in V$.

For the remainder of this theorem we shall suppose that $\dim(V) = n$, $\dim(W) = m$ and that both n and m are finite. We shall complete our proof by defining a basis of nm vectors for $\mathscr{L}(V \to W)$. It is well to recall that to define a linear transformation from V into W we need only define a mapping on a basis for V.

Let $\{v_1, \ldots, v_n\}$ and $\{w_1, \ldots, w_m\}$ be bases for V and W respectively. Define

$$\lambda_{ij}(v_k) = \begin{cases} 0 & \text{if } k \neq i \\ w_j & \text{if } k = i \end{cases}$$

Thus λ_{1j} takes v_1 into w_j and sends all other basis vectors into 0. To see that these nm linear transformations span $\mathscr{L}(V \to W)$, let Φ be any linear transformation. We have for each v_i that $\Phi(v_i) = \sum_{j=1}^{m} a_{ij} w_j$. Thus we have determined nm constants. We shall prove that $\Phi = \sum_{j=1}^{n}(\sum_{i=1}^{m} a_{ij}\lambda_{ij})$. Now, from our remark preceding Theorem 13, we need check our assertion only at the basis elements v_k.

$$\Big(\sum_{j=1}^{n}\Big(\sum_{i=1}^{m} a_{ij}\lambda_{ij}\Big)\Big)(v_k) = \sum_{j=1}^{n}\Big(\sum_{i=1}^{m} a_{ij}\lambda_{ij}(v_k)\Big) = \sum_{j=1}^{n} a_{kj}w_j = \Phi(v_k).$$

Finally we must prove that the λ_{ij} are linearly independent. Suppose $\sum a_{ij}\lambda_{ij} = \hat{0}$. In particular $(\sum_{i,j} a_{ij}\lambda_{ij})(v_k) = \hat{0}(v_k) = 0$. But then

$$\sum a_{kj}\lambda_{kj}(v_k) = 0 \quad \text{or} \quad \sum a_{kj}w_j = 0.$$

Hence $a_{kj} = 0$, for all k since the $\{w_1, \ldots, w_m\}$ is linearly independent. In this way, by letting $k = 1, \ldots, n$, we conclude the all coefficients a_{ij} are zero.

* * *

Theorem 14. Let V and W be vector spaces over a field F and let λ be a linear transformation from V into W with kernel K. λ is 1–1 if and only if dim $(K) = 0$.

PROOF. λ is a group homomorphism, hence Theorem 1.22 applies! Thus λ is 1–1 if and only if $K = \{0\}$, and $K = \{0\}$ if and only if dim $(K) = 0$.

$$* \quad * \quad *$$

Theorem 15. Let λ be a 1–1 linear transformation from V into W. Then there exists a linear transformation μ from W onto V such that the mapping from V into V given by the composite $\mu\,\lambda$ is the identity.

We shall prove this only in the case that dim (W) is finite.

PROOF. Let $\{v_1, \ldots\}$ be a basis for V. Since λ is 1–1, the kernel of λ is $\{0\}$ and thus, by Theorem 12, $\{\lambda(v_1), \ldots, \lambda(v_n)\}$ is a basis for the range space of λ. Extend this set to a basis for W: $\{\lambda(v_1), \ldots, \lambda(v_n), s_1, \ldots\}$. Now define μ on this basis by defining $\mu(\lambda(v_i)) = v_i$ and $\mu(s_i) = 0$. μ is linear by the extension process, and it is onto since every basis vector of V appears in the range space.

To complete the proof we need only show that $\mu\lambda$ is the identity, but this is easy to do since we need verify it only at the basis elements v_i where it does hold since we fixed it that way!

$$* \quad * \quad *$$

Of special interest is the case in which $W = V$ and the dimension is finite.

Theorem 16. Let V be a finite dimensional vector space over a field F. Let λ be a linear transformation of V into V. λ is 1–1 if and only if λ is onto. Moreover, the collection of nonsingular linear transformations of V onto V forms a group $\mathscr{L}(V)$ (called the full linear group) under the operation of composition of transformations.

PROOF. Let us suppose that λ is 1–1. Then $K = \{0\}$ and since dim $V = $ dim $(K) + $ dim (R) it follows that dim $(R) = $ dim (V) and, by Theorem 12, it follows that $R = V$, or that λ is onto. Conversely, suppose that λ is onto. The same equation now shows that dim $(K) = 0$ and hence λ is 1–1.

The set $\mathscr{L}(V)$ is closed under composition for it is an easy consequence of the definitions that the composition of linear transformations is again linear and if the kernel of each factor is $\{0\}$ then the kernel of the composition is $\{0\}$ also. The other group axioms now follow since we have proved associativity more generally, the identity transformation serves as the identity element, and Theorem 15 guarantees a left inverse.

$$* \quad * \quad *$$

Examples of nonsingular transformations are given by the transformations $E1$, $E2$, and $E3$ of Examples 18, 19, and 20. Furthermore, if $v_1, \ldots, v_n$ and $w_1, \ldots, w_n$ are any two bases for V_n then there is a linear transformation in (V_n) such that $(v_i) = \delta_{ij} w_j$ where $\delta_{ij} = 1$ if $i = j$ and 0 otherwise. Problem 5 in the next exercise set asks for a proof. In these examples it is almost trivial to verify that the kernel is $\{0\}$.

The content of the next theorem is illustrated in Figure 3.

Theorem 17. Let φ be a linear transformation from V into W and θ a nonsingular linear transformation from V onto V. Then $\varphi\theta$ and φ have the same range space and dim (kernel φ) = dim (kernel $\varphi\theta$).

PROOF. From the preceding theorem, θ has an inverse θ^{-1}. Thus $\varphi(v) = \varphi\theta\theta^{-1}(v) = \varphi\theta(\theta^{-1}(v))$. This shows that the range spaces are identical.

To prove the second half of the theorem note that if $\varphi(v) = 0$ then $\varphi\theta(\theta^{-1}(v)) = 0$. Since θ^{-1} is a 1–1 mapping, θ^{-1} induces a nonsingular, linear transformation from the kernel of φ onto the kernel of $\varphi\theta$. (We need only verify that θ^{-1} is 1–1 and onto on kernel φ.) In particular the two kernels have the same dimension.

$$* \quad * \quad *$$

Theorem 18. Let φ be a linear transformation from V into W and ψ be a nonsingular linear transformation from W onto W. Then φ and $\psi\varphi$ have the same kernel and dim (range φ) = dim (range $\psi\varphi$).

We shall omit the proof since it is so similar to that of the preceding theorem.

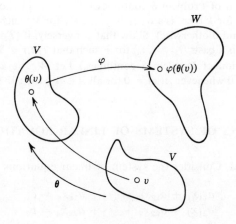

Figure 3

EXERCISE 4

1. Find explicitly the inverse of the transformation described in $E3$. Show that $E2$ can be accomplished by using a sequence of operations of types $E1$ and $E3$.

2. Let $V = V_3(\text{Ra})$ and $W = V_4(\text{Ra})$. A linear transformation λ takes $\varepsilon_1 = (1, 0, 0)$ into $(1, 0, 1, 0)$, $\varepsilon_2 = (0, 1, 0)$ into $(-1, 1, -1, 1)$, and $\varepsilon_3 = (0, 0, 1)$ into $(1, 2, 1, 2)$. Find a basis for the kernel and the range spaces.

3. Let $V = V_n(F)$ and $W = V_1(F) \cong F$. Show that if $\{b_1, \ldots, b_n\}$ is a basis for V, then $\mathscr{L}(V \to W) = V^*$ has a basis $f_1, \ldots, f_n$ so that $f_i(b_j) = \delta_{ij}$ where $\delta_{ij} = 1$ if $i = j$ and 0 if $i \neq j$. Show that if S is a subspace of V then $S' = \{f : f(v) = 0$ if and only if $v \in S\}$ is a subspace of V^* and $\dim S + \dim S' = n$.

4. Is the full linear group $\mathscr{L}(V)$ closed under the addition of $\mathscr{L}(V \to V)$.

5. Prove that if $\{v_1, \ldots, v_n\}$ and $\{w_1, \ldots, w_n\}$ are bases for $V = V_n(F)$ then there is a linear transformation $\lambda \in \mathscr{L}(V)$ such that $\lambda(v_i) = \delta_{ij}w_j$ where $\delta_{ij} = 1$ if $i = j$ and $= 0$ otherwise.

6. Show that if G is a finite group of order n then G is isomorphic to a subgroup of $\mathscr{L}(V_n)$. [*Hint:* Let $\{v_1, \ldots, v_n\}$ be a basis for V_n. If π is a permutation on $(1, \ldots, n)$ consider the linear transformation φ_π given by $\varphi_\pi(v_i) = v_{\pi(i)}$.]

7. Let $\{v_1, \ldots, v_n\}$ be a basis for $V = V_n(F)$. If $A \in \mathscr{L}(V \to V)$ is defined so that $A(v_i) = \sum \alpha_{ij}v_j$ and $B \in \mathscr{L}(V \to V)$ is defined so that $B(v_n) = \sum \beta_{hk}v_k$ then $BA(v_i) = \sum (\sum \alpha_{ih}\beta_{hj})v_j$.

8. Let $V = V_n(F)$. The vector space $V^* = \mathscr{L}(V \to F)$ of Theorem 14 is called the space of linear functionals of V into F. (V^* is often called the dual space of V.) Theorem 13 shows that the $\dim (V^*) = n$ and by Theorem 8, $V \cong V^*$ follows. Show this isomorphism explicitly as follows. Let $\{v_1, \ldots, v_n\}$ be a basis of V.

(i) Let $w = \sum \alpha_i v_i$ be a fixed vector. Show that the function $F = F_w$ defined by $F(s) = \sum \sigma_i \alpha_i$ if $s = \sum \sigma_i v_i$ is a member of V^*. (ii) Conversely show that if G is any member of V^* then there is a $w \in V$ such that $G = F_w$. (iii) Show that the mapping $w \to F_w$ is an isomorphism of V onto V^*.

★ **9.** (The notation of Problem 8 continues.) Theorem 13 shows that for every basis $\{w_1, \ldots, w_n\}$ for V there is a basis $W_1, \ldots, W_n$ for V^* such that $W_i(w_j) = \delta_{ij}$ ($\delta_{ij} = 1$ if $i = j$ and 0 otherwise). Show that conversely, if $\{T_1, \ldots, T_n\}$ is a basis for V^* then there is a basis $\{t_1, \ldots, t_n\}$ for V such that $T_i(t_j) = \delta_{ij}$.

★ **10.** (The notation of Problem 8 continues.) Let W^* be a subspace of V^*. Show that if $w = 0$ whenever $A(w) = 0$ for all $A \in W^*$ then $W^* = V^*$.

7.6. SOLUTIONS OF SYSTEMS OF LINEAR EQUATIONS

Let F be a field. Consider the system of linear equations ($a_{ij}, c_k \in F$):

1.

$$
\begin{aligned}
a_{11}x_1 + a_{12}x_2 + \cdots + a_{1n}x_n &= c_1 \\
a_{21}x_1 + a_{22}x_2 + \cdots + a_{2n}x_n &= c_2 \\
&\vdots \\
a_{m1}x_1 + a_{m2}x_2 + \cdots + a_{mn}x_n &= c_m.
\end{aligned}
$$

This system may be considered as an equation in $V_m(F)$ by writing vectors as columns:

$$a_1 = \begin{pmatrix} a_{11} \\ a_{21} \\ \vdots \\ a_{m1} \end{pmatrix}, \quad a_2 = \begin{pmatrix} a_{12} \\ a_{22} \\ \vdots \\ a_{m2} \end{pmatrix}, \quad \ldots, \quad a_n = \begin{pmatrix} a_{1n} \\ a_{2n} \\ \vdots \\ a_{mn} \end{pmatrix}, \quad \text{and} \quad c = \begin{pmatrix} c_1 \\ c_2 \\ \vdots \\ c_m \end{pmatrix}.$$

The system 1 now has the form

2.
$$\sum_{i=1}^{n} x_i a_i = c.$$

We can easily see that 2 will have a solution if and only if c belongs to the subspace spanned by $\{a_1, \ldots, a_n\}$. This may or may not be the case!

This system may also be considered in another way. Consider $V_n(F)$ and a linear transformation φ from $V_n(F)$ into $V_m(F)$ which is defined by

$$\varphi(1, 0, \ldots, 0) = \varphi(\varepsilon_1) = \begin{pmatrix} a_{11} \\ a_{21} \\ \vdots \\ a_{m1} \end{pmatrix}$$

$$\varphi(0, \ldots, 1, 0, \ldots, 0) = \varphi(\varepsilon_i) = \begin{pmatrix} a_{1i} \\ a_{2i} \\ \vdots \\ a_{mi} \end{pmatrix}$$

Then 2 will have a solution if and only if c belongs to the range space of φ.

The problem of solutions for system 1 is always twofold: Does a solution exist? Describe the totality of solutions if any exist. We first turn to the question of determining the totality of solutions, supposing one to exist.

The first thing to notice is that if $(u_1, \ldots, u_n)$ and $(v_1, \ldots, v_n)$ are solutions for 1, then $(u_1 - v_1, \ldots, u_n - v_n)$ is a solution for an associated system:

3.
$$\begin{aligned} a_{11}x_1 + a_{12}x_2 + \cdots + a_{1n}x_n &= 0 \\ a_{21}x_1 + a_{22}x_2 + \cdots + a_{2n}x_n &= 0 \\ \vdots \\ a_{m1}x_1 + \cdots + \cdots + a_{mn}x_n &= 0. \end{aligned}$$

This statement says nothing if 1 has only one solution, since then the solution $(u_1 - v_1, \ldots, u_n - v_n)$ of 3 is just $(0, 0, \ldots, 0)$, which is always a solution of 3. On the other hand 3 is a special case of 1, and so we must study systems like 3 for any general theory. Moreover, if we have a solution for 1, say $(u_1, \ldots, u_n)$ and know all solutions for 3, then the converse of our remarks in the paragraph above guarantee that all solutions for 1 have the form $(u_1 + w_1, \ldots, u_n + w_n)$ where $(w_1, \ldots, w_n)$ is a solution for 3. We begin therefore with an analysis of 3.

We prefer to consider the system 3 from the point of view of a linear transformation φ from $V_n(F)$ into $V_m(F)$. Thus a solution of 3 yields a vector $(u_1, \ldots, u_n)$ in the kernel of φ. This kernel, in a terminology reflecting the current problem, is often called the *solution* space of the system 3. If we find a basis for this solution space then any and all solutions come as linear combinations of these basis vectors. Hence given a system of equations 3, we should begin an immediate search for a basis of the solution space.

An important feature of this space is its dimension. The dimension of the kernel of φ is called the *nullity* of φ; the dimension of the range space is called the *rank* of φ. Note that the range space is the space spanned by the column vectors $\{a_1, \ldots, a_n\}$ in $V_m(F)$. Theorem 12 may now be stated: nullity + rank = dim $V_n(F) = n$.

Corollary. In the system of equations 3 if the number of unknowns exceeds number of equations (if $n > m$), then there is at least one nontrivial solution.

PROOF. The rank is the dimension of the space spanned by the column vectors and so cannot exceed the dimension of the space to which the column vectors belong. This number is m, the number of equations. Since $n > m$, the equation rank + nullity = n means that nullity > 0, which in turn implies the existence of a nonzero vector in the kernel.

$$* \quad * \quad *$$

To aid our search for a basis of the kernel we observe that we may alter the form 3 just as long as we do not alter the kernel. Theorem 18 shows that we can alter the form of the range space by a nonsingular transformation of $V_m(F)$ without affecting its dimension. In particular we may apply the transformations E1, E2, and E3 (see p. 189) to $V_m(F)$. This effectively means that we may change the coefficients of 3 by interchanging rows of equations (E2) or by adding a nonzero multiple of one equation to another (E1 and E3). Thus if

$$\psi(\varepsilon_1) = t\varepsilon_1 \qquad (t \neq 0)$$
$$\psi(\varepsilon_i) = \varepsilon_i \qquad (i = 2, \ldots, m),$$

then the equations representing the transformation $\psi\varphi$ become

$$ta_{11}x_1 + \cdots + ta_{1n}x_n = 0$$
$$\vdots$$
$$a_{m1}x_1 + \cdots + a_{mn}x_n = 0.$$

Thus we can carry out the elementary operations E1, E2, and E3 on the equations 3 without changing the solution space. We shall proceed to do this in a manner that will give an exceedingly simple form for the equations from which we shall be able to obtain all solutions for 3. The form bears the fancy name: row-reduced echelon form!

To begin with, we choose k_1 to be the least column index so that not all the coefficients $a_{1k_1}, \ldots, a_{mk_1}$ of x_{k_1} are zero. In this discussion we shall assume $k_1 = 1$ to avoid notational confusion. (If all coefficients are zero, it is not too hard to solve the system 3!) By an interchange of the equations, if necessary, we may transform the system into one in which the coefficient $a_{11} \neq 0$. By multiplying the first equation by a_{11}^{-1} we put the system into a form whose first equation is:

$$x_1 + b_{12}x_2 + \cdots + b_{1n}x_n = 0.$$

Then, by subtracting correct multiples of this equation from all the others, we can put the system into the form:

$$x_1 + b_{12}x_2 + \cdots + b_{1n}x_n = 0$$
$$b_{22}x_2 + \cdots + b_{2n}x_n = 0$$
$$\vdots$$
$$b_{m2}x_2 + \cdots + b_{mn}x_n = 0.$$

Now we proceed on the equations 2 through m just as above. And by repeating this process we arrive at a stage in which either all remaining coefficients are zero, or no equations remain! In this way we put the system 3 into the system

4.
$$x_{k_i} + \sum_{j=k_i}^{n} c_{ij}x_j = 0, \ 1 \leq i \leq s; s \leq n.$$

in which the ith equation is as shown or all coefficients are zero. Since we have put those equations with all zero coefficients at the bottom we have

$$1 \leq k_1 < k_2 < \cdots \leq n.$$

Ultimately our array of coefficients for the system 4 will look like this:

$$\begin{pmatrix} 1 & c_{12} & \cdots & 0 & c_{1(k_2+1)} & \cdots & 0 & c_{1(k_3+1)} & \cdots & 0 & \cdots & \cdots \\ 0 & 0 & \cdots & 1 & c_{2(k_2+1)} & \cdots & 0 & & \cdots & 0 & \cdots & \cdots \\ 0 & 0 & \cdots & 0 & & \cdots & 1 & c_{3(k_3+1)} & \cdots & 0 & \cdots & \cdots \\ \vdots & \vdots & \vdots & \vdots & \vdots & \vdots & 0 & \vdots & \vdots & \vdots & \vdots & \vdots \\ 0 & \cdots & \cdots & 0 & & \cdots & \cdots & \cdots & \cdots & 1 & c_{s(k_s+1)} & \cdots \\ 0 & \cdots & \cdots & 0 & 0 & \cdots & 0 & \cdots & \cdots & \cdots & \cdots & 0 \end{pmatrix}$$

$$\underset{\text{column 1}}{\uparrow} \qquad \underset{\text{column } k_2}{\uparrow} \qquad \underset{\text{column } k_3}{\uparrow}$$

Note that we have subtracted correct multiples of equation i from all the others so that in column k_i only one nonzero entry appears; the entry is 1. Clearly those columns k_i now corresponding to the coefficients x_{k_i} form a basis for the column space of 4, and by Theorem 17 its dimension is the dimension of the original range space. Thus from Theorem 12 it follows that if s is the number of nonzero rows of 4 then nullity $= n - s$.

Also from system 4 it is now easy to produce all solutions. We have for $k_1, k_2, \ldots, k_s$ that

$$x_{k_i} = -\Big(\sum_{j=k_i+1}^{n} c_{ij} x_i \Big).$$

Most important is the feature that no index k_j appears on the right-hand side of any equation of the above form. Hence, if $r_1, \ldots, r_t$ are the indexes which do not arise as one of the k_i, the values of $x_{r_1}, \ldots, x_{r_t}$ can be chosen *arbitrarily*. Then $x_{k_1}, \ldots, x_{k_s}$ (note that $s + t = n$) are determined by the above equations. Since any solution implies some choice for $x_{r_1}, \ldots, x_{r_t}$ it is clear that all solutions arise in this way. It remains to determine a basis for the solutions.

A basis for the null space may be achieved by choosing, in turn, $x_{r_j} = 1$, and all other $x_{r_j} = 0$. This, of course, gives an independent proof that the dim (Null Space) $= t$.

Now let us return to the problem of deciding whether the general system 1 has a solution and if so finding one. We may alter the equations in 1 just as we did those in 3 to obtain exactly the same form on the left-hand side of the equality symbol. In the process the coefficients $c = \begin{pmatrix} c_1 \\ \vdots \\ c_m \end{pmatrix}$ on the right-hand side have been altered. However, since each of $E1$, $E2$, and $E3$ is a non-singular transformation the result of the sequence of operations in the process is a nonsingular transformation ψ of $V_m(F)$, and the new coefficients on the right-hand side are $\psi(c)$. It follows that the new system of equations will have precisely the same set of solutions as the system 1. In row-reduced echelon form it is easy to decide whether a solution exists and to write down the solutions. The criterion is clearly that $\psi(c)$ must have zero coefficients in the last $(m - s)$ coordinate places.

EXERCISE 5

1. Find a basis for the subspace in $V_3(\mathrm{Ra})$ spanned by $(1, 2, 4)$, $(4, 8, -5)$, $(-8, -16, 10)$, $(2, 4, 1)$, $(1, 2, 3)$. Does $(5, 4, 3)$ belong to this subspace?

2. Let λ be a linear transformation from $V_3(\mathrm{Re})$ into itself. Let $a_1 = (1, 1, 2)$, $a_2 = (-1, 2, 1)$, $a_3 = (3, 0, 2)$. Let $\lambda(a_1) = a_2 + a_3$, $\lambda(a_2) = 3a_1$, $\lambda(a_3) = 2a_1 + 3a_3$. Find $\lambda(1, 0, 0)$, $\lambda(0, 1, 0)$, and $\lambda(0, 0, 1)$.

3. Consider the vector space $V_3(F)$ where F is the finite field of integers mod 5. Determine a value for k so that

$$(1, 3, k), \quad (0, 1, k - 1), \quad \text{and} \quad (3, 4, 1)$$

are linearly dependent.

4. Find all solutions of

$$x + 2z = 4$$
$$2x + 2y - 2z = 1$$
$$2x - y + z = 5.$$

Find a basis for the kernel and range space of the associated linear transformation over $V_3(Ra)$.

5. Let λ be any linear transformation from a finite dimensional vector space V into itself. By λ^m we denote the linear transformation obtained by m iterations of λ. Show that there is some integer m such that the kernel of λ^m and the range λ^m have only 0 in common.

6. What is the condition that integers a, b, c must satisfy in order that

$$2w - x + y - 3z = a$$
$$w + x - y = b$$
$$4w + x - y - 3z = c$$

can be solved in integers?

7.7. ALGEBRAS

Can vectors be multiplied? As a first example, recall that the complex numbers are a vector space over the real numbers, and indeed, there we *can* and do multiply vectors. What are the possibilities in general? Suppose that we have a vector space V and that we wish to define a multiplication on the elements of V—that is, we want a binary operation on V. With each pair of vectors u and v we desire to associate another *vector*, w. We write $u \circ v = w$. What properties shall this multiplication have? What shall its relation be with scalar multiplication and vector addition? Minimally we surely would wish to relate vector multiplication with scalar multiplication the following way: For all $u, v \in V$ and all $a \in F$,

1. $(au) \circ v = a(u \circ v) = u \circ (av)$.

We would also wish the distributive laws to hold:

2. $(u + v) \circ w = (u \circ w) + (v \circ w)$ and $w \circ (u + v) = (w \circ u) + (w \circ v)$.

If we desire these laws, then the multiplication is in fact completely determined by its effect on a basis. Thus if $(v_1, \ldots)$ is a basis for V, then 1 and 2 dictate: if $u = \sum a_i v_i$ and $v = \sum b_i v_i$ then

$$u \circ v = \left(\sum_i a_i v_i \right) \circ v = \sum_i ((a_i v_i) \circ v) = \sum_1 a_i(v_i \circ v)$$

$$= \sum_i a_i(v_i \circ \sum_j b_j v_j) = \sum_i a_i \left(\sum_j b_j(v_i \circ v_j) \right).$$

Thus

3.
$$u \circ v = \sum_{i,j} a_i b_j (v_i \circ v_j).$$

Hence we need only know $v_i \circ v_j$ for all pairs i, j. These products may again be expressed in terms of the basis vectors:

$$v_i \circ v_j = \sum_k c_{ijk} v_k$$

The coefficients c_{ijk} may be chosen in any arbitrary fashion and are called the structure constants of the multiplication. By using 3 as the definition for vector multiplication, properties 1 and 2 can be proved in a perfectly straight-forward manner. Any other properties, such as associativity and/or commutativity of multiplication, have to be established in each case; they may or may not hold.

Example 21. Let us view the complex numbers in this way, using the basis $\{1, i\}$. The structure constants are obtained from the following equations:

$$1 \circ 1 = 1 \cdot 1 + 0 \cdot i \qquad 1 \circ i = 0 \cdot 1 + 1 \cdot i$$
$$i \circ 1 = 0 \cdot 1 + 1 \cdot i \qquad i \circ 1 = -1 \cdot 1 + 0 \cdot i.$$

Definition. An *algebra* is a vector space V over a field F on which a multi-plication ($\circ$) between vectors has been defined so that for all $u, v, w \in V$ and all $a \in F$,

1. $(au) \circ v = a(u \circ v) = u \circ (av)$

and 2. $(u + v) \circ w = (u \circ w) + (v \circ w)$　and　$w \circ (u + v) = (w \circ u) + (w \circ v)$.

An algebra is called *associative* if the multiplication is associative. An associative algebra is thus a ring. The vector space $\mathscr{L}(V \to W)$ is an important example of such an algebra when ($\circ$) is taken to be composition of transformations.

Hereafter we shall omit the symbol denoting multiplication in favor of juxtaposition.

We shall give two further examples of algebras, both associative. First we establish one property.

Lemma 1. An algebra is associative if and only if the associative law holds for all the basis elements.

PROOF. The condition is trivially necessary for an algebra to be associative. Suppose then that $(xy)z = x(yz)$ for all triples of basis vectors from the basis $(v_1, \ldots)$. Let $u = \sum a_i v_i$, $v = \sum b_i v_i$, and $w = \sum c_i v_i$. We compute uv, $(uv)w$, vw, and $u(vw)$ and compare:

$$uv = \sum_{i,j} (a_i b_j)(v_i v_j), \quad vw = \sum_{j,k} b_j c_k (v_j v_k)$$

$$(uv)w = \left[\sum_{i,j} a_i b_j (v_i v_j) \right] \sum_k c_k v_k = \sum_{i,j} \left(\sum_k a_i b_j (v_i v_j)(c_k v_k) \right)$$

$$= \sum_{i,j} \left(\sum_k (a_i b_j) c_k ((v_i v_j) v_k) \right) = \sum_{ijk} (a_i b_j) c_k ((v_i v_j) v_k)$$

Similarly,

$$u(vw) = \sum_{ijk} a_i(b_j c_k)(v_i(v_j v_k)).$$

Thus, since by assumption $(v_i v_j)v_k = v_i(v_j v_k)$, and since $(a_i b_j)c_k = a_i(b_j c_k)$ holds in the field F, we have $u(vw) = (uv)w$.

* * *

Example 22 (*The Quaternions*). Let V be the vector space of dimension 4 over a field F. Let $\varepsilon_1 = (1, 0, 0, 0)$, $\varepsilon_2 = (0, 1, 0, 0)$, $\varepsilon_3 = (0, 0, 1, 0)$, $\varepsilon_4 = (0, 0, 0, 1)$, and the multiplication table for the basis vectors is

$$\varepsilon_1{}^2 = \varepsilon_1, \qquad \varepsilon_2{}^2 = \varepsilon_3{}^2 = \varepsilon_4{}^2 = -\varepsilon_1$$

$$\varepsilon_2 \varepsilon_3 = \varepsilon_4 \qquad \varepsilon_3 \varepsilon_2 = -\varepsilon_4$$

$$\varepsilon_3 \varepsilon_4 = \varepsilon_2 \qquad \varepsilon_4 \varepsilon_3 = -\varepsilon_2$$

$$\varepsilon_4 \varepsilon_2 = \varepsilon_3 \qquad \varepsilon_2 \varepsilon_4 = -\varepsilon_3$$

$$\varepsilon_1 \varepsilon_i = \varepsilon_i \varepsilon_1 \quad \text{for all } i.$$

(Note that $\varepsilon_i \varepsilon_j = -\varepsilon_j \varepsilon_i$ for all $i \neq j$; $i, j > 1$.)

Figure 4 provides a mnemonic device for remembering the multiplication table: use clockwise motion for "positive" products, or equivalently let $\varepsilon_2 = i$, $\varepsilon_3 = j$, $\varepsilon_k = k$ and remember $\varepsilon_i \cdot \varepsilon_j = \varepsilon_i \times \varepsilon_j$ as a vector product in 3-space using the usual right-hand rule.

From our previous discussion an algebra has been defined. However, this algebra of classical interest has many nice properties. In particular the multiplication is associative, but not commutative.

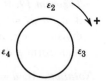

Figure 4

To prove associativity we need only, as the previous lemma shows, prove that $(\varepsilon_i \varepsilon_j)\varepsilon_k = \varepsilon_i(\varepsilon_j \varepsilon_k)$ for all choices of i, j, k. Thus there are $4^3 (= 64)$ cases to consider.
Since ε_1 acts as an identity, it is clear by inspection that associativity holds if one or more of the three is ε_1. This takes care of thirty-seven cases. Similarly the equality holds if $\varepsilon_1 \neq \varepsilon_i = \varepsilon_j = \varepsilon_k$. This takes care of three more cases. Now suppose that all three are distinct and no $\varepsilon_i = \varepsilon_1$. Then $\varepsilon_i \varepsilon_j = \pm \varepsilon_k$ while $\varepsilon_j \varepsilon_k = \pm \varepsilon_i$. If $\varepsilon_i \varepsilon_j = \varepsilon_k$, then the orientation around the circle must be as in Figure 4, in which case $\varepsilon_j \varepsilon_k = \varepsilon_i$. Thus $(\varepsilon_i \varepsilon_j)\varepsilon_k = -1 = \varepsilon_i(\varepsilon_j \varepsilon_k)$. Conversely if $\varepsilon_i \varepsilon_j = -\varepsilon_k$ then the orientation is reversed, and $(\varepsilon_i \varepsilon_j)\varepsilon_k = -\varepsilon_k{}^2 = 1 = -\varepsilon_i{}^2 = \varepsilon_i(\varepsilon_j \varepsilon_k)$. These cases cover six more possibilities. In the remaining cases exactly two of the three $\varepsilon_i, \varepsilon_j, \varepsilon_k$ must be equal.

Now suppose that $\varepsilon_i = \varepsilon_k$. Then $(\varepsilon_k \varepsilon_j)\varepsilon_k = -\varepsilon_k(\varepsilon_k \varepsilon_j) = -\varepsilon_k(-\varepsilon_j \varepsilon_k) = \varepsilon_k(\varepsilon_j \varepsilon_k)$. Thus the only cases remaining are $\varepsilon_i = \varepsilon_j$ or $\varepsilon_j = \varepsilon_k$. If $\varepsilon_i = \varepsilon_j \neq \varepsilon_k$ we must show $-\varepsilon_k = \varepsilon_i(\varepsilon_i \varepsilon_k)$. Now, as $\varepsilon_i \neq \varepsilon_k$, we have $\varepsilon_i \varepsilon_k = \pm \varepsilon_j$. If $\varepsilon_i \varepsilon_k = -\varepsilon_j$, the orientation of $\varepsilon_i, \varepsilon_j, \varepsilon_k$ around the circle is that of Figure 4 and $\varepsilon_i(\varepsilon_i\varepsilon_k) =$ $\varepsilon_i(-\varepsilon_j) = -(\varepsilon_i\varepsilon_j) = -\varepsilon_k$. If the orientation is reversed ($\varepsilon_i\varepsilon_k = \varepsilon_j$), we have $\varepsilon_i\varepsilon_j = -\varepsilon_k$. Hence associativity holds here. The case $\varepsilon_j = \varepsilon_k$ follows from the previous case together with the rule $\varepsilon_r\varepsilon_s = -\varepsilon_s\varepsilon_r$ for all $r \neq s$ if $r \neq 1$ and $s \neq 1$. Thus $(\varepsilon_i\varepsilon_j)\varepsilon_j = -\varepsilon_j(\varepsilon_i\varepsilon_j) = \varepsilon_j(\varepsilon_j\varepsilon_i)$, whereas $\varepsilon_i(\varepsilon_j\varepsilon_j) = -\varepsilon_i = (\varepsilon_j\varepsilon_j)\varepsilon_i$. In this way we establish that the associative law holds in a quaternion algebra.

Now let us compute a general product

$$u = \sum a_i\varepsilon_i; \qquad v = \sum b_j\varepsilon_j; \qquad uv = \sum_{i,j} a_ib_j(\varepsilon_i\varepsilon_j)$$

$$= (a_1b_1 - a_2b_2 - a_3b_3 - a_4b_4)\varepsilon_1 + \sum_{k=2}^{4} \Big(\sum_{\varepsilon_i\varepsilon_j = \varepsilon_k} a_ib_j \Big)_{\varepsilon_k}$$

$$= (a_1b_1 - a_2b_2 - a_3b_3 - a_4b_4)\varepsilon_1$$
$$+ (a_1b_2 + a_2b_1 + a_3b_4 - a_4b_3)\varepsilon_2$$
$$+ (a_1b_3 + a_3b_1 + a_4b_2 - a_2b_4)\varepsilon_3$$
$$+ (a_1b_4 + a_4b_1 + a_2b_3 - a_3b_2)\varepsilon_4.$$

In particular, if $v = a_1\varepsilon_1 - a_2\varepsilon_2 - a_3\varepsilon_3 - a_4\varepsilon_4$ (that is, $b_1 = a_1$ and $b_i = -a_i$), then $uv = (a_1^2 + a_2^2 + a_3^2 + a_4^2)\varepsilon_1$. Thus if $a_1^2 + a_2^2 + a_3^2 + a_4^2 = |u| \neq 0$, and $u_1 = 1/|u|(a_1\varepsilon_1 - a_2\varepsilon_2 - a_3\varepsilon_3 - a_4\varepsilon_4)$, then $u u_1 = \varepsilon_1$; that is, u has a multiplicative inverse. This result is stated as Theorem 19.

Note that Q contains a subring isomorphic to F via $x \to x\varepsilon_1$.

> **Theorem 19.** If F is a field in which $a_1^2 + a_2^2 + a_3^2 + a_4^2 = 0$ only
> if $a_1 = a_2 = a_3 = a_4 = 0$, then the quaternions over F form a
> division ring; in particular the quaternions over the rationals or the
> reals form a division ring.

> **Notation.** If $u = a_1\varepsilon_1 + a_2\varepsilon_2 + a_3\varepsilon_3 + a_4\varepsilon_4$, denote by $\bar{u}$ the element
> $a_1\varepsilon_1 - a_2\varepsilon_2 - a_3\varepsilon_3 - a_4\varepsilon_4$. Let the norm of u, $N(u)$, equal $u\bar{u} = a_1^2 + a_2^2 + a_3^2 + a_4^2$.

Lemma 2. $\overline{(uv)} = \bar{v}\bar{u}$ and $N(uv) = N(u)N(v)$.

PROOF. $\overline{(uv)} = \bar{v}\bar{u}$ follows by a direct calculation, or more simply by noting the symmetry of the roles of a_i and b_j in the calculation of uv. From this, $N(uv) = uv\overline{(uv)} = uv\bar{v}\bar{u} = u(v\bar{v})\bar{u} = u\bar{u}(v\bar{v}) = N(u)N(v)$. (Since $v\bar{v} \in F$ it is a scalar and so commutes with u.)

$*\quad*\quad*$

A less precise form of this lemma is that the product of two numbers, each of which is the sum of four squares, is again a sum of four squares. This identity is an important step in the proof of the theorem that every integer can be expressed as the sum of four squares. The identity shows that this need be proved only in the case of primes.

    Theorem 20. If F has characteristic $p \neq 0$, then the quaternions over F always have divisors of zero.

PROOF. From our previous work, we know that it suffices to show that there are in F nonzero elements a_1, a_2, a_3, a_4, such that $a_1^2 + a_2^2 + a_3^2 + a_4^2 = 0$. If the characteristic is 2, choose $a_1 = a_2 = a_3 = a_4 = 1$. Thus we may assume that $p \neq 2$. Let P be the prime subfield of F with p elements. We show that there are elements u, v in P such that $1 + u^2 + v^2 = 0$. We make a counting argument to show that some element of P appears in the form $1 + u^2$ and in the form $-v^2$ for suitable u and v. Now the number of distinct elements of the form u^2 is $(p - 1)/2 + 1 = (p + 1)/2$ since $x^2 = u^2$ if and only if $x = u$ or $x = -u$, and both equations hold only if $x = u = 0$. The number of elements of the form $1 + u^2$ is $(p + 1)/2$ as well. Hence as u takes on all possible values from P, $1 + u^2$ takes on $(p + 1)/2$ distinct values. Similarly $-v^2$ takes on $(p + 1)/2$ distinct values. Since $(p + 1)/2 + (p + 1)/2 = p + 1 > p$, some element of P has been duplicated; that is, $1 + u^2 = -v^2$ for suitable choices of u and v.

*   *   *

    We may view the quaternions over the real numbers as a suitable generalization of the complex numbers. A natural question immediately presents itself: Characterize all division algebras over the reals. This question has occupied algebraists since the discovery of the quaternions by Hamilton in 1843. Cayley found a division algebra of dimension 8 over the reals in 1845. The multiplication in this algebra was neither associative nor commutative. A hint of the type of theorem that was to be proved 79 years later was the result of Frobenius in 1878 that the only associative division algebras over the reals were the complex numbers and the quaternions. In 1940, Heinz Hopf, applying theorems from algebraic topology, showed that the dimension of any division algebra over the reals had to be a power of 2. In 1957, Raul Bott and John Milnor, and independently M. Kervaire, showed that the only possible dimensions were 1, 2, 4, and 8. This settled the matter—the only division algebras over the reals are the reals, the complex numbers, and the quaternions and the Cayley algebras. The supplementary reading list at the end of this chapter includes two special references. The classic work of L. E. Dickson on algebras contains an easy proof of the Frobenius theorem. The article by Charles Curtis is an engaging account of some problems in this area.

Example 23 (*Group Algebras*). Let G be a group. Let V be a vector space over a field F of dimension equal to the order of G. Denote a basis for V by the group elements. A multiplication is now defined using the group multiplication table as the structure constants. Thus if we denote the elements of G by g_i, then for $v \in V$

$$v = \sum a_i g_i$$

where all but a finite number on the a_i are 0. Then the structure constants are obtained from the equations $g_i g_j = g_k$, which are to hold in the algebra if and only if $g_i g_j = g_k$ in G. In general $(\sum a_i g_i)(\sum b_j g_j) = \sum (\sum_{g_i g_j = g_k} a_i b_j) g_k$.

The expression $\sum_{g_i g_j = g_k} a_i b_j$ is an element of V since at most a finite number of the a_i and b_j are different from zero; thus at most a finite number of nonzero products $a_i b_j$ can be formed regardless of whether $g_i g_j = g_k$ or not. In particular, for only a finite number of g_k does the sum $\sum_{g_i g_j = g_k} a_i b_j$ differ from zero.

It follows from Lemma 1 that this algebra is associative since all the basis elements satisfy the associative law, as implied by the associative law in G.

As a particular example let us take the cyclic group of order two: $\varepsilon_1, \varepsilon_2; \varepsilon_2^2 = \varepsilon_1$ over the finite field of two elements I_2. The elements of the group algebra are

$$0, \varepsilon_1, \varepsilon_2, \varepsilon_1 + \varepsilon_2$$

the addition and multiplication tables are

+	0	ε_1	ε_2	$\varepsilon_1 + \varepsilon_2$
0	0	ε_1	ε_2	$\varepsilon_1 + \varepsilon_2$
ε_1	ε_1	0	$\varepsilon_1 + \varepsilon_2$	ε_2
ε_2	ε_2	$\varepsilon_1 + \varepsilon_2$	0	ε_1
$\varepsilon_1 + \varepsilon_2$	$\varepsilon_1 + \varepsilon_2$	ε_2	ε_1	0

$\cdot$	ε_1	ε_2	$\varepsilon_1 + \varepsilon_2$
ε_1	ε_1	ε_2	$\varepsilon_1 + \varepsilon_2$
ε_2	ε_2	ε_1	$\varepsilon_2 + \varepsilon_1$
$\varepsilon_1 + \varepsilon_2$	$\varepsilon_1 + \varepsilon_2$	$\varepsilon_1 + \varepsilon_2$	0

This algebra has a zero divisor and indeed this happens "often" in a group algebra.

Lemma 3. Let G be a group and let F be a field. Let $S \neq \{1\}$ be a finite subgroup such that the order of S is not divisible by the characteristic of the field. Let $a = \sum_{s_i \in S} s_i$.

1. $a^2 = |S|a$
2. If $b = |S|^{-1}a$ then $b \neq 1$ and $(b - 1)b = 0$.

PROOF: 2 follows easily from 1. To prove 1 we calculate

$$a^2 = (\sum s_i)(\sum s_j) = \sum_k (\sum_{s_i s_j = s_k} 1 \cdot 1) s_k.$$

For a fixed k, the number of ordered pairs (s_i, s_j) such that $s_i s_j = s_k$ is just $|S|$ since s_j is determined once s_i is chosen.

This lemma shows that "most" group algebras have divisors of zero. The determination of the set of all divisors of zero in a group algebra is an unsolved problem.

EXERCISE 6

1. Show that in the quaternions over the reals the elements $\pm \varepsilon_i$ form a group of order 8. Show that the group is isomorphic to the group with generators a, b, c, d, and with defining relations $a^2 = b^2 = c^2 = d$, $d^2 = 1$, $ab = c$, $bc = a$, and $ca = b$.

2. Show that the group algebra G of the abstract group in (1) is not the quaternions Q but that mapping

$$1 \to \varepsilon_1$$
$$a \to \varepsilon_2$$
$$b \to \varepsilon_3$$
$$c \to \varepsilon_4$$
$$d \to -\varepsilon_1$$

maps G onto Q homomorphically.

3. Let Q be the system of quaternions over the real field Re. Show that for every $x \in Q$ there exist $r, s \in$ Re such that $x^2 - rx + s = 0$. For $x \in$ Re define $t(x) = 2x$, $n(x) = x^2$. For $x \notin$ Re let $t(x) = r$, $n(x) = s$ where $x^2 - rx + s = 0$, $r, s \in F$. Prove the following properties.

(i) For $a \in$ Re, $t(ax) = at(x)$
(ii) $t(x + y) = t(x) + t(y)$
(iii) $n(xy) = n(x)n(y)$
(iv) $t(xy) + n(x + y) = t(x)t(y) + n(x) + n(y)$.

4. Let V and W be finite dimensional vector spaces over F. Show that $\mathcal{L}(V \to W)$ is an associative algebra. Find the structive constants corresponding to the basis given in Theorem 13. $\mathcal{L}(V \to W)$ is called a linear algebra; give some reasons for this name.

SUPPLEMENTARY READING

C. W. Curtis, The four and eight square problem and division algebras, *Studies in Mathematics*, vol. 2 (A. A. Albert editor), Mathematical Association of America, Buffalo, New York (1963).

L. E. Dickson, *Algebras and their Arithmetics* (First Edition, 1923), New York: Dover (1960).

N. Jacobson, *Lectures in Abstract Algebra*, vol. II, Princeton, N.J.: Van Nostrand (1953).

P. R. Halmos, *Finite-Dimensional Vector Spaces*, Princeton, N.J.: Van Nostrand (1958).

I. Niven and H. S. Zukerman, *An Introduction to the Theory of Numbers*, New York: John Wiley & Sons (1960).

O. Schreier and E. Sperner, *Introduction to Modern Algebra and Matrix Theory* (translated by Davis and Hausner), New York: Chelsea (1955).

8 | Field Extensions and Finite Fields

In this chapter we take a deeper look into the relations between a field and its extensions and subfields. Our immediate goal is a proof of Theorem 6.10. In many respects this is the fundamental theorem of algebra; certainly it is the fundamental theorem of field theory.

8.1. CONSTRUCTION OF FIELD EXTENSIONS

Theorem 1 (*Kronecker*). Let F be a field. If $p(x)$ is a nonscalar polynomial in $F[x]$, there exists a field $E \supseteq F$ in which $p(x)$ has a zero.

PROOF. It clearly suffices to prove this theorem for irreducible polynomials, and we now assume that $p(x)$ is irreducible. Let $p(x) = c_0 + c_1 x + \cdots + c_n x^n$. From (7) of Theorem 6.6 we know that $\bar{E} = F[x]/\langle p(x)\rangle$ is a field. We shall see that up to an isomorphism, $\bar{E}$ satisfies the conclusion of the theorem. That isomorphism begins with the identification of the elements in F with the scalar polynomials in $F[x]$, and it is continued by the natural mapping $\varphi : F[x] \to F[x]/\langle p(x)\rangle$. Recall from the proof of Theorem 2.4 that the ring homomorphism φ is defined so that for all $a(x) \in F[x]$, $\varphi(a(x)) = a(x) + \langle p(x)\rangle = \overline{a(x)}$, the residue class of the ideal $\langle p(x)\rangle$ to which $a(x)$ belongs. Moreover $\varphi(a(x)) = \varphi(b(x))$ if and only if $p(x) \mid a(x) - b(x)$. In particular this means that the restriction of φ to the scalar polynomials c ($c \in F$) is an isomorphism of the scalar polynomials, hence of F onto the residue classes of the form $\bar{c} = c + \langle p(x)\rangle$.

Now by the division algorithm for all $f(x) \in F[x]$ there is a unique polynomial $r(x)$ such that $f(x) = p(x)q(x) + r(x)$ where $r(x) = 0$ or $\deg(r) < \deg(p) = n$. Since $\varphi(f) = \varphi(r)$, this means that each residue class of $\langle p(x)\rangle$

has a unique representative of degree less than n. If we let $\bar{x}$ denote the residue class to which x belongs we have

$$\bar{E} = \{\bar{a}_0 + \bar{a}_1\bar{x} + \cdots + \bar{a}_{n-1}\bar{x}^{n-1} : a_i \in F\}.$$

Now we have $p(x) \in \langle p(x) \rangle = \bar{0}$; consequently, since φ is a ring homomorphism,

$$\begin{aligned}
\bar{0} = \varphi(0) = \varphi(p(x)) &= \varphi(c_0 + c_1 x + \cdots + c_n x^n) \\
&= \varphi(c_0) + \varphi(c_1 x) + \cdots + \varphi(c_n x^n) \\
&= \bar{c}_0 + \bar{c}_1\bar{x} + \cdots + \bar{c}_n\bar{x}^n.
\end{aligned}$$

That is, $\bar{x} = \varphi(x) = x + \langle p(x) \rangle$ is a zero of the polynomial $\bar{c}_0 + \bar{c}_1 x + \cdots + \bar{c}_n x^n$ in $\bar{E}[x]$.

Now it should be clear where we go from here. F is isomorphic to a subfield of $\bar{E}$. This isomorphism carries over to an isomorphism between the polynomials of $F[x]$ and a subring of $\bar{E}[x]$. $p(x) = c_0 + c_1 x + \cdots + c_n x^n$, irreducible in $F[x]$, corresponds to the polynomial $\bar{p}(x) = \bar{c}_0 + \bar{c}_1 x + \cdots + \bar{c}_n x^n$ in $\bar{E}[x]$ which has a zero, $\bar{x}$, in $\bar{E}$. To avoid confusion of the different roles of x we shall use a new symbol θ for the residue class $\bar{x}$, identify $c \in F$ with $\bar{c} \in \bar{E}$, and so say that $\bar{E}$ is an extension of F, and conclude that $p(x)$ has the zero θ in $\bar{E}$. Finally we drop the $(^-)$ on E. In summary,

$$E = \{a_0 + a_1\theta + \cdots + a_{n-1}\theta^{n-1} : a_i \in F\}.$$

Calculations are carried out in this field with the relation $c_0 + c_1\theta + \cdots + c_n\theta^n = 0$.

* * *

If we identify F with a subfield of $F[x]/\langle p(x) \rangle$ we have that $F[x]/\langle p(x) \rangle$ is a vector space over F. From the proof of Theorem 1 we obtain our next result.

Corollary. If $p(x)$ is an irreducible polynomial of degree n ($n > 0$) in $F[x]$ then $\{\bar{1}, \bar{x}, \cdots, \bar{x}^{n-1}\}$ is a basis for $F[x]/\langle p(x) \rangle$ over F.

PROOF. The proof of Theorem 1 shows that $\{\bar{1}, \bar{x}, \cdots, \bar{x}^{n-1}\}$ spans $F[x]/\langle p(x) \rangle$ considered as a vector space over F. If this set of residue classes were dependent over F then we should have $\sum_{i=0}^{i=n-1} \bar{a}_i\bar{x}^i = \bar{0}$ and hence that $g(x) = \sum_{i=0}^{i=n-1} a_i x^i$ belongs to $\langle p(x) \rangle$; that is, that $p(x) \mid g(x)$. But since $\deg(g(x)) \le n-1$ while $\deg(p(x)) = n$, this is possible only if $g(x)$ is the zero polynomial; that is only if $a_i = 0$ for all i. Thus $\{\bar{1}, \bar{x}, \cdots, \bar{x}^{n-1}\}$ is a basis and the corollary holds.

* * *

Example 1. Let us carry out this proof in a specific case. (In section 6.4 we viewed the complex numbers in this way.) Let us consider $x^5 - 2$ over the rational numbers Ra. It is easy to show that there is no fifth root of 2 in Ra, and indeed by Eisenstein's criteria $x^5 - 2$ is irreducible in $\text{Ra}[x]$. Each residue class of $\text{Ra}[x]/\langle x^5 - 2 \rangle$ has a unique representative of degree less than 5 by the division algorithm. Hence

$$\text{Ra}[x]/\langle x^5 - 2 \rangle = \{a_0 + a_1 x + a_2 x^2 + a_3 x^3 + a_4 x^4 + \langle x^5 - 2 \rangle : a_i \in \text{Ra}\}$$
$$= \{\bar{a}_0 + \bar{a}_1 \bar{x} + \bar{a}_2 \bar{x}^2 + \bar{a}_3 \bar{x}^3 + \bar{a}_4 \bar{x}^4 : a_i \in \text{Ra}$$
$$\text{and } \bar{x} = x + \langle x^5 - 2 \rangle \}.$$

Employing the identifications and the symbol θ of the proof we have

$$E = \{a_0 + a_1 \theta + a_2 \theta^2 + a_3 \theta^3 + a_4 \theta^4 : a_i \in \text{Ra}, \theta^5 - 2 = 0\}.$$

Here are some sample calculations:

$$\theta^4(\theta^3 + 1) = \theta^7 + \theta^4 = \theta^2 \theta^5 + \theta^4 = 2\theta^2 + \theta^4.$$

It is an interesting exercise to compute $(1 + \theta + \theta^3)^{-1}$, or, in high school algebra terms, to rationalize $1/(1 + \sqrt[5]{2} + \sqrt[5]{8})$. We use the euclidean algorithm to obtain a solution for the congruence $(1 + x + x^3)s(x) \equiv 1 \pmod{x^5 - 2}$ as required by Theorem 5.16 and its corollary; equivalently we find polynomials $s(x)$ and $t(x)$ such that $(1 + x + x^3)s(x) + (x^5 - 2)t(x) = 1$. Thus in $\text{Ra}[x]/\langle x^5 - 2 \rangle$ we shall have $(\bar{1} + \bar{x} + \bar{x}^3)\bar{s}(\bar{x}) = \bar{1}$, or $(1 + \theta + \theta^3)s(\theta) = 1$. We calculate

$$x^5 - 2 = (x^3 + x + 1)(x^2 - 1) - (x^2 - x + 1)$$
$$x^3 + x + 1 = (x^2 - x + 1)(x + 1) + x$$
$$x^2 - x + 1 = x(x - 1) + 1;$$

thus $(x^3 + x + 1)(x^4 - x^2 - x + 1) - (x^5 - 2)x^2 = 1$. Hence $(\theta^3 + \theta + 1)^{-1} = \theta^4 - \theta^2 - \theta + 1$ or $1/(1 + \sqrt[5]{2} + \sqrt[5]{8}) = \sqrt[5]{16} - \sqrt[5]{4} - \sqrt[5]{2} + 1$.

Since $x^5 - 2$ has a zero θ in E we know that $x - \theta$ divides $x^5 - 2$ in $\mathcal{E}[x]$. We calculate

$$x^5 - 2 = (x - \theta)(x^4 + \theta x^3 + \theta^2 x^2 + \theta^3 x + \theta^4).$$

We may ask whether the second factor has a zero in E. If it does we may factor further; if not we may construct, by the same process, an extension of E in which an irreducible factor of $x^5 - 2$ in $E[x]$ has a root. We may continue in this way until we construct a sufficiently large field so that $x^5 - 2$ factors into linear factors. That is, a field to which all the zeros of $x^5 - 2$ belong. Theorem 2 gives us the result in general.

Definition. Let $f(x) \in F[x]$. $f(x)$ is said to *split* in an extension E of F if $f(x)$ can be factored as a product of linear factors in $E[x]$. E is said to be a *splitting field* for $f(x)$ over F if $f(x)$ splits in E but in no proper subfield of E which contains F.

Example 2. A splitting field of $x^2 + 1$ over the field of real numbers is the field of complex numbers. However this field is not a splitting field of $x^2 + 1$

over the rationals. A splitting of $x^2 + 1$ over the rationals, Ra, is $\mathrm{Ra}(i) \cong \mathrm{Ra}[x]/\langle x^2 + 1 \rangle$. (The notation $\mathrm{Ra}(i)$ was introduced on p. 118.)

Lemma 1. Let $f(x) \in F[x]$ have degree n. Let E be an extension of F. If $f(x) = c(x - a_1)(x - a_2)\ldots(x - a_n)$ in $E[x]$ then $F(a_1, \cdots, a_n)$ is a splitting field for $f(x)$ over F.

PROOF. Recall the definition from Section 4.3.

$F(a_1, \cdots, a_n) = \bigcap \{K : K \text{ a subfield of } E, F \subseteq K \subseteq E \text{ and } \{a_1, \cdots, a_n\} \subseteq K\}$.

In any event $f(x)$ splits in $H = F(a_1, \cdots, a_n)$ since each factor $x - a_i \in H[x]$. Now suppose $f(x)$ splits in K where $F \subseteq K \subseteq E$. In particular $x - a_i \in K[x]$ and so $a_i \in K$. Thus $\{a_1, \cdots, a_n\} \subseteq K$, and so $H \subseteq K$, and we have shown that $f(x)$ can split in no proper subfield of H which contains F.

* * *

Theorem 2 (*Existence of Splitting Fields*). For all fields F and for all $f(x) \in F[x]$ such that $\deg (f) \geq 1$, there is an extension K of F which is a splitting field for $f(x)$ over F.

PROOF. The proof is by induction on $\deg (f)$. If $\deg (f) = 1$ then $K = F$ since $f(x)$ is already a linear polynomial. For our induction hypothesis we assume the theorem for all fields and for all polynomials of degree less than n. Now suppose that $\deg (f) = n$. Let $p(x) \in F[x]$ be an irreducible factor of $f(x)$. By Theorem 1 there is a field $E \cong F[x]/\langle p(x) \rangle$ in which $p(x)$ has a root a_1, and by the factor theorem, in $E[x]$ we have $p(x) = (x - a_1)q(x)$, hence in $E[x]$ we have $f(x) = (x - a_1)q(x)g(x)$. Now $q(x)g(x)$ has degree $n - 1$, so by hypothesis there is a splitting field $H \supseteq E$ for $q(x)g(x)$ containing zeros $a_2, \cdots, a_n$ of $f(x)$ (see Figure 1). Clearly $f(x)$ splits in H, and so by Lemma 1 $F(a_1, \cdots, a_n) \subseteq H$ is a splitting field for $f(x)$ over F.

$$H$$
$$E$$
$$F$$

$E[x]$
$f(x) = (x - a_1)q(x)g(x)$

$F(x)$
$f(x) = p(x)g(x)$

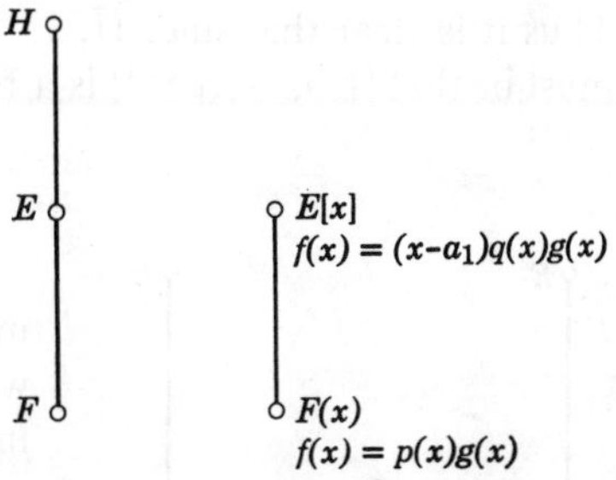

Figure 1

* * *

The question of unicity is a little more complicated. Let us reconsider the example $x^5 - 2$. We know that in the field of complex numbers $x^5 - 2$ has five distinct roots and indeed they are $\sqrt[5]{2}e^{2k\pi i/5}$; $k = 0, 1, 2, 3,$ and 4, as we showed in Chapter 4. One root is real, the others complex. Which root is θ? Our construction does not even show that E is a subfield of the complex numbers, but even in a splitting field constructed by successive steps, according to Theorem 2, we would be hard-pressed to distinguish the roots, except by the symbols used in the construction and properties of the rational numbers. Clearly E does not depend, up to isomorphism, on the identification of θ as a particular complex number. Our next theorems treat the isomorphism problem.

> **Theorem 3.** Let E be an extension of F. Let $p(x)$ be an irreducible polynomial of $F[x]$, and let $a \in E$ be a zero of $p(x)$. Then $F(a) \cong F[x]/\langle p(x) \rangle$ and if $\deg(p(x)) = n$ then $\{1, a, \cdots, a^{n-1}\}$ is a basis for $F(a)$ over F.

PROOF. We simply consider the mapping φ of $F[x] \to E$ given by defining $\varphi(f(x)) = f(a)$. As we observed in Theorem 6.3, φ is a ring homomorphism. The kernel of φ clearly contains $\langle p(x) \rangle$. We claim the kernel of φ is precisely $\langle p(x) \rangle$. If $f(x) \in F[x]$ and $f(a) = 0$, then by Lemma 6.4, since f and p have a common root in E, in $F[x]$ it follows that $\mathrm{GCD}(f,p) \neq 1$. As $p(x)$ is irreducible in $F[x]$ it follows that $p(x) \mid f(x)$, and so $f(x) \in \langle p(x) \rangle$. Thus the kernel is $\langle p(x) \rangle$ and so it follows from Theorem 2 that the range $\mathcal{R}_\varphi$ of φ is isomorphic with $F[x]/\langle p(x) \rangle$. But $F[x]/\langle p(x) \rangle$ is a field, hence $\mathcal{R}_\varphi$ is a field. On the other hand $\mathcal{R}_\varphi = \{f(a) : f(x) \in F[x]\}$, so $a \in \mathcal{R}_\varphi$ and any subfield of E containing F and a contains $\mathcal{R}_\varphi$. Thus $\mathcal{R}_\varphi \supseteq F(a) \supseteq \mathcal{R}_\varphi$.

Under the isomorphism $\mathcal{R}_\varphi \cong F[x]/\langle p \rangle$ the image of a is $\bar{x} = x + \langle p(x) \rangle$. Thus it is clear that since $\{\bar{1}, \bar{x}, \cdots, \bar{x}^{n-1}\}$ is a basis for $F[x]/\langle p(x) \rangle$ over F it must be that $\{1, a, \cdots, a^{n-1}\}$ is a basis for $F(a)$ over F.

* * *

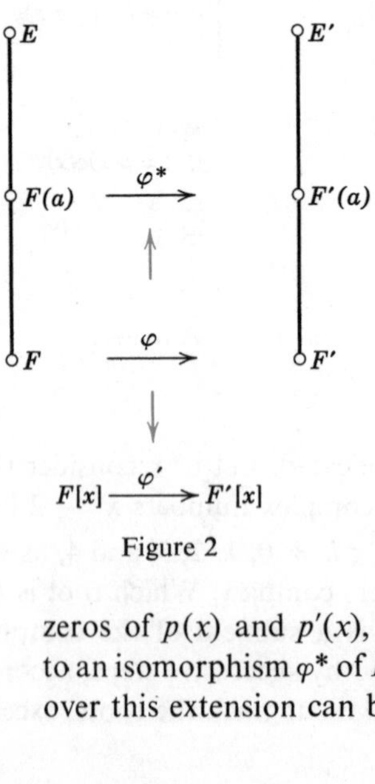

Figure 2

Our next theorem generalizes this isomorphism in a very useful way. Figure 2 will help picture the relationships described in the theorem.

> **Theorem 4.** Let F and F' be fields and φ be an isomorphism from F onto F'. Let F be a subfield of E and F' be a subfield of E'. Let $p(x) = c_0 + c_1 x + \cdots + c_n x^n$ be an irreducible polynomial in $F[x]$ and $p'(x) = \varphi(c_0) + \cdots + \varphi(c_n)x^n$ be the corresponding polynomial in $F'[x]$. If there are elements $a \in E$ and $a' \in E'$ which are respective zeros of $p(x)$ and $p'(x)$, then the isomorphism φ can be extended to an isomorphism φ^* of $F(a)$ onto $F'(a')$ such that $\varphi^*(a) = a'$. Moreover this extension can be made in only one way.

PROOF. We can easily extend φ to an isomorphism φ' of $F[x]$ onto $F'[x]$ by defining $\varphi'(a_0 + \cdots + a_m x^m) = \varphi(a_0) + \cdots + \varphi(a_m)x^m$. Under this isomorphism it is clear that $p'(x)$ is irreducible in $F'[x]$. From Theorem 3 we have isomorphisms $\theta : F(a) \rightarrow F[x]/\langle p(x)\rangle$ and $\Psi : F'(a') \rightarrow F'[x]/\langle p'(x)\rangle$. We now need only verify that $F[x]/\langle p(x)\rangle$ is isomorphic with $F'[x]/\langle p'(x)\rangle$. This must be the case since φ is but a "name-changing" apparatus. In detail,

$$F[x]/\langle p(x)\rangle = \{f(x) + \langle p(x)\rangle\}$$

and

$$F'[x]/\langle p'(x)\rangle = \{f'(x) + \langle p'(x)\rangle\}$$

and since φ' is an isomorphism, $\varphi' : F[x] \rightarrow F'[x]$, it is clear that the mapping φ'' is defined by $\varphi''(f(x) + \langle p(x)\rangle) = \varphi(f'(x)) + \langle p'(x)\rangle$ is indeed an isomorphism. Thus $\varphi^* = \Psi^{-1}\varphi''\theta$ is an isomorphism,

$$\varphi^* : F(a) \rightarrow F'(a').$$

We have $\varphi^*(f) = \varphi(f)$ for all $f \in F$ and $\varphi^*(a) = a'$, for $\varphi^*(a) = \Psi^{-1}\varphi''\theta(a) = \Psi^{-1}\varphi''(\bar{x}) = \Psi^{-1}(\bar{x}) = a'$, and if $f \in F$, then $\varphi^*(f) = \Psi^{-1}\varphi''\theta(f) = \Psi^{-1}\varphi''(f + \langle p(x)\rangle) = \Psi^{-1}(\varphi'(f) + \langle p_1(x)\rangle) = \varphi(f)$.

The unicity of φ^* as an extension of φ such that $\varphi^*(a) = a'$ follows from the fact that $\{1, a, \cdots, a^{n-1}\}$ is a basis for $F(a)$ over F. Thus any linear transformation, a fortiori any isomorphism of $F(a)$, is completely determined by its effect on this basis. If we require $\varphi^*(a) = a'$ the effect of φ^* on this basis is uniquely determined and so φ^* is determined uniquely.

* * *

Corollary. Let $p(x)$ be irreducible in $F[x]$ and $E \supseteq F$. If $p(x)$ has two zeros a, b in E, then $F(a) \cong F(b)$ by a unique isomorphism fixing all elements of F and taking a into b.

PROOF. In Theorem 4 take $F = F'$, $E = E'$, and $\varphi = $ identity isomorphism. The isomorphism φ^* of Theorem 4 is the desired isomorphism.

* * *

Theorem 5. Let φ be an isomorphism of a field F onto F'. Let $f(x) = a_0 + \cdots + a_n x^n \in F[x]$ and $f'(x) = \varphi(a_0) + \cdots + \varphi(a_n)x^n \in F'[x]$. If $E \supseteq F$ is a splitting field for $f(x)$ and if $E' \supseteq F'$ is a splitting field for $f'(x)$, then φ can be extended to an isomorphism Φ of E onto E'.

PROOF. The proof is by induction on the deg $(f(x))$. Figure 3 may be of help in picturing the proof. If deg $(f) = 1$, then $E = F$, and $E' = F'$ and $\Phi = \varphi$. Now we assume the theorem for all such situations where the degree of the polynomial is less than n. First we extend φ to an isomorphism φ' of $F[x]$ onto $F'[x]$, as in Theorem 4. Let $p(x)$ be an irreducible factor of $f(x)$. Then in

$F[x]$, $f(x) = p(x)g(x)$, and in $F'[x]$, $f'(x) = p'(x)g'(x)$. Let $a \in E$ be a zero of $p(x)$ and $a' \in E'$ be a zero of $p'(x)$. By Theorem 4 we may extend φ to an isomorphism φ^* of $K = F(a)$ onto $K' = F'(a')$. Clearly we may extend φ^* to an isomorphism $\varphi^{*'}$ of $K[x]$ onto $K'[x]$. Now in $K[x]$ we have $p(x) = (x - a)q(x)$, and in $K'[x]$ we have $p'(x) = (x - a')q'(x)$. Moreover, since $\varphi^{*'}$ is an isomorphism taking $p(x)$ into $p'(x)$ and $(x - a)$ into $(x - a')$, under $\varphi^{*'}$ we must have $q(x)$ mapped into $q'(x)$; thus $\varphi^{*'}$ takes $q(x)g(x)$ onto $q'(x)g'(x)$, which has degree $n - 1$.

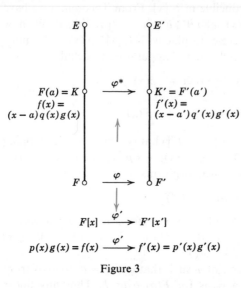

Figure 3

We claim that E is a splitting field for $[q(x)g(x)]$ over K. Surely $q(x)g(x)$ splits in E, and since $a \in E$, if $q(x)g(x)$ were to split in any proper subfield of E containing K, then $f(x)$ would split in that subfield. Similarly E' is a splitting field for $[q'(x)g'(x)]$ over K'. Hence by the induction hypothesis, we can extend φ^* to an isomorphism Φ of E onto E'.

* * *

Corollary. Let $f(x) \in F[x]$. Any two splitting fields for $f(x)$ over F are isomorphic.

PROOF. Let E and E' be two splitting fields for $f(x)$ over F. In Theorem 5 take $F = F'$ and φ to be the identity isomorphism.

* * *

Definition. Let $E \supseteq F$ and $a, b \in E$. a and b are called *conjugates over F* if a and b are zeros of the same irreducible polynomial in $F[x]$.

Example 3. The complex number $a = r + si$ ($r, s \in$ Re) and its complex conjugate $\bar{a} = r - si$ are conjugates over Re. If $s = 0$ then $a = \bar{a}$ while if $s \neq 0$ then $a \notin$ Re and $x^2 - 2rx + (r^2 + s^2)$ is irreducible in Re$[x]$ as it has no real zero—its zeros being a and $\bar{a}$.

It is important to note in the definition that conjugacy is relative to a particular field and that irreducible polynomials are required. Thus $\sqrt{2}$ and $-\sqrt{2}$ are conjugates in Re over Ra, but they are not conjugates in C over Re.

Theorem 6. Let $E \supseteq F$. The relation $\underset{\sim}{c}$ defined on E by $a \underset{\sim}{c} b$ if and only if $a = b$ or a and b are conjugates over F is an equivalence relation on E. Moreover if σ is any automorphism of E fixing each element of F, then for all $a \in E$, $a \underset{\sim}{c} \sigma(a)$.

PROOF. We shall omit the easy verification that $\underset{\sim}{c}$ is an equivalence relation on E. Let σ be an automorphism of E such that $\sigma(f) = f$ for all $f \in F$ and let $p(x) = c_0 + \cdots + c_n x^n$ be an irreducible polynomial of which a is a root. Then $0 = \sigma(0) = c_0 \sigma(a) + \cdots + c_n \sigma(a)^n$ and so $p(\sigma(a)) = 0$.

$$* \quad * \quad *$$

EXERCISE 1

1. Let $F = I/\langle 2 \rangle$ be the field of two elements. Show that $p(x) = x^3 + x + 1$ is irreducible in $F[x]$. Find the eight elements of $E = F[x]/\langle p(x) \rangle$. Write down the multiplication table for E. Show that E is a splitting field for $p(x)$.

2. Show that $f(x) = 2x^3 + 9x + 6$ is irreducible over the field Ra of rational numbers. In a field containing a zero θ of $f(x)$, express the multiplicative inverse of $\theta + 1$ in the form $a + b\theta + c\theta^2$.

3. Prove that the field H mentioned in the proof of Theorem 2 is the splitting field for $f(x)$.

4. Replace the "identification" process in the proof of Theorem 1 by an actual set-theoretic construction of a field E containing F as an actual subset (rather than an isomorphic copy of F) and such that $p(x)$ has a zero in E.

5. Let F be a field whose characteristic is not 2. Let E be a splitting field for $(x^2 - a)(x^2 - b) \in F[x]$. Let α be a zero of $x^2 - a$ and β a zero of $x^2 - b$. Under what conditions on a and b will $E = F(\alpha + \beta)$?

8.2.   CLASSIFICATION OF EXTENSIONS

The idea used in the proof of Theorem 3 can be used to classify the elements in an extension E of a field F with respect to their relation to F. In this section let E be a fixed extension of F.

Theorem 7. If $a \in E \supseteq F$ then either

$$F(a) \cong F(x), \text{ the field of quotients of } F[x],$$

or a is a zero of an irreducible polynomial $p(x) \in F[x]$ such that

$$F(a) \cong F[x]/\langle p(x) \rangle.$$

PROOF. As in Theorem 3 we consider the ring homomorphism $\varphi : F[x] \to E$ defined by $\varphi(f(x)) = f(a)$ and examine its kernel K_φ. If $K_\varphi \neq 0$ then $K_\varphi = \langle p(x) \rangle$ by (6) of Theorem 6.6, and as the range of φ is an integral domain it follows from Theorems 2.6 and 2.12 that $p(x)$ must be irreducible. A brief independent argument runs as follows. If $p(x) = g(x)h(x)$ then $0 = g(a)h(a)$ so that either $g(a) = 0$ or $h(a) = 0$. If $g(a) = 0$ then $g(x) \in K_\varphi$, and so $p(x) \mid g(x)$; hence $g(x)$ is an associate of $p(x)$. Thus $p(x)$ must be irreducible. But then, from Theorem 3, we have $F(a) \cong F[x]/\langle p(x)\rangle$.

Thus we may suppose that $K_\varphi = \{0\}$. This means that φ is an isomorphism and so $\mathscr{R}_\varphi \cong F[x]$. But now we can extend φ to an isomorphism φ^* of $F(x)$ onto $F(a)$ by defining $\varphi^*(f(x)/g(x)) = f(a)g(a)^{-1}$. The verification that φ^* is an isomorphism is left as an exercise.

*   *   *

Definition. Let $a \in E \supseteq F$. a is called *transcendental over F* if $F(a) \cong F(x)$. a is called *algebraic over F of degree n* if a is a zero of an irreducible polynomial $p(x) \in F[x]$ of degree n. In this case $F(a) \cong F[x]/\langle p(x)\rangle$.

It is conceivable that a could be algebraic over F of several different degrees. However Lemma 6.4 assures us that two irreducible polynomials in $F[x]$ with a common zero must have the same degree. Indeed Problem 6 of Exercises 6.4 establishes that two such polynomials are associates.

> **Theorem 8.** If $a \in E \supseteq F$ then a is algebraic over F if and only if there is a polynomial $f(x)$ of degree ≥ 1 so that $f(a) = 0$.

PROOF. The proof amounts to the observation that a is a zero of a polynomial $f(x)$ if and only if it is the zero of an irreducible factor of $f(x)$.

*   *   *

Definition. An extension $E \supseteq F$ is called an *algebraic* extension of F if every element in E is algebraic over F. If E is not an algebraic extension of F, then E is called a *transcendental* extension of F.

Note that if E is a transcendental extension of F then E contains at least one element which is transcendental over F. Here E may or may not have elements other than those of F which are algebraic over F.

Example 4. Every element of F is algebraic over F, for if $a \in F$ then a is a zero of $x - a$.

Example 5. Every complex number is algebraic over Re (the real numbers), for if $c = a + bi$ then c is a zero of $(x - c)(x - \bar{c}) = x^2 - 2ax + (a^2 + b^2) \in \text{Re}[x]$.

Example 6. Many, indeed most, real numbers are transcendental over the rationals. Among these are π and e. It is not easy to prove that these real numbers are transcendental over the rationals. We refer the interested reader to references at the end of this chapter. A famous theorem states that if a and b are algebraic over the rationals and b is irrational, then a^b is transcendental. Thus, in particular, $2^{\sqrt{2}}$ is transcendental over the rationals. This theorem was proved in 1934 independently by A. D. Gelfond and by Th. Schneider.

Another classification of extensions comes from the dimension of E as a vector space over F, as described in Example 8 of Chapter 7.

Definition. An extension $E \supseteq F$ is called a *finite* extension of F of degree n if E is a finite dimensional vector space of dimension n over F. Otherwise E is said to be an *infinite* extension of F. We write $[E:F]$ for the degree of E over F.

As a consequence of our definition we have immediately that if E is a finite extension of F of degree n then there exists a set $\{a_1, \cdots, a_n\} \subseteq E$ such that $E = F(a_1, \cdots, a_n)$. Indeed if $\{a_1, \cdots, a_n\}$ is a basis of E as a vector space over F, then $E = F(a_1, \cdots, a_n) = \{c_1 a_1 + \cdots + c_n a_n : c_i \in F\}$.

> **Theorem 9.** If $E \supseteq F$ and $[E:F]$ is finite, then E is an algebraic extension of F.

PROOF. Let $[E:F] = n$ and let $s \in E$. Then $1, s, s^2, \cdots, s^n$ are $(n+1)$ elements in a vector space of dimension n and hence must be linearly dependent over F. Thus there exist in F, $a_0, a_1, \cdots, a_n$, not all 0, such that $a_0 + a_1 s + \cdots + a_n s^n = 0$. That is, s is a zero of $0 \neq f(x) = a_0 + a_1 x + \cdots + a_n x^n$, and so by Theorem 8, s is algebraic over F.

*   *   *

We include the next theorem for completeness. It is an immediate consequence of our definitions in the light of the corollary to Theorem 1 and Theorem 3.

> **Theorem 10.** If $p(x)$ is an irreducible polynomial of degree n $(n > 0)$ in $F[x]$ then $E = F[x]/\langle p(x) \rangle$ is a finite extension of F of degree n. Moreover if $F \subseteq K$ and $a \in K$ is algebraic over F of degree n then $[F(a):F] = n$.

The next theorem is in some sense an analogue of the theorem of Lagrange for finite dimensional extensions. Figure 4 illustrates the relationship of the theorem.

> **Theorem 11.** If D is a finite extension of E and E is a finite extension of F, then $[D:F] = [D:E][E:F]$.

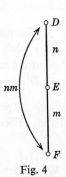

PROOF. Let $[D:E] = n$ and $[E:F] = m$. Let $a \in D$, and let $\{d_1, \cdots, d_n\}$ be a basis for D over E. This means that there exist elements $a_1, \cdots, a_n$ in E such that $a = a_1 d_1 + \cdots + a_n d_n$. Now we can get an expression for each a_i involving

Fig. 4

coefficients from F. Let $\{e_1, \cdots, e_m\}$ be a basis of E over F. Then, for each i, there are elements $b_{ij} \in F$ such that $a_i = b_{i1}e_1 + \cdots + b_{im}e_m$. Thus

$$a = \sum_{i=1}^{n} a_i d_i = \sum_{i=1}^{n} \left(\sum_{j=1}^{m} b_{ij}e_j \right) d_i = \sum_{i,j} b_{ij}(e_j d_i).$$

Now since $b_{ij} \in F$ and $e_j d_i \in D$ we have shown that the nm elements $\{e_j d_i : j = 1, \cdots, m$ and $i = 1, \cdots, n\}$ span D as a vector space over F. Hence $[D:F] \leq nm$. Next we shall show that the elements $e_j d_i$ are linearly independent over F. Suppose for some elements $b_{ij} \in F$ we have

$$0 = \sum_{i,j} b_{ij} e_j d_i.$$

The $0 = \sum_{i=1}^{n} (\sum_{j=1}^{m} b_{ij}e_j)d_i$. Since, for each i, $\sum_{j=1}^{m} b_{ij}e_j \in E$ and the set $\{d_1, \cdots, d_n\}$ is linearly independent over E, it follows that for all i, $0 = \sum_{j=1}^{m} b_{ij}e_j$. However, the set $\{e_1, \cdots, e_m\}$ is linearly independent over F; hence for all j, $b_{ij} = 0$.

8.3. TRANSCENDENTAL EXTENSIONS

In this section we shall obtain a few results about isomorphisms between transcendental extensions.

Theorem 12. Let $E \supseteq F$ and $\bar{E} \supseteq \bar{F}$. Let $\varphi : F \to \bar{F}$ be an isomorphism of F onto $\bar{F}$. If $a \in E$ is transcendental over F and $\bar{a} \in \bar{E}$ is transcendental over $\bar{F}$ then φ can be extended to an isomorphism Φ of $F(a)$ onto $\bar{F}(\bar{a})$ such that $\Phi(a) = \bar{a}$.

PROOF. From the definition there is an isomorphism $\psi : F(a) \to F(x)$ and an isomorphism $\theta : \bar{F}(y) \to \bar{F}(\bar{a})$ such that $\psi(a) = x$ and $\theta(y) = \bar{a}$. We may extend φ to an isomorphism φ' of $F(x)$ onto $\bar{F}(y)$ so that $\varphi'(x) = y$. Thus $\Phi = \theta\varphi'\psi$ is an isomorphism from $F(a)$ onto $\bar{F}(\bar{a})$ and $\Phi(a) = \bar{a}$.

$$* \quad * \quad *$$

Theorem 13. Let $E \supseteq F$. If $A = \{a_1, \cdots, a_n\}$ is a set of elements in E such that for each i, a_i is transcendental over $F(a_1, \cdots, a_{i-1})$ then there is an isomorphism $\Phi : F(a_1, \cdots, a_n) \to F(x_1, \cdots, x_n)$ such that $\Phi(a_i) = x_i$.

PROOF. Recall that $F(x_1, \cdots, x_i)$ is the field of quotients of $F[x_1, \cdots, x_i]$. From Theorem 6.20 we have that if $F^{(i)}$ denotes $F(x_1, \cdots, x_i)$ then $F(x_1, \cdots, x_{i+1}) \cong F^{(i)}(x_{i+1})$. Now by definition there is an isomorphism $\varphi : F(a_1) \to F(x_1) = F^{(1)}$ such that $\varphi(a_1) = x_1$. We proceed by induction on n. We have, by the induction hypothesis, that there is an isomorphism

$\theta : F(a_1, \cdots, a_{n-1}) \to F(x_1, \cdots, x_{n-1}) = F^{(n-1)}$ such that $\theta(a_i) = x_i$. Hence by Theorem 12 we may extend this isomorphism to an isomorphism $\theta' : F(a_1, \cdots, a_{n-1})(a_n) = F(a_1, \cdots, a_n) \to F^{(n-1)}(x_n)$, which by Theorem 6.20 is isomorphic to $F(x_1, \cdots, x_n)$. The composition of these isomorphisms yields the desired isomorphism Φ.

$$* \quad * \quad *$$

Definition. Let $E \supseteq F$. Let $A = \{a_1, \cdots, a_n\}$ be a set of n distinct elements in E. The set A is called *algebraically independent* over F if, $\sum f_{i_1 \ldots i_n} a_1^{i_1} \cdots a_n^{i_n} = 0$, for coefficients $f_{i_1 \ldots i_n} \in F$, implies all coefficients $f_{i_1 \ldots i_n} = 0$.

Example 7. In $F(x_1, \cdots, x_n)$ the elements $x_1, \cdots, x_n$ are algebraically independent. It follows immediately from Theorem 6.21 that in this case the definition is satisfied.

> **Theorem 14.** Let $E \supseteq F$. Let $A = \{a_1, \cdots, a_n\} \subseteq E$. A is algebraically independent over F if and only if for each $i \leq n$, a_i is transcendental over $F(a_1, \cdots, a_{i-1})$.

PROOF. It is easy to show that if A is algebraically independent then a_i is transcendental over $F(a_1, \cdots, a_{i-1})$. To prove the converse we make use of the isomorphism between $F(a_1, \cdots, a_n)$ and $F(x_1, \cdots, x_n)$ given by Theorem 13. If $\sum f_{i_1 \ldots i_n} a_1^{i_1} \ldots a_n^{i_n} = 0$, then from the isomorphism we should have $\sum f_{i_1 \ldots i_n} x_1^{i_1} \cdots x_n^{i_n} = 0$; but by Theorem 6.21 this entails that all coefficients $f_{i_1 \ldots i_h}$ be equal to zero.

> **Theorem 15.** Let $E \supseteq F$. Let $A = \{a_1, \cdots, a_n\}$ be algebraically independent over F. If φ is any permutation on A then it may be extended to an automorphism Φ of $F(a_1, \cdots, a_n)$.

PROOF. From Theorem 14, $\varphi(a_i)$ is transcendental over $F(\varphi(a_1), \cdots, \varphi(a_{i-1}))$ for all i and so, by Theorem 13, $F(\varphi(a_1), \cdots, \varphi(a_n)) \cong F(x_1, \cdots, x_n)$ by an isomorphism sending $\varphi(a_i)$ into x_i. By the same reason, $F(x_1, \cdots, x_n) \cong F(a_1, \cdots, a_n)$ by an isomorphism sending x_i into a_i. The composition of these isomorphisms yields the desired automorphism Φ.

$$* \quad * \quad *$$

Corollary. For every permutation σ on $\{1, \cdots, n\}$ there is an automorphism σ of $F(x_1, \cdots, x_n)$ such that $\sigma(x_i) = x_{\sigma(i)}$. This isomorphism sends $\sum f_{i_1 \ldots i_n} x_1^{i_1} \ldots x_n^{i_n}$ into $\sum f_{i_1 \ldots i_n} x_{\sigma(1)}^{i_1} \cdots x_{\sigma(n)}^{i_n}$. In a more succinct notation, $\sigma(f(x_1, \cdots, x_n)) = f(x_{\sigma(1)}, \cdots, x_{\sigma(n)})$.

8.4. ALGEBRAIC EXTENSIONS

In this section we shall consider only algebraic extensions of a field F. As a first goal we shall prove that "an algebraic extension of an algebraic extension is an algebraic extension."

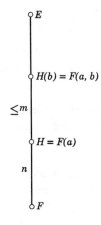

Figure 5

Theorem 16 Let a and b be elements of an extension field $E \supseteq F$. If a and b are algebraic over F, then $a + b$, ab, $-b$; and, if $b \neq 0$, b^{-1} are algebraic over F.

PROOF. By definition, a and b are zeros, respectively, of irreducible polynomials $p(x)$ and $q(x)$ of degree n and m. Moreover $H = F(a) = F[x]/\langle p(x)\rangle$ has degree n over F. Now consider $q(x) \in H[x]$. By Theorem 8, b is algebraic over H, and hence b is a zero of an irreducible polynomial $q_1(x) \in H[x]$, and $H(b) \cong H[x]/\langle q_1(x)\rangle$. Necessarily, $q_1(x) \mid q(x)$ so that $[H(b):H] \leq m$, and so $[H(b):F] \leq nm$, and $H(b)$ is algebraic over F (see Figure 5). But now, since $a, b \in H(b) = F(a, b)$, it follows that $a + b$, ab, $-b$, and if $b \neq 0$, $b^{-1} \in H(b)$ so that they too are algebraic over F.

$$* \quad * \quad *$$

Corollary. Let $E \supseteq F$. The set $A = \{a : a \in E \text{ and } a \text{ algebraic over } F\}$ of elements in E form a subfield of E.

PROOF. Theorem 16 establishes the necessary closure properties.

$$* \quad * \quad *$$

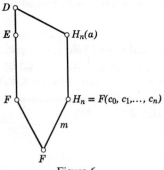

Figure 6

Theorem 17. Let D, E, and F be fields such that $D \supseteq E \supseteq F$. If E is an algebraic extension of F and $a \in D$ is algebraic over E, then a is algebraic over F.

PROOF. By definition, a is a root of $p(x) = c_0 + c_1 x + \cdots + c_n x^n \in E[x]$. By assumption, each c_i is algebraic over F and it follows from Theorem 10 that $[F(c_i):F]$ is finite. Then in successive steps we form $H_0 = F(c_0)$ and, inductively, $H_{i+1} = H_i(c_{i+1})$. c_{i+1} is algebraic over H_i since it is algebraic over $F \subseteq H_i$. Hence $[H_i : H_{i-1}]$ is finite. By Theorem 11, H_n is finite over F (see Figure 6). Now a is algebraic over H_n

and hence $[H_n(a) : H_n]$ is finite, and so $[H_n(a) : F]$ is finite. In particular a is algebraic over F.

*   *   *

Corollary. If D is an algebraic extension of E and E is an algebraic extension of F, then D is an algebraic extension of F.

We shall leave the proof of this important corollary as an exercise. In the proof of Theorem 17 note that we have dodged the issue of just what polynomial in $F[x]$ has the element $a \in D$ as a zero. To exhibit the polynomial we need other techniques, which we shall develop later. (See Section 10.7 and Problem 4 of Exercise 10.3).

An important tool for investigating properties of a field extension $E \supseteq F$ is the set of automorphisms of E which fix every element of F. As we observed in the corollary to Theorem 4.5, this set of these automorphisms forms a group $\mathscr{G}(E/F)$. Theorems 4 and 5 show that if E is the splitting field of an irreducible polynomial $f(x)$ with at least two distinct zeros, then $\mathscr{G}(E/F)$ has some members other than ι—the identity automorphism—indeed, if a and b are two distinct roots of $f(x)$ we have an isomorphism $\varphi : F(a) \to F(b)$ with $\varphi(a) = b$, which may be extended to an automorphism of E. Under the assumption that E is a splitting field of a polynomial we shall be able to say a great deal about $\mathscr{G}(E/F)$. This is the primary topic of the Galois Theory of Chapter 10. For now we shall obtain some more modest results. Our first result is a direct corollary of Theorem 6.

> ***Theorem 18.*** Let $E = F(a)$. If a is algebraic over F of degree n then the order of $\mathscr{G}(E/F)$ is at most n. If a is the zero of an irreducible polynomial of degree n in $F[x]$ which has n distinct zeros in E then $\mathscr{G}(E/F)$ has order n.

PROOF. Let $p(x)$ be an irreducible polynomial in $F[x]$ of which a is a zero. As we observed in the proof of Theorem 4, an automorphism σ of E fixing the elements of F is completely determined by $\sigma(a)$. On the other hand, from Theorem 6, we know that $\sigma(a)$ is a root of $p(x)$ and since $p(x)$ has at most n zeros we have that $|\mathscr{G}(E/F)| \le n$. On the other hand, if $p(x)$ has n distinct zeros in E then E is a splitting field for $p(x)$ over F. From the Corollary to Theorem 4 and Theorem 5, for every zero a' of $p(x)$ there is an automorphism σ of E such that $\sigma(a) = a'$. In this automorphism each element of F is left fixed since it is an extension of the identity automorphism of F. Thus $|\mathscr{G}(E/F)| \ge n$.

*   *   *

Definition. A field E is called *algebraically closed* if E has no proper algebraic extensions.

Example 8. The field of complex numbers is algebraically closed. This is a consequence of the next theorem and of the Fundamental Theorem of

Algebra, which says that every polynomial with complex coefficients has a complex zero; this in turn implies that only linear polynomials are irreducible.

> **Theorem 19.** Let E be an algebraic extension of F. The following conditions are equivalent.
>
> 1. E is algebraically closed.
> 2. Every irreducible polynomial in $E[x]$ is linear.
> 3. Every polynomial in $F[x]$ splits in E.

PROOF. Statement 1 implies 2: If $p(x)$ is irreducible and has degree > 1, then $E_1 = E[x]/\langle p(x) \rangle$ is a proper algebraic extension of E. Hence deg $(p) = 1$.

Statement 2 implies 3: Let $f(x) \in F[x]$ and let $p(x)$ be an irreducible polynomial in $E[x]$ dividing $f(x)$. From 2, we have that $p(x) = x - a$ with $a \in E$. Thus $f(x)$ splits in $E[x]$.

Statement 3 implies 1: Suppose that E has a proper algebraic extension E_1. Hence there exists $a \in E_1$ such that $a \notin E$. a is algebraic over E, hence, by Theorem 17, a is algebraic over F, and so a is a zero of an irreducible polynomial $p(x)$ in $F[x]$. But $p(x)$ splits in E, hence $p(x) = e(x - e_1)(x - e_2) \cdots (x - e_n)$ in $E[x]$. Since a is a zero of $p(x)$ we must have $a = e_i \in E$ for some i, contrary to the choice of a.

* * *

Our next theorem tells us, for example, that starting with the rational numbers, we may successively adjoin zeros of polynomials until we obtain a field which contains all zeros of all polynomials with rational coefficients. We shall prove this theorem when the number of elements in the field is countable.

Definition. A set S is called countable if there is a 1–1 function from S into I_+. In particular, a finite set is countable.

We employ a technical trick in our proof to define a 1–1 function from $F[x]$ into I_+. The device we use was invented by the contemporary logician Kurt Gödel, and is called a Gödel numbering.

> **Theorem 20.** Let F be a countable field. There exists an algebraic extension E of F which is algebraically closed.

PROOF. Let γ be the 1–1 mapping of F into I_+. We first define a 1–1 mapping θ of $F[x]$ into I_+. Let $(p_0, p_1, \ldots)$ be the sequence of primes in I_+. $p_0 = 2$, $p_1 = 3$, etc. Now let $f(x) = a_0 + a_1 x + \cdots + a_n x^n \in F[x]$. Let $\theta(f) = \prod_{i=0}^{n} p_i^{\gamma(a_i)}$. The 1–1 nature of θ follows from the unique factorization theorem for I_+. Now we define inductively a sequence of finite extensions of F:

$\Phi(1) = F$.   If $n > 1$,

$$\Phi(n + 1) = \begin{cases} \Phi(n) \text{ if } n \notin \text{range of } \theta, \text{ otherwise,} \\ \text{splitting field of } \theta^{-1}(n) \text{ over } \Phi(n). \end{cases}$$

The fields $\Phi(n)$ form a chain $F = \Phi(1) \subseteq \Phi(2) \subseteq \ldots$, and we assert that the set union of this chain, call it E,

$$E = \bigcup \{\Phi(n) : n \in I_+\}$$

is the desired field. We must, of course, define binary operations appropriately in E, but this is done in a very natural way. If $a, b \in E$ then there is least integer n such that $a, b \in \Phi(n)$. Define $a + b = c$ if and only if $a + b = c$ in in $\Phi(n)$ and $a \cdot b = d$ if and only if $ab = d$ in $\Phi(n)$. This clearly defines two binary operations on E and

  1. $\langle E, +, \cdot \rangle$ is a field.
  2. For every n, $\Phi(n)$ can be regarded as a subfield of E.
  3. Every element in E is algebraic over F.
  4. E is algebraically closed.

The proofs of 1, 2, and 3 are easy. Property 4 follows by noting that condition 3 of Theorem 19 is satisfied; indeed we constructed E by adjoining all roots of all polynomials in F.

$$* \quad * \quad *$$

Definition. A field E is called an algebraic closure of F if E is an algebraically closed field which is an algebraic extension of F.

We have proved that every countable field has an algebraic closure. It is true that every field has an algebraic closure. There is a proof of this theorem which is essentially the same as that given above, except that the chain of field extensions must be defined by a transfinite induction. An equivalent method is to secure the algebraic closure by employing the maximum principle on a suitably defined set of field extensions of F. The interested reader may consult some of the references listed at the end of this chapter. There he will also find proofs of the following uniqueness theorem: Any two algebraic closures of a field are isomorphic.

EXERCISE 2

1. Let E be an extension of a field F. Let $a \in E$. Regarding E as a vector space over F show that the subspace spanned by $\{1, a, a^2, \ldots\}$ is a field if and only if a is algebraic over F.

2. Let R be a ring and E and F fields such that $E \supseteq R \supseteq F$. (We suppose that F and R are subrings of E.) If E is an algebraic extension of F prove that R is a field.

3. Let $f(x)$ and $g(x)$ be irreducible over F. Let deg $(f) = n$, deg $(g) = m$, and $(n, m) = 1$. Let $g(x)$ have a zero $a \in E \supseteq F$. Show that $f(x)$ is irreducible over $F(a)$.

4. Complete the details in the proof of Theorem 7.

5. Let $E = F(x)$. Show that σ^* defined by $\sigma^*(f(x)) = f(x + 1)$ is an automorphism of $F[x]$ which may be extended to an automorphism σ of E. Show that if char $(F) = 0$ then $F = \{a \in E : \sigma(a) = a\}$. What can be said about $\{a \in E : \sigma(a) = a\}$ if char $(F) = p$?

6. Prove, using if necessary the Fundamental Theorem of Algebra (Theorem 4.11) that it is impossible to define an addition and multiplication in $V_3(\mathrm{Re})$ so that this vector space becomes a field. (Recall that we made such a construction in $V_2(\mathrm{Re})$ in defining the complex numbers.)

8.5. FINITE FIELDS

We are now in a position to obtain a great deal of information about finite fields. This theory is of considerable interest in its own right and it provides a particularly beautiful example of how the general theory of the preceding chapters fits together to provide a rather detailed description of all finite fields. We already know something about finite fields. The prime subfield P of a finite field F is isomorphic with $I/\langle p \rangle$, where p is a prime integer. Theorem 7.9 states that the number of elements in F is then p^n where n is the dimension of F as a vector space over P; that is, F is a finite extension of P of degree n and is thus an algebraic extension of P. Our next result was a problem in Exercise 4.2, but we shall state it here for future reference.

Lemma 2. Let p be a prime. If R is a commutative ring in which $pr = 0$ for all $r \in R$ then $(a + b)^{p^n} = a^{p^n} + b^{p^n}$ for all $a, b \in R$ and for all $n \in I_+$.

PROOF. The proof is by induction on n. For $n = 1$ we may calculate $(a + b)^p$ by the binomial formula, since R is commutative: $(a + b)^p = \sum_{k=0}^{n} \binom{p}{k} a^k b^{p-k}$. Now if $0 < k < p$ then $\binom{p}{k} = p!/k!(p - k)! \equiv 0 \pmod{p}$ since $p \nmid k!(p - k)!$ for $0 < k < p$. Hence $\binom{p}{k} a^k b^{p-k} = 0$ in R and so $(a + b)^p = a^p + b^p$. Now $(a + b)^{p^n} = ((a + b)^p)^{p^{n-1}} = (a^p + b^p)^{p^{n-1}} = (a^p)^{p^{n-1}} + (b^p)^{p^{n-1}} = a^{p^n} + b^{p^n}$. The third equality holds by the induction hypothesis.

$$* \quad * \quad *$$

A consequence of this lemma is that in a commutative ring R in which $pr = 0$ for all r, the mapping $\varphi(a) = a^p$ is an endomorphism of R. The lemma tells us $\varphi(a + b) = \varphi(a) + \varphi(b)$ while $\varphi(ab) = \varphi(a)\varphi(b)$ holds trivially by commutativity.

Lemma 3. If F is a field of characteristic p, then $S = \{a : a \in F \text{ and } a^{p^n} - a = 0\}$ is a subfield of F.

PROOF. S contains 0 and 1 and has the appropriate closure properties because $(a + b)^{p^n} = a^{p^n} + b^{p^n}$ in a field of characteristic p, and always $(ab)^{p^n} = a^{p^n} b^{p^n}$. Finally then, if $a \in S$ we have $-a = (p - 1)a \in S$, and if $0 \neq a \in S$ we have $(a^{-1})^{p^n} = (a^{p^n})^{-1} = a^{-1}$.

* * *

Theorem 21 (*Existence and Uniqueness of Finite Fields*). For every prime p and every integer n there exists a finite field with p^n elements. Any field with p^n elements is isomorphic to the splitting field of $x^{p^n} - x$ over $P = I/\langle p \rangle$.

The motivation for this theorem comes from the fact that if F has p^n elements then the nonzero elements form a finite group of $p^n - 1$ elements; thus if $0 \neq a \in F$ then $a^{p^n - 1} = 1$ by Lagrange's theorem, and so every element of F is a zero of $x^{p^n} - x$. On the other hand this polynomial can have at most p^n zeros, and Lemma 3 tells us that the zeros of this polynomial form a subfield of its splitting field. This is essentially the proof!

PROOF (*Existence*). Consider the polynomial $x^{p^n} - x$ in $P[x]$. Let F be its splitting field over P. We note first of all that $x^{p^n} - x$ has p^n distinct zeros in F since its derivative is $p^n x^{p^n - 1} - 1 = -1$ in $P[x]$ and so can have no common factor with $x^{p^n} - x$. We shall show that F consists precisely of these p^n elements. This amounts to the observation that F contains the subfield S of Lemma 3, but on the other hand $x^{p^n} - x$ must split in S since S contains all its zeros. Thus $F = S$, and so F has p^n elements.

(*Uniqueness*). From our observations about the motivation for this theorem, it is clear that if F is a finite field with p^n elements, then $x^{p^n} - x$ splits in F and has p^n zeros. On the other hand the polynomial could split in no proper subfield since no proper subfield has p^n elements; hence F must be a splitting field for $x^{p^n} - x$. Thus the uniqueness follows from the uniqueness of splitting fields—which was established by Theorem 5 and its corollary.

* * *

In view of this theorem we may speak of *the* finite field of p^n elements. Finite fields are called Galois fields in honor of Evariste Galois, and traditionally the finite field of p^n elements is denoted by $\mathrm{GF}(p^n)$. Our next theorem tells us the nature of all subfields of $\mathrm{GF}(p^n)$.

Theorem 22. If H is a subfield of $\mathrm{GF}(p^n)$ then $H \cong \mathrm{GF}(p^m)$ where $m \mid n$. Conversely, if $m \mid n$ then there is exactly one subfield with p^m elements.

PROOF. From the previous theorem, if a subfield exists it is isomorphic to $\mathrm{GF}(p^m)$ where $m \leq n$. Theorem 11 on the multiplicative property of degrees tells us that $n = [\mathrm{GF}(p^n):P] = [\mathrm{GF}(p^n):\mathrm{GF}(p^m)][\mathrm{GF}(p^m):P]$. Hence $m = [\mathrm{GF}(p^m):P]$ divides n.

There can be at most one subfield with p^m elements in $\mathrm{GF}(p^n)$, because any such field contains all the zeros of $x^{p^m} - x$, and if there were two distinct subfields of order p^m in $\mathrm{GF}(p^n)$ then there would be more than p^m zeros of $x^{p^m} - x$ in $\mathrm{GF}(p^n)$.

Now if $m \mid n$, then from Lemma 4.8 we have $p^m - 1 \mid p^n - 1$; also by Lemma 4.8, $x^{p^m-1} - 1 \mid x^{p^n-1} - 1$. Thus $x^{p^m} - x \mid x^{p^n} - x$, the division taking place in $I[x]$, hence also in $P[x]$. Thus every zero of $x^{p^m} - x$ is a zero of $x^{p^n} - x$ and so belongs to $\mathrm{GF}(p^n)$. Consequently, $\mathrm{GF}(p^n)$ must contain as a subfield—a splitting field of $x^{p^m} - x$—which we know to be $\mathrm{GF}(p^m)$.

* * *

Theorem 23. The multiplicative group of nonzero elements in $\mathrm{GF}(p^n)$ is cyclic.

PROOF. Since this group is abelian we may apply the corollary of Theorem 5.18. Let m be the positive integer such that for $0 \neq a \in \mathrm{GF}(p^n)$ we have $a^m = 1$, and let $g \in \mathrm{GF}(p^n)$ have order m. Since $a^m = 1$ for all nonzero a, it follows that $x^m - 1$ has $p^n - 1$ distinct zeros in $\mathrm{GF}(p^n)$, hence $m \geq p^n - 1$; however, since the order of g is m it must be that $m \leq p^n - 1$—the order of the group. Hence $m = p^n - 1$ and so the group is cyclic, and g is its generator.

* * *

Theorem 24. If g is a generator of the cyclic group of nonzero elements of $\mathrm{GF}(p^n)$ then g is algebraic over $P = \mathrm{GF}(p)$ of degree n.

It is no trick to prove that g is algebraic over P; the trick is to prove that g is the zero of an irreducible polynomial of degree n in $P[x]$. For notational ease let $H = \mathrm{GF}(p^n)$. Since the powers of g generate all nonzero elements of H it is clear that $P(g) = H$. On the other hand, g is the zero of some polynomial $g(x)$ irreducible in $P[x]$ and, by Theorem 7, $P(g) \cong P[x]/\langle g(x)\rangle$. Since the degree of $g(x)$ and the degree of $[P(g):P]$ coincide, and we know the latter to be n, the theorem follows.

* * *

Corollary. In $\mathrm{GF}(p)[x]$ there exist irreducible polynomials of degree n for all positive integers n. Moreover $\mathrm{GF}(p^n)$ is the splitting field of an irreducible polynomial in $\mathrm{GF}(p)[x]$.

Theorem 25. Let $g(x)$ be an irreducible polynomial over $\mathrm{GF}(p)$ of degree d. $g(x) \mid x^{p^n} - x$ if and only if $d \mid n$.

PROOF. If $g(x) \mid x^{p^n} - x$, then $g(x)$ has a zero in $H = GF(p^n)$ and so, by Theorem 3, H contains a subfield isomorphic to $P[x]/\langle g(x) \rangle$, which has degree d over P. By Theorem 22, $d \mid n$. Conversely, if $d \mid n$, then H contains the subfield $GF(p^d)$, and since $E = P[x]/\langle g(x) \rangle$ has degree d and p^d elements, it follows from Theorem 21 that $E \cong GF(p^d)$; thus $GF(p^d)$ contains a zero of $g(x)$. Hence $g(x)$ and $x^{p^d} - x$ have a zero in common and as $g(x)$ is irreducible it follows that $x^{p^d} - x$ is divisible by $g(x)$.

* * *

An important corollary follows. We leave the proof as an exercise.

Corollary. If an irreducible polynomial $g(x) \in GF(p)[x]$ has a zero in $GF(p^n)$ then $g(x)$ splits in $GF(p^n)$. Any irreducible polynomial has simple zeros and any two irreducible polynomials of the same degree have isomorphic splitting fields.

Theorem 26. $x^{p^n} - x$ is the product of all the irreducible monic polynomials $p(x)$ in $GF(p)[x]$ such that degree $(p(x))$ divides n.

PROOF. In view of Theorems 25 and 5.11 we have only to show that the irreducible monic polynomials of $GF(p)[x]$ are mutually coprime. Let $p(x)$ and $q(x)$ be distinct irreducible monic polynomials of $GF(p)[x]$. Since both are irreducible, they are either coprime or associates. If $p(x) = cq(x)(c \in GF(p))$, then since $p(x)$ and $q(x)$ are monic, it follows that $c = 1$, by comparing their leading coefficients.

* * *

Corollary. If $W_p(d)$ is the number of irreducible monic polynomials of degree d in $GF(p)[x]$ then $p^n = \sum_{d/n} d W_p(d)$.

PROOF. In the factorization of $x^{p^n} - x$ over $GF(p)$, given in Theorem 26, we simply compare the degrees on both sides. On the left we have p^n while on the right we have a sum of the degrees of all the irreducible monic polynomials of $GF(p)[x]$. If $d \mid n$, there are, by Theorem 25, $W_p(d)$ summands equal to d. If $d \nmid n$, there are no summands equal to d.

* * *

This corollary gives us a perfectly good way of calculating $W_p(n)$. For example, $W_3(6)$ can be obtained as $3^6 = 1W_3(1) + 2W_3(2) + 3W_3(3) + 6W_3(6)$. Thus we must first calculate $W_3(1)$, $W_3(2)$, and $W_3(3)$. Note that $W_p(1) = p$ since the number of irreducible polynomials of the form $x + b$ is just the number of choices for b which is p. Thus if q is a prime, $qW_p(q) = [p^q - p]$, and so we obtain $6W_3(6) = 3^6 - [W_3(1) + 2W_3(2) + 3W_3(3)] = 3^6 - (3 + 6 + 24)$, and so $W_3(6) = 116$.

It is an interesting exercise involving a little elementary number theory to obtain an explicit formula for $W_p(n)$ in terms of a number-theoretic function, called the Möbius μ-function after A. F. Möbius (1790–1868). Since we shall have occasion to use this again we proceed in a general setting.

Definition. The Möbius μ-function is a function from the nonnegative integers into $\{-1, 0, 1\}$ defined by

$\mu(0) = 0,$
$\mu(1) = 1,$
$\mu(n) = 0$ if $p^2 \mid n$ for some prime p,
$\mu(n) = (-1)^k$ if $n = p_1 \cdots p_k$ where $\{p_1, \cdots, p_k\}$ is a set of distinct primes.

From this definition we have $\mu(p) = -1$ for any prime p and, for example, $\mu(4) = 0$, $\mu(6) = 1$, $\mu(12) = 0$, and $\mu(30) = -1$.

Lemma 4. For all integers $d \geq 1$,

$$\sum_{d \mid n} \mu(d) = \begin{cases} 1 \text{ if } n = 1 \\ 0 \text{ if } n > 1. \end{cases}$$

PROOF. For $n = 1$ this formula is trivial. It is easily verified when $n = p$, a prime. If $n = p_1^{e_1} \cdots p_k^{e_k}$ is the factorization of n into distinct prime powers and $m = p_1 \cdots p_k$ then $\sum_{d \mid n} \mu(d) = \sum_{d \mid m} \mu(d)$ for the divisors of n such that $\mu(d) \neq 0$ are precisely the divisors of m. Now the number of divisors $d \mid m$ such that $\mu(d) = 1$ is the number of subsets of $P = \{p_1, \cdots, p_k\}$ with an even number of elements (we include the empty set, corresponding to $d = 1$) whereas the number of $d \mid m$ such that $\mu(d) = -1$ is the number of subsets of P with an odd number of elements. Since these two numbers of subsets are the same (Theorem 0.8) the lemma follows.

$$* \quad * \quad *$$

Theorem 27 (*Möbius inversion formula*). Let $f : I_+ \to I_+$ and $F : I_+ \to I_+$ be two functions related by

$$F(m) = \sum_{d \mid m} f(d).$$

Then
$$f(m) = \sum_{d \mid m} \mu\left(\frac{m}{d}\right) F(d) = \sum_{d \mid m} \mu(d) F\left(\frac{m}{d}\right).$$

PROOF. The last two sums are clearly the same by replacing the dummy index d by $d_1 = m/d$. Now we calculate

$$\sum_{d \mid m} \mu(d) F\left(\frac{m}{d}\right) = \sum_{d \mid m} \mu(d) \sum_{c \mid (m/d)} f(c)$$

$$= \sum_{cd \mid m} \mu(d) f(c) = \sum_{c \mid m} f(c) \sum_{d \mid (m/c)} \mu(d)$$

$$= f(m).$$

The last equality follows since $\sum_{d \mid (m/c)} (d) = 0$ unless $m/c = 1$; that is, $m = c$.

*   *   *

Now we apply this theorem to obtain a

Corollary. $W_p(n) = (1/n) \cdot \sum_{d \mid n} \mu(n/d) p^d$.

PROOF. Let $f(a) = a W_p(a)$ and $F(a) = p^a$. The corollary to Theorem 26 completes the hypothesis of the Möbius inversion formula.

Next we shall determine the group $\mathscr{G} = \mathscr{G}(\mathrm{GF}(p^n)/\mathrm{GF}(p))$ of automorphisms of $\mathrm{GF}(p^n)$ over $\mathrm{GF}(p)$. Since any automorphism of $\mathrm{GF}(p^n)$ necessarily fixes each element of the prime subfield which in this case is $\mathrm{GF}(p)$, $\mathscr{G}$ is the group of all automorphisms of $\mathrm{GF}(p^n)$.

*   *   *

Theorem 28. The group $\mathscr{G}$ of automorphisms of $\mathrm{GF}(p^n)$ is a cyclic group of order n.

PROOF. From the Corollary to Theorem 24, $\mathrm{GF}(p^n)$ is the splitting field of an irreducible polynomial in $\mathrm{GF}(p)[x]$ of degree n. From Theorem 18 it follows that $|\mathscr{G}| = n$.

The automorphisms are given as follows. Let $\tau(a) = a^p$ for all a in $\mathrm{GF}(p^n)$. Since, by the remark after Lemma 2, τ is an endomorphism and moreover since $a^p = 0$ if and only if $a = 0$, it follows that τ is 1–1; therefore, since $\mathrm{GF}(p^n)$ is a finite set, it follows that τ is an automorphism of $\mathrm{GF}(p^n)$. Finally we claim that $\iota, \tau, \tau^2, \tau^3, \cdots, \tau^{n-1}(\tau^n = \iota)$ are all distinct. Let g be a generator of the multiplicative group of $\mathrm{GF}(p^n)$. The multiplicative order of g is $p^n - 1$. Suppose that $\tau^t = \iota$. Then $\tau^t(g) = g^{p^t} = g$ and thus $p^t - 1$ is divisible by $p^n - 1$ which is impossible if $0 < t < n$.

*   *   *

EXERCISE 3

1. Prove, without recourse to Theorem 22, that if $\mathrm{GF}(p^m)$ is a subfield of $\mathrm{GF}(p^n)$ then $m \mid n$. [*Hint:* Show first that $p^m - 1 \mid p^n - 1$.]

2. How many monic polynomials of degree n are there that are irreducible over $\mathrm{GF}(p)$ and whose zeros are generators of the multiplicative group of nonzero elements in $\mathrm{GF}(p^n)$?

3. Find all irreducible polynomials of degree 1, 2, and 4 in $\mathrm{GF}(2)[x]$. Verify that the product of all of these is $x^{16} - x$. Find the multiplicative order of each nonzero element in $\mathrm{GF}(16)$.

4. Prove the corollary to Theorem 25.

5. $x^3 - x + 1$ and $x^3 - x - 1$ are both irreducible in GF(3)[x]. The corollary to Theorem 25 states that their splitting fields over GF(3) are isomorphic. Exhibit this isomorphism for these two polynomials.

6. Construct a splitting field E for $x^4 + x + 1$ over GF(2). List, in a suitable notation, all the elements of this field. What can you say about the reducibility of $x^4 + x^3 + 1$ over E? Find the complete factorization of $x^4 + x^2 + 1$ over E.

7. Let S be a subfield of GF(p^n). Let $\mathscr{G}$ be the group of automorphisms of GF(p^n) over GF(p). Let $\mathscr{G}_S = \{\sigma \in \mathscr{G} : \sigma(a) = a \text{ for all } a \in S\}$. Show that the mapping $\Phi(S) = \mathscr{G}_S$ is a 1–1 mapping from the subfields of GF(p^n) onto the subgroups of $\mathscr{G}$.

8. Let $a \in$ GF(p) show that $x^{p^n} - x + na$ is always divisible by $x^p - x + a$ over GF(p). (p is a prime.)

9. Show that for every positive prime p, $x^p - x + a$ where $0 \neq a \in$ GF(p) is always irreducible over GF(p).

10. Let a, b be elements in GF(2^n) where n is odd. Show that $a^2 + ab + b^2 = 0$ implies $a = b = 0$.

11. Show that if G is a finite subgroup of the multiplicative group of any field, then G is cyclic.

8.6. SIMPLE EXTENSIONS

We have seen that there is an element $g \in$ GF(p^n) such that GF(p^n) = GF(p)(g). By adjoining g to GF(p) we generate all of the extension GF(p^n). When a field extension can be generated by adjoining a single element we have a relatively simple situation to consider. In fact we now make this a technical definition!

Definition. An extension $E \supseteq F$ is called *simple* if there exists an $a \in E$ such that $E = F(a)$. The element a is called a *primitive* element of E over F.

Example 9. GF(p^n) is a simple extension of GF(p).

Example 10. Let x be an indeterminate for F. $F(x)$ is a simple extension of F. x is a primitive element.

Example 11. If $p(x)$ is an irreducible polynomial of $F[x]$ then $F[x]/\langle p(x) \rangle$ is a simple extension of F. $\bar{x}$ is a primitive element.

We shall be mostly interested in algebraic extensions. Our main result is that if F is a field of characteristic 0 then every finite extension of F is a simple extension. Since every finite extension can be generated by adjoining a finite set of elements to the subfield it suffices to prove that if $E \supseteq F$ and char(F) = 0 and a, $b \in E$ then $F(a, b)$ is simple. The most natural candidate for the primitive element of $F(a, b)$ is $a + b$. Unfortunately this is not always a primitive element, but it is close to one; we prove that for some $c \in F$, $a + bc$ is a primitive element for $F(a, b)$.

Theorem 29. Let F be a field of characteristic 0. Let $a, b \in E \supseteq F$ be algebraic over F. Then $F(a, b)$ is a simple extension of F, and there is an element $c \in F$ such that $d = a + bc$ is a primitive element of $F(a, b)$ over F.

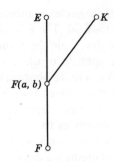

Figure 7

PROOF. Let $p(x)$ be an irreducible polynomial in $F[x]$ of which a is a zero, and let $q(x)$ be an irreducible polynomial of $F[x]$ of which b is a zero. Let K be a splitting field of $p(x)q(x)$ over $F(a, b)$ (see Figure 7). Let $\{a = a_1, a_2, \cdots, a_n\}$ be the set of distinct conjugates of a over F, and let $\{b = b_1, \cdots, b_m\}$ be the set of distinct conjugates of b over F. These elements of course belong to K. Now choose $c \in F$ so that $c \neq 0$ and so that it is not equal to $(a_i - a_h)/(b_k - b_j)$ for any 4-tuple (i, j, h, k). Since F is infinite this is possible. We claim that $d = a + bc$ is a primitive element of $F(a, b)$. Clearly $d \in F(a, b) = F(b, d) = F(a, d)$.

Now consider the polynomial $p(d - cx) \in F(d)[x]$. b is a zero of $p(d - cx)$ as $d - cb = a$. b is also a zero of $q(x) \in F(d)[x]$, hence in $F(d)[x]$, $p(d - cx)$ and $q(x)$ have a monic common factor $t(x) \in F(d)[x]$ such that $t(b) = 0$. (This is a consequence of Lemma 6.4.) It is our contention that $t(x) = x - b$ and so, in particular, $b \in F(d)$. From this we have easily that $F(d) = F(b, d) = F(a, b)$. To prove that $t(x) = x - b$ we note that at least $t(x)$ divides $q(x)$ and $p(d - cx)$ in $F[d](x)$ while in $K[x]$, $(x - b) \mid t(x)$. Now any zero of $t(x)$ is a root of $q(x)$ and $p(d - cx)$. Thus if there is another zero of $t(x)$ different from b it is b_i $(i > 1)$. But then $d - cb_i$ is a zero of $p(x)$; hence $d - cb_i = a_j$, $(j \geq 1)$ and so $d = a + bc = a_j + cb_i$, or $c = (a - a_j)/(b_i - b)$, contrary to the choice of c. Thus in $K[x]$, $t(x) = (x - b)^e$. However, since F has characteristic 0, $q(x)$ has only simple zeros; hence $e = 1$. This completes the proof.

$$* \quad * \quad *$$

Corollary. A field which is a finite extension of a field of characteristic 0 is a simple extension.

As we have observed, a finite field is a simple extension of any of its subfields. While this corollary can be generalized somewhat, there are examples of finite extensions which are not simple. See, for example, the book by van der Waerden, mentioned in the supplementary reading list at the end of this chapter.

8.7. ROOTS OF UNITY

In this section we shall discuss the splitting field of $x^n - 1$ over the rational numbers. The zeros of $x^n - 1$ are the nth roots of unity. Since we know that the complex numbers are algebraically closed we know that $x^n - 1$ splits over this field. The nth roots of unity, as complex numbers, are $e^{2k\pi i/n}$. Hence we know, from the corollary to Theorem 5, that a splitting field is isomorphic to a subfield of the complex numbers. If we call this subfield S we know that S is a finite, simple extension of Ra. $e^{2\pi i/n}$ can be taken as a primitive element for this extension. (Why?)

Without depending on our knowledge of the complex numbers, our theory permits us to determine all of the above remarks except that $e^{2\pi i/n}$ is a root of unity, since we have no machinery to develop e. As a matter of fact, the theorems we desire do not seem to be made easier by the knowledge that we are discussing fields isomorphic with subfields of the complex numbers.

Before starting our investigation we need one more fact about finite cyclic groups. This fact was given as Problem 3 of Exercises 3.4.

Lemma 5. If C is a cyclic group of order n with generator g then the order of g^k is n/d where $d = \text{GCD}(n, k)$.

PROOF. Let $n = dn_1$ and $k = dk_1$. (Recall that $(n_1, k_1) = 1$.) Thus $(g^k)^{n_1} = g^{dk_1 n_1} = (g^n)^{k_1} = 1$. Thus the order of g^k divides n_1. Conversely, if $(g^k)^m = 1$ then $n \mid km$; hence $n_1 \mid k_1 m$, and as $(n_1, k_1) = 1$, it follows that $n_1 \mid m$. Therefore the order of g^k is $n_1 = n/d$.

* * *

It would be well to recall the Euler φ-function mentioned in Problem 5 of Exercise 3.4. $\varphi(n)$ is the number of positive integers less than or equal to n and relative prime to n. From Lemma 5 it follows that the number of generators of the cyclic group of order n ($=$ number of elements of order n) is just $\varphi(n)$. In this section φ will always denote the Euler φ-function.

Now we are off!

Lemma 6. $x^n - 1$ has n distinct zeros in a splitting field Z_n over Ra.

PROOF. We apply the derivative test; $\text{GCD}(x^n - 1, nx^{n-1}) = 1$ since $x^n - 1$ and nx^{n-1} can have no common zeros. Theorem 2 tells us a splitting field exists.

* * *

Lemma 7. The zeros of $x^n - 1$ form a multiplicative group T_n of order n in Z_n. This group is cyclic and hence has $\varphi(n)$ generators.

PROOF. It is easy to verify that the n zeros of $x^n - 1$ form a multiplicative group in Z_n. From the corollary of Theorem 5.18 there is an integer m such that $\zeta^m = 1$ for all $\zeta \in T_n$, and T_n has an element of order m. If $m < n$, then $x^m - 1$ would have n zeros, contrary to Theorem 6.12. Hence $m = n$, and there is an element ζ of order n in T_n. The rest comes from Lemma 5.

* * *

Definition. The generators of $T_n = \{\zeta : \zeta^k = 1\}$ are called the primitive nth roots of unity in Z_n.

If $T_n = \langle \zeta \rangle$, Lemma 5 tells us that the primitive nth roots of unity are ζ^k where $(k, n) = 1$.

Lemma 8. $Z_n = \mathrm{Ra}(\zeta)$ where ζ is a primitive nth rooth of unity.

PROOF. We have only to observe that $x^n - 1$ has all its zeros in $\mathrm{Ra}(\zeta)$ since they are all powers of ζ.

*   *   *

Definition. In $Z_n[x]$ let $\Phi_n(x) = \prod_{(k,n)=1} (x - \zeta^k)$.

Here $\Phi_n(x)$ is a polynomial whose zeros are precisely the primitive nth roots of unity. $\Phi_n(x)$ is called the nth cyclotomic polynomial. Its degree is $\varphi(n)$.

Lemma 9. $x^n - 1 = \prod_{d|n} \Phi_d(x)$.

PROOF. Each nth root of unity is a primitive dth root of unity for exactly one d. If ζ^t is an nth root of unity then d is the order of ζ^t in T_n and in fact Lemma 5 shows that $d = n/(n, k)$. Since $x^n - 1 = \prod_{0 \le t < n} (x - \zeta^t)$, the formula in Lemma 9 just collects those factors $(x - \zeta^t)$ where t is a primitive dth root of unity.

*   *   *

Corollary. $n = \sum_{d|n} \varphi(d)$.

PROOF. Calculate the degree on both sides of the equality in Lemma 9.

*   *   *

> **Theorem 30.** $\Phi_n(x) \in I[x]$; that is, the nth cyclotomic polynomial has integer coefficients.

PROOF. We prove this by induction on n. Note that in any event $\Phi_n(x)$ is a monic polynomial. Now $\Phi_1(x) = x - 1$ and $\Phi_2(x) = x + 1$. From Lemma 9 we have $x^n - 1 = [\prod_{d|n,\ d \ne n} \Phi_d(x)]\Phi_n(x)$. Now by induction $\Phi_d(x) \in I[x]$, and so $f(x) = \prod_{d|n,\ d \ne n} \Phi_d(x) \in I[x]$ and is a monic polynomial. Now in $I[x]$ we know $x^n - 1 = f(x)q(x) + r(x)$ with $0 = r(x)$ or $\deg(r) < \deg(f)$ by Lemma 6.2. This equation also holds in $Z_n[x]$, and moreover the $q(x)$ and $r(x)$ are unique (Theorem 6.5). But in $Z_n[x]$ we have $x^n - 1 = f(x)\Phi_n(x)$; hence $r(x) = 0$ and $q(x) = \Phi_n(x)$; that is, $\Phi_n(x) \in I[x]$.

*   *   *

Example 12. If p is a prime, $\Phi_p(x) = (x^p - 1)/(x - 1) = x^{p-1} + \cdots + x + 1$ which we showed to be irreducible.

$$\Phi_4(x) = \frac{x^4 - 1}{\Phi_1(x)\Phi_2(x)} = \frac{x^4 - 1}{x - 1}\frac{x - 1}{x^2 - 1}$$

$$= \frac{x^4 - 1}{x_2 - 1} = x^2 + 1.$$

$$\Phi_6(x) = \frac{x^6 - 1}{\Phi_1(x)\Phi_2(x)\Phi_3(x)} = \frac{x^6 - 1}{x - 1}\frac{x - 1}{x^2 - 1}\frac{x - 1}{x^3 - 1}$$

$$= \frac{(x^6 - 1)(x - 1)}{(x^2 - 1)(x^3 - 1)} = x^2 - x + 1.$$

Theorem 31. $\Phi_n(x) = \prod_{d|n} (x^d - 1)^{\mu(n/d)}$ where μ is the Möbius μ-function.

PROOF. We shall use the Möbius inversion formula by employing a formal logarithm: $x^n - 1 = \prod_{d|n} \Phi_d(x)$; hence

$$\log(x^n - 1) = \sum_{d|n} \log \Phi_d(x),$$

hence

$$\log \Phi_n(x) = \sum_{d|n} \mu\left(\frac{n}{d}\right) \log(x^d - 1),$$

hence

$$\Phi_n(x) = \prod_{d|n} (x^d - 1)^{\mu(n/d)}.$$

$$* \quad * \quad *$$

If you object to this "proof," as well you may, you may obtain a correct proof by replacing, in the proof of Theorem 27, every $\sum$ by $\prod$ and every coefficient by an exponent. That proof becomes, mutatis mutandis, a correct proof here.

Example 13. $\Phi_8(x) = (x - 1)^{\mu(8)}(x^2 - 1)^{\mu(4)}(x^4 - 1)^{\mu(2)}(x^8 - 1)^{\mu(1)}$

$$= \frac{x^8 - 1}{x^4 - 1} = x^4 + 1.$$

$$\Phi_{12}(x) = \frac{(x^2 - 1)(x^{12} - 1)}{(x^4 - 1)(x^6 - 1)} = x^4 - x^2 + 1.$$

We include in the next lemma a result which we shall need later.

Lemma 10. If $0 < r < n$ and $r \mid n$ then $\Phi_n(x) \mid [(x^n - 1)/(x^r - 1)]$ in $I[x]$.

PROOF. We know $\Phi_n(x) \mid (x^n - 1)$ and $x^n - 1 = (x^r - 1)[(x^n - 1)/(x^r - 1)]$. We claim that $\text{GCD}(\Phi_n(x), x^r - 1) = 1$. This is so because, since $r \mid n$, the polynomials $\Phi_n(x)$ and $(x^r - 1)$ have no common zero. Hence it follows that $\Phi_n(x) \mid [(x^n - 1)/(x^r - 1)]$.

* * *

All the examples of $\Phi_n(x)$ which we have given have coefficients that are 0, 1, or -1. It is natural to conjecture that this is always the case. This conjecture is true in the range $1 \le n < 105$; however, the cyclotomic polynomial $\Phi_{105}(x)$ has a coefficient whose absolute value is 2. In 1883, A. Migotti showed that if p and q are distinct primes every coefficient of $\Phi_{p^\alpha q^\beta}(x)$ is either 0, 1, or -1. In 1931, I. Schur showed that for any positive integer N there is an n such that $\Phi_n(x)$ has a coefficient whose absolute value exceeds N. The paper by Emma Lehmer mentioned in the reading list at the end of this chapter contains a proof of Schur's result as well as an account of this problem and some additional results. More precise information on the growth of the coefficients in $\Phi_n(x)$ has been obtained by Paul Erdös.

Another interesting and important result, but one we shall not need in this book, is that $\Phi_n(x)$ is always irreducible in $\text{Ra}[x]$.

8.8. WEDDERBURN'S THEOREM

We have now almost enough machinery to prove the theorem of Wedderburn[1] which states that every finite division ring is a field. This means that in a finite system in which all the field properties except commutativity of multiplication are assumed, the multiplication must also be commutative. The proof we give here is due to E. Witt.[2] Wedderburn's proof appeared in 1905. Witt's proof, appearing in 1931, was one of the first of several short and elegant proofs. The recent articles by I. N. Herstein and T. J. Kaczynski mentioned in supplementary reading list show that new proofs are still being discovered.

Basically each proof considers a subring of the finite division ring which is a field and obtains a numerical relation between the multiplicative group of the field and the multiplicative group of the whole division ring. From this relationship, Witt obtains, from information about the cyclotomic polynomial, a contradiction—unless the field is all of the division ring. Before beginning the proof proper we need to recall from Example 9 of Chapter 7 that if E is a division ring and F a subdivision ring which is a field, then E is a vector space over F. It then follows that if F is finite with q elements, and E has finite dimension n over F then E has q^n elements. This is so because, as a vector space, $E \cong V_n(F)$ by Theorem 7.8.

[1] J. H. M. Wedderburn, *Trans. Am. Math. Soc.*, **6** (1905), 349–352.

[2] E. Witt, Über die Kommutativität endlicher Schiefkörper, *Abh. Math. Sem. Univ. Hamburg*, **8** (1931), 413.

We also need a result about groups which we previously included as an exercise. Since the result is important for this and subsequent work we shall digress to develop it here.

Theorem 32. Let G be a group.

1. The relation defined $a \sim b$ if and only if there exists $u \in G$ such that $a = ubu^{-1}$ is an equivalence relation on G. If $a \sim b$ we say that a and b are conjugate in G, and the equivalence class $[a]$ to which a belongs is called a conjugacy class of G.

2. The set $N_a = \{w : waw^{-1} = a\}$ is a subgroup of G called the normalizer (or centralizer) of a.

3. $|[a]| = [G : N_a]$.

PROOF. The proofs for 1 and 2 are straightforward verifications which we omit. To prove 3 we show that the distinct conjugates of a are in 1–1 correspondence with the left cosets of N_a in G. We claim that $\sigma(tN_a) = tat^{-1}$ is the desired 1–1 mapping. We must show (i) that σ is a function, that is, if $tN_a = sN_a$ then $tat^{-1} = sas^{-1}$; (ii) σ is onto, and (iii) if $tat^{-1} = sas^{-1}$, then $tN_a = sN_a$. To prove (i), from $tN_a = sN_a$ we know that $s \in tN_a$ so that $s = tw$ for some $w \in N_a$. Then $sas^{-1} = twa(tw)^{-1} = twaw^{-1}t^{-1} = tat^{-1}$. To prove (ii), if $b \sim a$, then $b = uau^{-1}$ and so $\sigma(uN_a) = uau^{-1} = b$. To prove (iii), from $tat^{-1} = sas^{-1}$ we have $s^{-1}tat^{-1}s = a$, or $(s^{-1}t)a(s^{-1}t)^{-1} = a$, so that $s^{-1}t \in N_a$. Thus $s^{-1}t = w \in N_a$ and so $t = sw$. Thus $t \in sN_a$ and so $tN_a = sN_a$, from Theorem 1.11.

* * *

Corollary (*Class Equation*). If G is a finite group then

$$|G| = \sum_a [G : N_a]$$

where the summation is over a complete set of distinct conjugacy class representatives.

PROOF. From Theorem 0.5 we have that $G = \bigcup_a [a]$ where the set union runs over a complete set of distinct conjugacy class representatives. The corollary follows since the distinct conjugacy classes are mutually exclusive.

* * *

Theorem 33 (*Wedderburn*). A finite division ring is a field.

PROOF. Let D be a finite division ring. We shall use the notation that if E is a subdivision ring of D then E^* shall denote its multiplicative group of nonzero elements. Let $Z = \{z : zd = dz \text{ for all } d \in D\}$. It is almost obvious and we omit the verification that Z is a field. Thus $Z = \mathrm{GF}(p^m)$. Let $q = p^m$. Now D is a vector space over Z of dimension n (see Figure 8), and so D has q^n

elements. We shall show that $D = Z$, or equivalently that $n = 1$. Let us suppose, to the contrary that $n > 1$.

Now let $a \in D$ and define $N_a = \{x : ax = xa \text{ for } x \in D\}$. Again it is clear that N_a is a division ring and $N_a \supseteq Z$. Thus N_a has q^r elements. We wish to show that $r \mid n$ (see Figure 9). In any event, from considering $D^* \supseteq N_a^*$ we

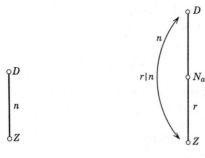

Figure 8   Figure 9

know that $q^r - 1 \mid q^n - 1$. If $n = rs + t$ with $0 < t < r$ then $q^n - 1 = q^{rs}q^t - 1 = q^t(q^{rs} - 1) + (q^t - 1)$. Now $q^r - 1$ divides $q^n - 1$ by hypothesis and also $(q^{rs} - 1)$, by Lemma 4.8, thus we have that $q^r - 1$ divides $q^t - 1$. But $q^t - 1 < q^r - 1$—a contradiction. Thus $t = 0$ and $r \mid n$. Moreover $r = n$ if and only if $N_a = D$, and $N_a = D$ if and only if $a \in Z$.

Next we observe that if $a \neq 0$, the normalizer of a in D^* is exactly N_a^*. Again this observation is just a matter of definition and we shall omit the verification.

Finally we consider the class equation for D^*. $|D^*| = \sum_a |[a]|$ where the sum is over a system of distinct conjugate class representatives in D^*. $[a]$ contains $(q^n - 1)/|N_a^*|$ elements; in particular $[a]$ has one element if and only if $a \in Z^*$. Hence the class equation becomes

$$q^n - 1 = (q - 1) + \sum_a \frac{(q^n - 1)}{|N_a^*|}.$$

Here, $(q - 1)$ is the number of elements in Z^*. The summation is over a system of distinct conjugate class representatives a, where $a \notin Z^*$. Now each N_a^* has $q^r - 1$ elements for some r which depends on the class $[a]$, but all we need to know is that $r \mid n$. We also know that $r < n$, since otherwise $a \in Z^*$. Hence

(*) $$q^n - 1 = (q - 1) + \sum \frac{q^n - 1}{q^r - 1},$$

where the summation is over certain divisors r of n, $r < n$.

Witt's chief contribution occurs here; by assuming $n > 1$ we shall produce a contradiction by considering the divisibility properties of $\Phi_n(q)$ where $\Phi_n(x)$ is the cyclotomic polynomial. From Lemma 10 we know that if $0 < r < n$ and $r \mid n$, $\Phi_n(x) \mid (x^n - 1)/(x^r - 1)$, hence $\Phi_n(q) \mid (q^n - 1)/(q^r - 1)$

if $r \mid n$. From (*) we then conclude that $\Phi_n(q) \mid (q - 1)$. However, from $\Phi_n(x) = \prod_{(k,n)=1} (x - \zeta^k)$ we have, as complex numbers,

$$|\Phi_n(q)| = \prod_{(k,n)=1} |q - \zeta^k| \geq \prod_{(k,n)=1} \big||q| - |\zeta^k|\big| = \prod_{(k,n)=1} (q - 1) > (q - 1)$$

if $n > 1$ since $q = p^m \geq 2$. This contradicts $\Phi_n(q) \mid (q - 1)$ and hence $n = 1$, $Z = D$, and our theorem is proved.

* * *

EXERCISE 4

1. $\Phi_n(x)$ denotes the nth cyclotomic polynomial. For $n > 1$ show that for every q, $\Phi_n(q) \equiv 1 \pmod{q}$. Prove that $\Phi_n(0) = 1$. Prove that $\prod_{(k,n)=1} (-\zeta^k) = 1$ if ζ is a primitive nth root of unity.

2. Let $E = F(a)$ be a transcendental extension of F.   Find all the primitive elements for this extension.

3. Let $a, b \in E = \mathrm{GF}(2^m)$ and let $P = \mathrm{GF}(2)$. Show that if $P(a) \cap P(b) = P$ then $P(a, b) = P(a + b)$.

4. (D. E. Knuth) Let E be an algebraic extension of P, the prime subfield of E. Let A be a nonempty subset of E such that (i) A is a vector space over P, and (ii) whenever $a \in A$ then for all positive integers n, $a^n \in A$. Show that A is a subfield of E.

5. Prove the following relations on cyclotomic polynomials in $\mathrm{Ra}[x]$.

(i) $\Phi_n(x) = \Phi_{n_0}(x^m)$ where $n = n_0 m$ and n_0 is the product of the distinct prime factors of n.

(ii) $\Phi_{2n}(x) = \Phi_n(-x)$ if n is odd.

(iii) $\Phi_{np}(x) = \Phi_n(x^p)/\Phi_n(x)$ if $p \nmid n$ and p is an odd prime.

SUPPLEMENTARY READING

A. A. Albert, *Fundamental Concepts of Higher Algebra*, Chicago, Illinois: Chicago University Press (1956).

P. Erdös, On the coefficients of the cyclotomic polinomial, *Bulletin of the American Mathematical Society*, **52** (1946), 179–184.

S. Fefferman, *The Number Systems*, Reading, Massachusetts: (1964).

I. N. Herstein, Wedderburn's theorem and a theorem of Jacobson, *American Mathematical Monthly*, **68** (1961), 249–251.

T. J. Kaczynski, Another proof of Wedderburn's theorem, *American Mathematical Monthly*, **71** (1964), 652–653.

Emma Lehmer, On the magnitude of the coefficients of the cyclotomic polynomial, *Bulletin of the American Mathematical Society*, **42** (1936), 389–392.

R. C. Mullin, A combinatorial proof of the existence of Galois fields, *American Mathematical Monthly*, **71** (1964), 901–902.

K. Rogers, Skew fields of prime characteristic, *American Mathematical Monthly*, **69** (1962), 287–288.

O. Zariski and P. Samuel, *Commutative Algebra*, vol. 1, Princeton, New Jersey: Van Nostrand (1958).

9 | Finite Groups

In this chapter we extend our study of groups by paying special attention to finite groups. In the first sections we obtain information about the subgroups of a finite group G from information about the order of G, in particular the prime power decomposition of $|G|$.

9.1. CAUCHY'S THEOREM

We begin by proving the weak converse of Lagrange's theorem. This theorem is attributed to Cauchy. The proof we give utilizes the class equation of F obtained as the corollary to Theorem 8.32.

Definition. Let G be a group. The *center Z* of a group G is the set

$$Z = \{a : ga = ag \text{ for all } g \in G\}.$$

It is easy to see that Z is a subgroup of G and that

$$Z = \{a : gag^{-1} = a \text{ for all } g \in G\}$$
$$= \{a : N_a = G\}.$$

In light of this definition we may recast the corollary of Theorem 8.32 as follows.

Lemma 1. If G is a group then

$$|G| = |Z| + \sum_{a \notin Z} [G : N_a]$$

where the summation is over a complete set (possibly empty) of distinct conjugacy class representatives which do not belong to the center of G.

Theorem 1. If p is a prime dividing the order of a group G then G has an element of order p.

PROOF. Our proof is by induction on the order of G. However, we must also know that this theorem is true for all abelian groups as we proved in Theorem 1.31. (Consequently the theorem is true if $G = 1, 2, 3, 5, 7$ and since we know all the groups of order 4 and 6, we know that it is true for groups of those orders also!) Let $|G| = n$. Now if S is a proper subgroup of G and $p \mid |S|$, then by induction S has an element of order p. Thus we may suppose that for every subgroup $S \neq G$ we have $p \nmid |S|$. Since $p \mid |G|$ and $|G| = [G:S]|S|$ it follows that for all subgroups $S \neq G$, $p \mid [G:S]$. (Figure 1 illustrates the relationships. We draw the line from G to S in red to emphasize that $p \mid [G:S]$.) Now consider the class equation

$$|G| = |Z| + \sum_{a \notin Z} [G:N_a]$$

where the sum extends over a complete set of distinct conjugacy class representatives. If $G \neq N_a$, that is, if $a \notin Z$, then $p \mid [G:N_a]$. Since $p \mid |G|$ it follows that p divides $|Z|$. Thus Z cannot be a proper subgroup, and so $Z = G$. This means that G is abelian and so G must have an element of order p.

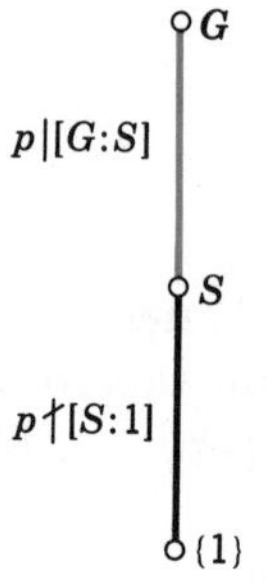

G

$p \mid [G:S]$

S

$p \nmid [S:1]$

(1)

Fig. 1

* * *

We need to extend the notion of the normalizer N_a of an element $a \in G$ by defining the normalizer of a subset D of G. To facilitate some of our definitions let us remember what in Chapter 1 was called complex multiplication in a group G. In particular, if $g \in G$ and D is a subset of G, then

$$gD = \{gd : d \in D\} \quad \text{and} \quad gDg^{-1} = \{gdg^{-1} : d \in D\}.$$

The proof of the following lemma is routine and we shall omit it.

Lemma 2. Let G be a group; let D and E be subsets of G and let $g \in G$. The following conditions are equivalent:

1. $gD = Eg$,
2. $Dg^{-1} = g^{-1}E$,
3. $gDg^{-1} = E$,
4. $D = g^{-1}Eg$.

Moreover for all $g, h \in G$ we have $(gh)D = g(hD)$.

Definition. Let D be a subset of G. The set

$$N_D = \{g : gDg^{-1} = D\}$$

is called the *normalizer* of D in G.

Let D and E be subsets of G and let S be a subgroup of G. D and E are called *conjugate under* S if there is an element $s \in S$ such that $sDs^{-1} = E$. We write $D \overset{S}{\sim} E$ if D and E are conjugates under S.

Theorem 2. For any subset D of a group G and for any subgroup $S \subseteq G$,

1. N_D is a subgroup of G.
2. The relation $(\overset{S}{\sim})$ is an equivalence relation on the set of all subsets of G.
3. If D is a subset of G then the number of subsets conjugate to D under S is $[S : S \cap N_D]$.

PROOF. We shall omit the routine verifications required for 1 and 2. The proof of 3 is analogous to the proof of Theorem 8.32. We define a 1–1 function φ from the cosets of $S \cap N_D$ in S into the conjugates of D under S as follows:

$$\varphi(s(S \cap N_D)) = sDs^{-1}.$$

We must show that for all pairs $s, t \in S$ then $s(S \cap N_D) = t(S \cap N_D)$ if and only if $sDs^{-1} = tDt^{-1}$. Let us suppose that $t \in s(S \cap N_D)$. Then $t = sg$ for $g \in S \cap N_D$. Thus $tDt^{-1} = (sg)D(g^{-1}s^{-1}) = s(gDg^{-1})s^{-1} = sDs^{-1}$. Conversely, if $s, t \in S$ and $sDs^{-1} = tDt^{-1}$ then $t^{-1}sDs^{-1}t = D$ and so $t^{-1}s \in N_D$. As S is a subgroup $t^{-1}s \in S$ so that $t^{-1}s \in S \cap N_D$ or $s \in t(S \cap N_D)$ and so $s(S \cap N_D) = t(S \cap N_D)$ as cosets in S.

*   *   *

It is important to note that if D is a subgroup of G, and $D^* = gDg^{-1}$ is any conjugate of D, then $D^* \cong D$ since $\sigma(x) = gxg^{-1}$ is an automorphism of G. Moreover, if D is a subgroup, then D is a normal subgroup of N_D; indeed, N_D is the largest subgroup of G in which D is normal. Thus D is a normal subgroup of G if and only if $N_D = G$.

9.2. *p*-GROUPS

Definition. Let p be a prime. A group G is called a *p*-group if the order of every element of G is finite and is a power of p.

From Theorem 1 it follows that the order of every finite *p*-group must be a power of p. The converse is, of course, just a consequence of the theorem of Lagrange; if $|G| = p^n$, then G is a *p*-group. These groups have many special properties. The theorems of this section deal with finite *p*-groups and show that if G is a finite *p*-group, for every subgroup $S \neq G$, the normalizer N_S is a properly larger group. We shall derive an important consequence from this fact.

Theorem 3. The center Z of a finite *p*-group G is larger than $\{1\}$.

PROOF. This is a direct consequence of the class equation for a *p*-group. We have $|G| = |Z| + \sum_{a \notin Z} [G : N_a]$. Since G is a *p*-group, $p \mid |G|$ and

$p \mid [G:N_a]$ unless $G = N_a$, which can happen only if $a \in Z$. Thus the class equation tells us that $p \mid |Z|$; in particular $|Z| \neq 1$ and so $Z \neq \{1\}$.

* * *

Corollary. If G is a finite p-group then G contains a normal subgroup of order p.

PROOF. Consider the center Z. Since $p \mid |Z|$, Z has an element c of order p. It is easy to see that $C = \langle c \rangle = \{1, c, \ldots, c^{p-1}\}$ is a *normal* subgroup of G for if $x \in G$, then, since $c^i \in Z$, we have $xc^ix^{-1} = c^i$; hence $xCx^{-1} = C$.

* * *

Theorem 4. If G is a finite p-group of order p^r then there is a chain of subgroups

$$\{1\} = G_0 \subset G_1 \subset G_2 \subset \cdots \subset G_r = G$$

such that G_i is a normal subgroup of G and $[G_{i+1}:G_i] = p$.

PROOF. The proof is by induction on r. If $r = 1$ then $G_1 = G$ and there is nothing to prove. In general, from the preceding corollary, G has a normal subgroup G_1 of order p. Consider $\bar{G} = G/G_1$ and the natural homomorphism $\varphi : G \to \bar{G}$. Figure 2 illustrates the relationships. Now $|\bar{G}| = p^{r-1}$ and by the induction hypothesis there is a chain

$$\{\bar{1}\} = \bar{G}_1 \subset \bar{G}_2 \subset \cdots \subset \bar{G}_r = \bar{G}$$

such that $\bar{G}_i$ is normal in $\bar{G}$ and $[\bar{G}_{i+1}:\bar{G}_i] = p$. From Theorem 1.29 and its proof, the set G_i of preimages of $\bar{G}_i$, $G_i = \{g : g \in G$ and $\varphi(g) \in \bar{G}_i\}$ is a normal subgroup of G; by Theorem 1.30, $G_{i+1}/G_i \cong \bar{G}_{i+1}/\bar{G}_i$, in particular $[G_{i+1}:G_i] = p$.

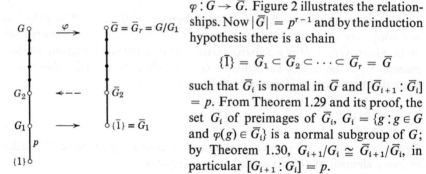

Figure 2

* * *

Theorem 5. Let G be a finite p-group and let S be a subgroup of G. If $S \subset G$, then $S \subset N_S$.

PROOF. We have already remarked that $S \subseteq N_S$. We wish to show that N_S is larger than S. The proof is by induction on $|G|$. If G is abelian (in particular, if $|G| = p$), then every subgroup is normal in G so that $N_S = G \supset S$. Also observe that the center Z of G is contained in N_S for all subsets S. Hence if $Z \nsubseteq S$ it follows that $N_S \supset S$. From now on we suppose that $Z \subseteq S$. (We show in Figure 3 the relationship of the various subgroups considered.) Let $\varphi : G \to G/Z = \bar{G}$ be the natural homomorphism. Since $|Z| > 1$, it follows

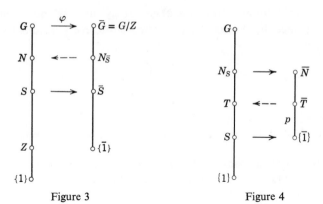

Figure 3   Figure 4

that $|G/Z| < |G|$ and, of course, G/Z is a *p*-group. By the induction hypothesis the normalizer $N_{\bar{S}}$ of $\bar{S}$ in $\bar{G}$ is larger than $\bar{S}$. Let N be the preimage of $N_{\bar{S}}$ under φ. Since $N_{\bar{S}} \supset \bar{S}$, it follows from Theorem 1.29 that $N \supset S$. To complete the proof we claim that $N \subseteq N_S$. To see this, note that if $g \in N$ and $s \in S$, then $\varphi(gsg^{-1}) = \varphi(g)\varphi(s)\varphi(g^{-1})$, which must belong to $\bar{S}$ since $\varphi(g) \in N_{\bar{S}}$. Consequently $gsg^{-1} \in S$ and so $gSg^{-1} \subseteq S$ for all $g \in N$. In particular, since N is a subgroup, $g^{-1}Sg \subseteq S$ and so $S \subseteq gSg^{-1}$. This proves that if $g \in N$ then $gSg^{-1} = S$ and so $N \subseteq N_S$.

*   *   *

Corollary. Every subgroup of index p in a finite *p*-group is a normal subgroup.

PROOF. Let S be a subgroup of index p in G. We have $p = [G:S] = [G:N_S][N_S:S]$ and since $N_S \supset S$ it follows that $[N_S:S] > 1$; hence $p = [N_S:S]$ and $1 = [G:N_S]$, or $G = N_S$.

*   *   *

Theorem 6. Let G be a finite *p*-group and S a subgroup of G. If $S \subset G$ then there exists a subgroup T such that (1) $S \subset T \subseteq G$, (2) S is a normal subgroup of T, and (3) $[T:S] = p$.

PROOF. We know that S is a proper normal subgroup of N_S. In $\bar{N} = N_S/S$ there is a subgroup $\bar{T}$ of order p. (See Figure 4.) This is Theorem 1. By Theorem 1.29, its preimage T in the natural homomorphism $N_S \to \bar{N}$ is a subgroup of N_S containing S and, since $\{\bar{1}\}$ is normal in $\bar{T}$, S is normal in T.

*   *   *

Corollary. If G is a finite *p*-group, then for every proper subgroup S of G, there is a chain $S = H_0 \subset H_1 \subset \cdots \subset H_m = G$ such that H_i is normal in H_{i+1} and $[H_{i+1}:H_i] = p$.

PROOF. The proof follows from the theorem by an easy induction on the index $[G:S]$ since, by the corollary to Theorem 5, every maximal subgroup of G is normal in G.

*   *   *

EXERCISE 1

1. Show that the center of S_n is the identity.

2. In the proof of Theorem 5, and using the notation of the proof, show that $N = N_S$.

3. Show that a group whose order is p^2 (p a prime) is abelian.

4. Let G be a finite group. Show that G is a cyclic p-group if and only if G has a unique maximal subgroup.

5. Let S be a subgroup of a finite p-group G. Show that there exist subgroups A_i and B_j such that

$$\{1\} = A_0 \subseteq A_1 \subseteq \cdots \subseteq A_n = S = B_0 \subseteq B_1 \subseteq \cdots \subseteq B_m = G,$$

and A_i and B_j are normal subgroups, respectively, in A_{i+1} and B_{j+1} of index p. Show that if S is a normal subgroup of G then A_i and B_j may be chosen normal in G for all i and j.

6. Find all groups of order 8 and 9.

★7. Find all groups of order 16.

9.3.   THE SYLOW THEOREMS

These theorems deal with finite groups and constitute an introduction to the arithmetic theory of finite groups. By the "arithmetic theory" of groups we mean the information about a finite group implied by the arithmetic properties of the order of the group. These theorems were first demonstrated by L. Sylow (1814–1897), and they have been considerably extended by the work of the contemporary mathematicians, Philip Hall and Helmut Wielandt.

Definition. Let G be a finite group and p a prime. Let $|G| = p^r n$ where $p \nmid n$. A subgroup P of G is called a p Sylow subgroup (p–SSG) of G if $|P| = p^r$.

It is not at all obvious that a p–SSG exists. Of course, if $p \nmid |G|$ then $r = 0$, and a p–SSG is the identity. On the other hand, if G is abelian, we have proved that G has a p–SSG for all p; we have even shown (Theorem 5.18) that G is the direct product of its Sylow subgroups for those primes that divide G. Note that if P is a p–SSG of G then every conjugate gPg^{-1} is also a p–SSG of G. For an arbitrary group we shall prove three main theorems:

1. For all primes p, a p–SSG exists.
2. Any two p–SSG are conjugate in G, and any subgroup of G which is a p-group is contained in some p–SSG.
3. If k_p is the number of p–SSG then $k_p \equiv 1 \pmod{p}$, and $k_p = [G:N_p]$ and so divides the order of G.

Theorem 7 (*First Sylow Theorem*). For all primes p, every group has a p–SSG.

PROOF. Our proof is by induction on $|G|$. If $|G| = 1$ or $p \nmid |G|$ then Theorem 7 is trivial. Let $|G| = p^r n$ where $p \nmid n$ and where we assume that $r > 0$. Now if G has a subgroup S such that $S \neq G$ and $p \nmid [G:S]$, then it must be that $p^r \mid |S|$; thus, by induction S has a p–SSG of order p^r, which is therefore a p–SSG of G. Hence we may suppose that for every subgroup S of G, $p \mid [G:S]$. From an examination of the class equation

$$|G| = |Z| + \sum_{a \notin Z} [G:N_a],$$

this implies that $p \mid |Z|$. Now Z has an element a of order p (Theorem 1) and as $a \in Z$, it follows that $\langle a \rangle$ is a normal subgroup of G. We consider $\bar{G} = G/\langle a \rangle$ (see Figure 5). $|\bar{G}| = p^{r-1}n$ and, by the induction hypothesis, $|\bar{G}|$ has a p–SSG, $\bar{P}$, of order p^{r-1}. Let P be the preimage of $\bar{P}$ under the natural homomorphism. We claim that $|P| = p^r$. From Theorem 1.29 we know $\bar{P} = P/\langle a \rangle$ and $|\bar{P}| = |P|/|\langle a \rangle|$, or $|P| = |\bar{P}| \cdot |\langle a \rangle| = p^r$.

$$* \quad * \quad *$$

Before proceeding further we need one more result from the theory of group homomorphisms, the so-called diamond theorem (see Figure 6).

Theorem 8. Let A and B be subgroups of G. If B is a normal subgroup of $A \vee B$, then $A \cap B$ is a normal subgroup of A; moreover $A \vee B = AB$ and $(A \vee B)/B \cong A/(A \cap B)$.

PROOF. Problem 7 of Exercise 6 in Chapter 1 asked for a proof that $A \cap B$ is normal in A and $A \vee B = AB$. The first is elementary, the second is essentially the observation that if B is normal in $A \vee B$ then for all $a \in A$, $aB = Ba$ and so $(ab)(a'b') = a(ba')b' = a(a'b^*)b' = a''b''$. Now since $A \vee B = AB$ every coset of B in $A \vee B$ has the form aB for some $a \in A$.

To prove $A \vee B/B \cong A/A \cap B$, we define a mapping $\theta: A \vee B/B \to A/A \cap B$ by $\theta(aB) = a(A \cap B)$. First of all, if $aB = a^*B$ then $a^{-1}a^*B = B$,

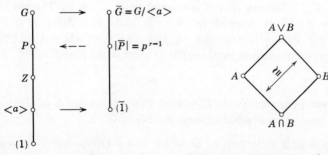

Figure 5   Figure 6

and so $a^{-1}a^* \in A \cap B$, so that $a^*(A \cap B) = a(A \cap B)$. From this it follows that θ is a function, and it is clearly a mapping from the cosets of B in $A \vee B$ onto the cosets of $A \cap B$ in A. Since B is normal in $A \vee B$ we have $\theta(aB \cdot a'B)$ $= \theta(aa'B) = aa'(A \cap B)$. Since $A \cap B$ is normal in A we have $aa'(A \cap B) =$ $a(A \cap B) \cdot a'(A \cap B) = \theta(aB) \cdot \theta(a'B)$. This shows that θ is a homomorphism of $A \vee B/B$ onto $A/A \cap B$. Finally, if aB belongs to the kernel of θ, then $a(A \cap B) = A \cap B$ and in particular $a \in B$; hence $aB = B$. Thus the kernel of θ is the identity of $A \vee B/B$, and so we have shown that θ is the desired isomorphism.

* * *

Next we prove a special lemma to facilitate the proof of the second Sylow theorem.

Lemma 3. Let G be a finite group. Let S be a subgroup of G which is a p-group. Let P be a p–SSG of G and N_P its normalizer. Under these conditions $N_P \cap S = P \cap S$.

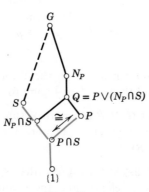

Figure 7

Figure 7 shows the subgroup relations of the hypothesis. A red line from a subgroup A to a subgroup B indicates that $p \mid [A:B]$, whereas a black line indicates that $p \nmid [A:B]$. We shall apply Theorem 8 to show that, unless the conclusion of the lemma is true, a pair of factor groups are isomorphic while their colors show that they have different orders!

PROOF. Since $N_P \supseteq P$ clearly $N_P \cap S \supseteq P \cap S$. We shall prove that $N_P \cap S \subseteq P \cap S$. Since $N_P \cap S \subseteq S$ it clearly suffices to prove $N_P \cap S \subseteq P$. Suppose this is not the case; then $N_P \cap S \neq P \cap S$ and so $p \mid [N_P \cap S : P \cap S]$. Moreover $Q = (N_P \cap S) \vee P \neq P$. But since $P \subseteq Q \subseteq N_P$ and P is normal in N_P, it follows that P is normal in Q. Thus by Theorem 8, $P \cap (N_P \cap S) = P \cap S$ is normal in $N_P \cap S$ and $N_P \cap S/P \cap S \cong Q/P$, in particular $[Q:P] = [N_P \cap S : P \cap S]$. But $p \nmid [Q:P]$ whereas $p \mid [N_P \cap S : P \cap S]$. This contradiction implies that Q must equal P and so $P \supseteq N_P \cap S$.

* * *

Theorem 9 (*Second Sylow Theorem*). Every subgroup S of G which is a p-group is contained in some p–SSG of G.

PROOF. Let S be a subgroup of G which is a p-group. Let P be a p–SSG. We shall show that S is contained in a conjugate of P in G.

Let $P = P_1, \ldots, P_t$ be the distinct conjugates of P under G. By Theorem 2, setting $S = G$, it follows that $t = [G : N_P]$ where N_P is the normalizer of P in G and since $N_P \supseteq P$ we know that $p \nmid t$. We now partition $\{P_1, \ldots, P_t\}$ into equivalence classes under the equivalence relation ($\overset{S}{\sim}$) of Theorem 2. By Theorem 2 the number of subgroups P_j conjugate to P_i under S is $[S : S \cap N_{P_i}]$. Hence corresponding to the partitioning of $\{P_1, \ldots, P_t\}$ under ($\overset{S}{\sim}$) we obtain

$$\text{(*)} \qquad\qquad t = [G : N_P] = \sum [S : S \cap P_i]$$

where the sum is over a set of ($\overset{S}{\sim}$)-equivalence class representatives. Now $p \nmid t$, yet since S is a p-group we have $p \mid [S : S \cap P_i]$ unless $[S : S \cap P_i] = 1$. Thus it must be the case that $[S : S \cap P_i] = 1$ for some i, but this means that $S = S \cap P_i$, or that $S \subseteq P_i$.

* * *

As a corollary to the proof we obtain

> **Theorem 10** (*Third Sylow Theorem*). Any two p–SSG of G are conjugate under G. The number k_p of p–SSG's of G is a divisor of $|G|$ and $k_p \equiv 1 \pmod{p}$.

PROOF. Let P and P^* be two p–SSG of G. Put $S = P^*$ and $P = P$ in the proof of the Theorem 9. We have that P^* is contained in some conjugate P_i of P. But $|P^*| = |P_i|$ and hence $P^* = P_i$.

Now put $S = P$ and the formula (*) becomes $t = [G : N_P] = \sum [P : P \cap P_i]$. Since the groups P_i are all distinct for exactly one i we have $1 = [P : P \cap P_i]$ while $p \mid [P : P \cap P_i]$ otherwise. Hence $t \equiv 1 \pmod{p}$. We know $[G : N_P] = t$ and from Lagrange's theorem we know that $t \mid |G|$.

* * *

In view of the third Sylow theorem any two p–SSG's are isomorphic. If there is only one p–SSG then it must be a normal subgroup, indeed a characteristic subgroup since its order uniquely determines it. (A subgroup H of G is called *characteristic* if $\varphi(H) = H$ for every automorphism φ of G.)

The Sylow theorems are extremely helpful in determining all abstract groups of a given order. We shall give two examples.

Example 1. Any group of order 15 is cyclic. Let G be a group of order 15. Since $15 = 3 \times 5$ we know that G has 3–SSG's and 5–SSG's. The number of 3–SSG's has the form $1 + 3k$ and divides 15; thus $k = 0$ is the only possibility. Hence there is only one subgroup of order 3, call it C_3, which is cyclic and is a normal subgroup of G. Similarly the number of 5–SSG's is $1 + 5h$, and this number divides 15. Hence $h = 0$ and there is only one 5–SSG, call it C_5, which is cyclic and is normal in G. Since $C_3 \cap C_5 = \{1\}$ it follows that $C_3 \vee C_5 = G \cong C_3 \times C_5 \cong C_{15}$, a cyclic group of order 15.

Example 2. We shall determine, up to isomorphism, all groups of order 12. Let G be a group of order $12 = 4 \times 3$. G has 2–SSG's, each of order 4, and 3–SSG's, each a cyclic group of order 3. The 2–SSG's are all isomorphic to either the cyclic group of order 4, C_4, or to the four-group, V_4. Their number is $1 + 2k$ and hence there are either 1 or 3 of these subgroups in G. Similarly there are $1 + 3h$ subgroups of order 3; hence there are 1 or 4 3–SSG's. Consequently, there are at most eight possibilities according to the number and the type of the Sylow subgroups.

First we show that there is no group of order 12 with four 3–SSG's and three 2–SSG's. Any two 3–SSG's intersect in $\{1\}$ and so these four subgroups would account for 9 elements in G. Any 2–SSG adds 3 more distinct elements, since a 2–SSG and a 3–SSG intersect in $\{1\}$. Now we have a total of 12 elements and hence there could not exist another distinct 2–SSG in G.

Another easy case occurs when there is one 2–SSG, A, and one 3–SSG, C_3. Since each is normal and $A \cap C_3 = \{1\}$ while $|A \vee C_3| = |AC_3| = 12$, it follows that $G \cong A \times C_3$. Two cases arise according as $A \cong C_4$ or $A \cong V_4 = C_2 \times C_2$.

Case 1. $G \cong C_4 \times C_3 \cong C_{12}$ is a cyclic group of order 12.

Case 2. $G \cong V_4 \times C_3 \cong C_2 \times C_2 \times C_3$.

These cases include all the abelian groups of order 12, since from Theorem 5.18 we know that if G is abelian then $G = S_4 \times S_3$ and we have just listed all the possibilities for S_4 and S_3.

Before proceeding, note that if A is a 2–SSG and B is 3–SSG then $|A \vee B| \geq |A \cdot B| = |A| \, |B|/|A \cap B| = 4 \cdot 3/1 = 12$ so that $A \vee B = A \cdot B = G$.

Case 3. G has one 2–SSG which is C_4 and G has four 3–SSG's. Let $C_4 = \langle a \rangle = \{1, a, a^2, a^3 : a^4 = 1\}$ and let $S_3 = \langle c \rangle = \{1, c, c^2 : c^3 = 1\}$ be a 3–SSG. Since C_4 is normal we have $cac^{-1} \in C_4$. If $cac^{-1} = a$ then $G = \langle a, c \rangle$ is abelian, thus since cac^{-1} has order 4 the only remaining possibility is $cac^{-1} = a^3$, or $ca = a^3c$. But then $(ac)^2 = a(ca)c = aa^3cc = c^2$, an element of order 3. Thus 3 divides the order of (ac). Also $(ac)^3 = (ac)(ac)^2 = acc^2 = a$, an element of order 4. Thus 4 must also divide the order of (ac) and so 12 must divide the order of (ac); that is, $G = \langle ac \rangle$ is cyclic, a case we have excluded. Indeed all of this is nonsense since if G is cyclic, then G is abelian, but we assumed that $ac \neq ca$! Thus there can be no group of order 12 in the category of Case 3.

Case 4. G has one 2–SSG, V_4, which is isomorphic to the four-group and G has four 3–SSG's. Let

$$V_4 = \{1, r, s, rs : rs = sr = t, r^2 = s^2 = t^2 = 1\}$$

and let

$$S_3 = \langle a \rangle = \{1, a, a^2 : a^3 = 1\}.$$

Since V_4 is normal we must have $ara^{-1} \in V_4$. If $aga^{-1} = g$ for all g in V_4 then $G = S_3 \vee V_4$ is abelian. Hence, without loss of generality we may assume $ara^{-1} = s$. Hence $ar = sa$ and $r = a^{-1}sa$ and so $a^{-1}ra = a^{-2}sa^2 = asa^{-1}$. If $asa^{-1} = r$ then $a^{-1}ra = r$, or $ra = ar$, a contradiction. If $asa^{-1} = s$, then $as = sa = ar$, or $s = r$—a contradiction. Hence it must be that $asa^{-1} = rs = t$ and $ata^{-1} = ara^{-1}asa^{-1} = st = r$. Thus we have as relations, $ar = sa$, $as = ta$, and $at = ra$. From this information it is possible to write down a multiplication table for the group, if it exists. Such a group does exist because the alternating group $\mathscr{A}_4$ of Problem 11 of Exercise 1.5 satisfies these relations. Thus there is a group in the category of Case 4 and any such group is isomorphic to $\mathscr{A}_4$.

Case 5. G has one 3–SSG, S_3, and three 2–SSG's, each isomorphic to the four-group. Let $S_3 = \{1, c, c^2 : c^3 = 1\}$ and let $A = \{1, a, b, ab\}$ be a 2–SSG. Since S_3 is normal it follows that aca and bcb belong to S_3. If $aca = c^2$ and $bcb = c^2$ then $(ab)c(ab) = abcba = ac^2a = c$. So without loss of generality (or by renaming the elements of A) we may assume $aca = c$. If $bcb = c$ then $abcab = c$ and so $G = S_3 \vee A$ is abelian; hence we suppose that $bcb = c^2$ and so $abcab = bacab = bcb = c^2$. Therefore, we have the relations $ac = ca$, and $bc = c^2b$. From this information it is possible to write down a multiplication table for G, if such a group exists.

To show that there does exist a group in the category we put $x = ac$ and $y = b$. We calculate $x^6 = 1$, $y^2 = 1$, and $yx = bac = abc = ac^2b = x^5y$. From Theorem 1.10, it follows that G is isomorphic to the dihedral group of order 12, which we know exists.

Case 6. G has one 3–SSG and three 2–SSG's each of which is a cyclic group of order 4. Let $S_3 = \langle c \rangle = \{1, c, c^2 : c^3 = 1\}$ and $A = \langle a \rangle = \{1, a, a^2, a^3 : a^4 = 1\}$. Since S_3 is normal, we have that $aca^{-1} \in S_3$. If $aca^{-1} = c$ then $G = S_3 \vee A$ is abelian and so we suppose that $aca^{-1} = c^2$. Hence $ac = c^2a$. From this information we may write down a multiplication table. It turns out that this multiplication table is the Cayley table of a group. One method of exhibiting such a group is to write out the Cayley table and then by using the Cayley representation theorem get a group of permutations which satsify the above relations. The permutations are of course the rows of the Cayley table. This method, while tedious, does ultimately demonstrate the existence of such a group. However, Problem 4 of the next exercise set shows how to construct a group in this category.

EXERCISE 2

1. Give a new proof that a finite abelian group is the direct product of its Sylow subgroups by using the Sylow theorems.

2. Find all groups of order 18 and 20.

3. Identify the group $S_3 \times C_2$ as one of the cases in Example 2. (S_3 is the symmetric group on 3 letters, C_2 is a cyclic group of order 2.) Find all the subgroups of this group. (Save your work for Problem 7 in Exercise 10.1.)

4. Show that there is a subgroup of $S_3 \times C_4$ which is a group in the category of Case 6 of Example 2.

5. Find sufficient conditions on primes p and q ($p < q$) such that all groups of order pq are cyclic. (★) Are your conditions also necessary?

6. Find all groups of order 30.

9.4. SOLVABLE GROUPS

This section deals with properties of groups which are not related directly to the arithmetic properties of the order of the group but with properties which are related to the set of subgroups partially ordered by set inclusion. In particular we are interested in special chains of subgroups. The theorems selected here for study will help us study automorphism groups of field extensions and ultimately permit us to state conditions under which an equation $f(x) = 0$, ($f(x) \in F[x]$) has a solution "in radicals." Indeed the term "solvable" which we shall introduce presently is used because the concept arose in the study of the theory of equations.

Definition. Let G be a group and let

$$\{1\} = A_0 \subseteq A_1 \subseteq \cdots \subseteq A_n = G$$

be a chain of subgroups in G. The chain is called a *subnormal* chain if each A_i is a normal subgroup of A_{i+1}. The chain is called a *normal* chain for G if each A_i is a normal subgroup of G. The chain is called a *composition* series for G if each A_i is a maximal normal subgroup of A_{i+1}; that is, $A_i \neq A_{i+1}$, and if $A_i \subset H \subseteq A_{i+1}$ and H is normal in A_{i+1} then $H = A_{i+1}$.

Most of our concern will be with subnormal chains and composition series. Every group has the subnormal chain $\{1\} \subseteq G$ since 1 is a normal subgroup of G. For finite groups it is not difficult to prove, by induction on $|G|$, that every group has a composition series. For let A_{n-1} be a maximal normal subgroup of G. ($A_{n-1} = \{1\}$ is possible!) Then by induction A_{n-1} has a composition series, and by adding $A_n = G$ to that series we clearly obtain a composition series for G.

We remark that even though A is normal in B and B is normal in G, A need not be normal in G. An example is provided by S_4 which contains $B = \{\iota, (1, 2)(3, 4), (1, 3)(2, 4), (1, 4)(2, 3)\}$ as a normal subgroup whereas B contains $A = \{\iota, (1, 2)(3, 4)\}$, but A is not a normal subgroup of S_4.

Lemma 4. Let A, B, S be subgroups of G. If A is normal in B then $A \cap S$ is normal in $B \cap S$. If in addition S is normal in G then $A \vee S$ is normal in $B \vee S$.

Figure 8 illustrates the relationships, but we do not mean to imply that $A = B \cap (A \vee S)$ or that $B = A \vee (B \cap S)$.

PROOF. We suppose that A is normal in B. If $x \in B \cap S$ and $y \in A \cap S$ then $xyx^{-1} \in S$ as both x and y lie in S and $xyx^{-1} \in A$ as $y \in A$, $x \in B$, and A is normal in B. Thus $A \cap S$ is normal in $B \cap S$ from Theorem 1.26.

If S is normal in G then by Theorem 8 we have $A \vee S = AS$ and $B \vee S = BS$ and so $A \vee S = \{as : a \in A \text{ and } s \in S\}$ and $B \vee S = \{bt : b \in B \text{ and } t \in S\}$. Thus $(bt)as(bt)^{-1} = btast^{-1}b^{-1} = btb^{-1}bab^{-1}bst^{-1}b^{-1}$. But since S is normal in G, $btb^{-1} = t_1 \in S$ and $b(st^{-1})b^{-1} = s_1 \in S$; and since A is normal in B, $bab^{-1} = a_1 \in A$; hence $bt(as)(bt)^{-1} = t_1 a_1 s_1 \in A \vee S$. Thus $A \vee S$ is normal in $B \vee S$.

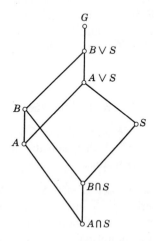

Figure 8

*   *   *

Definition. A finite group G is called *solvable* if G has a composition series $1 = A_0 \subseteq A_1 \subseteq \cdots \subseteq A_n = G$ in which every index $[A_{i+1} : A_i]$ is a prime integer. (Let us agree to call the group consisting of a single element solvable also!)

Example 3. Let $G = S_3$, the full symmetric group on three letters. Let C be the cyclic subgroup of order 3 which we know to be normal (it has index 2 in S_3 for one reason). We have the composition series $\{1\} \subset C \subset S_3$. Thus S_3 is solvable.

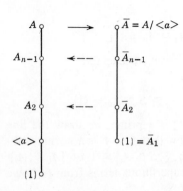

Figure 9

Example 4. Let $G = \mathscr{A}_4$, the alternating group on four letters. Using the notation of Problem 11 of Exercise 1.5 we have the composition series $\{1\} \subset \{1, r\} \subset \{1, r, s, t\} \subset \mathscr{A}_4$.

Example 5. Every p-group is solvable. Theorem 4 may be restated in exactly this form.

Theorem 11. Every finite abelian group is solvable.

PROOF. Our proof is by induction on the order of the group. If $|A| = p$ where p is a prime, then $\{1\} \subset A$ is a composition series. In general, if A is an abelian group and p is prime dividing $|A|$, we argue as follows (Figure 9 may help in picturing the details of the proof). By Theorem 1 there is an element $a \in A$ whose order is p, and so $\langle a \rangle$ is a subgroup, a fortiori—a normal subgroup of G of order p. We consider $\bar{A} = A/\langle a \rangle$. Since $|\bar{A}| < |A|$ we have, by induction, that $\bar{A}$ is solvable (why is $\bar{A}$ abelian?). Let $\bar{A} = \bar{A}_n \supset \bar{A}_{n-1} \supset \cdots \supset \bar{A}_1 = \{\bar{1}\}$ be a composition series for $\bar{A}$. Let A_i be the preimage of $\bar{A}_i$ in the natural homomorphism of A onto $\bar{A}$. From Theorems 1.29 and 1.30 it follows that $A = A_n \supset A_{n-1} \supset \cdots \supset A_1 = \langle a \rangle \supset \{1\}$ and that A_i is a normal subgroup of A_{i+1}; moreover $A_{i+1}/A_i \cong \bar{A}_{i+1}/\bar{A}_i$, in particular $[A_{i+1} : A_i] = [\bar{A}_{i+1} : \bar{A}_i]$ is a prime integer.

*   *   *

The proof of this theorem has an important generalization.

> **Theorem 12.** Let G be a finite group. If G has a normal subgroup S which is solvable and such that G/S is also solvable, then G is solvable.

PROOF. Let $\bar{G} = G/S$, and let $\bar{G} = \bar{B}_m \supset \cdots \supset \bar{B}_0 = \{\bar{1}\}$ be a composition series for $\bar{G}$. Just as in the proof of Theorem 11, if B_i is the preimage of $\bar{B}_i$ in the natural homomorphism $G \to \bar{G}$, then $G = B_m \supset B_{m-1} \supset \cdots \supset B_0 = S$ is a subnormal chain from G to S in which $[B_{i+1} : B_i]$ is a prime. Now since S is solvable, we have a composition series from S to $\{1\}$ and so by putting them together we obtain a composition series for G.

*   *   *

We now prove a strong converse of this theorem.

> **Theorem 13.** If G is a finite solvable group then every subgroup of G is solvable and every homomorphic image of G is solvable.

PROOF. Let

$$(C) \qquad G = A_n \supset A_{n-1} \supset \cdots \supset A_1 \supset A_0 = \{1\}$$

be a composition series for G, which for this proof we keep fixed.

Let S be a subgroup of G. Form the chain

$$(C^*) \qquad S = S \cap A_n \supseteq S \cap A_{n-1} \supseteq \cdots \supseteq S \cap A_0 = \{1\}.$$

(Figure 10 shows the relationships. If $[R : T]$ is a prime, we draw the line from R to T in red.) From Lemma 4, we know that $S \cap A_i$ is a normal subgroup of $S \cap A_{i+1}$. We claim that $[S \cap A_{i+1} : S \cap A_i] = 1$ or $[A_{i+1} : A_i]$, the latter being a prime. Thus by deleting superfluous terms from (C^*) we shall have exhibited a composition series for S.

Now we have that $A_i \subseteq A_i \vee (S \cap A_{i+1}) \subseteq A_{i+1}$ and, since A_i is normal in A_{i+1}, it follows that A_i is normal in $A_i \vee (S \cap A_{i+1})$. Hence, from Theorem 8, $A_i \vee (S \cap A_{i+1})/A_i \cong (S \cap A_{i+1})/A_i \cap S$. Since $[A_i \vee (S \cap A_{i+1}) : A_i] \mid [A_{i+1} : A_i]$ our claim has been proved.

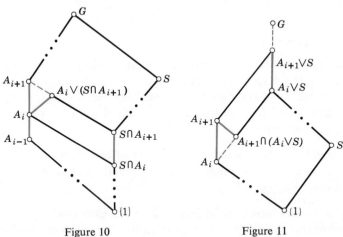

Figure 10   Figure 11

Now we prove the second part of the theorem. Let $\bar{G}$ be a homomorphic image of G. From our theorems on homomorphisms (Theorems 1.24, 1.25, 1.29, and 1.30), it suffices to show that if S is a normal subgroup of G then there is a subnormal chain $G = B_m \supset B_{m-1} \supset \cdots \supset B_1 \supset S$ such that $[B_{i+1} : B_i]$ is a prime integer. We shall construct this chain from the composition chain (C) for G in the following natural way. As shown in Figure 11 we have

$$(C^{**}) \quad G = A_n \vee S \supseteq A_{n-1} \vee S \supseteq \cdots \supseteq A_1 \vee S \supseteq A_0 \vee S = S.$$

By Lemma 4 we have that $A_i \vee S$ is normal in $A_{i+1} \vee S$, and by an argument similar to that given in the first part of this proof we have that $[A_{i+1} \vee S : A_i \vee S] = 1$ or $[A_{i+1} : A_i]$. Thus by deleting superfluous terms from (C^{**}) we obtain the desired subnormal chain from G to S.

*   *   *

As we have seen, any abelian group is solvable and, in view of Theorem 11, it may be useful to look for homomorphic images of G which are abelian. The question of the existence of homomorphic images of G which are abelian is an interesting one in itself. The first results along these lines were part of Exercise 1.6. We shall formalize these results here.

We begin with the observation that if A is an abelian group and $\varphi : G \to A$ is a homomorphism of G into A then for all $x, y \in G$ we have $\varphi(xyx^{-1}y^{-1}) = 1 \in A$. This is true since $\varphi(xyx^{-1}y^{-1}) = \varphi(x)\varphi(y)\varphi(x)^{-1}\varphi(y)^{-1} = 1$ as A is abelian. Thus $xyx^{-1}y^{-1}$ belongs to the kernel of φ. Conversely, if $xyx^{-1}y^{-1}$ belongs to the kernel of a homomorphism for all $x, y \in G$ it follows that the homomorphic image is abelian.

Definition. Let G be a group. The elements of the set

$$C = \{xyx^{-1}y^{-1} : x, y \in G\}$$

are called *commutators* of G.

Note that the inverse of the commutator $(xyx^{-1}y^{-1})$ is $yxy^{-1}x^{-1}$ by Theorem 1.2 and so is a commutator of G also. In addition, a conjugate $a(xyx^{-1}y^{-1})a^{-1} = (axa^{-1})(aya^{-1})(ax^{-1}a^{-1})(ay^{-1}a^{-1}) = x_1y_1x_1^{-1}y_1^{-1}$ is a commutator of G. It is not true in general that the product of two commutators is a commutator.

Definition. Let G be a group and C its set of commutators. The subgroup $G' = \langle C \rangle$ which is generated by the commutators is called the *derived* or *commutator* subgroup of G.

If G is abelian then $C = \{1\}$ and so $G' = \{1\}$. Conversely, if $C = G' = \{1\}$ this means that $xyx^{-1}y^{-1} = 1$ or $xy = yx$ for all $x, y \in G$ and so G is abelian. Thus the size of G' is in a certain sense a measure of the noncommutativity in G.

> **Theorem 14.** The derived group G' of a group G is a normal subgroup of G. G/G' is abelian. If $G \supseteq N \supseteq G'$ then N is normal and G/N is abelian. Conversely, if G/N is abelian, then $N \supseteq G'$.

PROOF. Since the conjugate of a commutator is a commutator it follows that every inner automorphism of G fixes the set of commutators and hence the group G', which they generate. Thus G' is normal in G.

To see that $\bar{G} = G/G'$ is abelian, let φ be the natural mapping of G into $\bar{G}$. If $\bar{x}, \bar{y} \in \bar{G}$ and $\varphi(x) = \bar{x}$ and $\varphi(y) = \bar{y}$ then as $xyx^{-1}y^{-1} \in G'$ we must have $\bar{1} = \varphi(xyx^{-1}y^{-1}) = \bar{x}\bar{y}(\bar{x})^{-1}(\bar{y})^{-1}$ and so $\bar{x}\bar{y} = \bar{y}\bar{x}$.

Now suppose $G \supseteq N \supseteq G'$. To show that N is normal let $n \in N$ and $g \in G$. We know that $gng^{-1}n^{-1} \in G' \subseteq N$ and so $gng^{-1} = (gng^{-1}n^{-1})n \in N$. Since the kernel of $G \to G/N$ contains G' it follows that G/N is abelian as we remarked when we were motivating the definition of a commutator. The last assertion of the theorem now follows in an analogous manner.

$$* \quad * \quad *$$

Lemma 5. Let S and T be subgroups of G. If $S \supseteq T$ then $S' \supseteq T'$.

PROOF. We note that every commutator of T is a commutator of S and so the conclusion of the lemma is immediate.

$$* \quad * \quad *$$

Definition. Let G be a group. Let $G^{(1)} = G'$, the derived group of G. Inductively let $G^{(k+1)} = (G^{(k)})'$ be the derived group of $G^{(k)}$. The *derived* series of G is the chain

$$G \supseteq G^{(1)} \supseteq G^{(2)} \supseteq \cdots.$$

If G is finite we note that there must exist an integer m such that $G^{(m)} = G^{(m+r)}$ for all $r \geq 0$.

Theorem 15. Let G be a finite group. The following conditions are equivalent.

    1. There is a positive integer h such that $G^{(h)} = \{1\}$.
    2. G has a subnormal series

$$\{1\} = A_0 \subset A_1 \subset \cdots \subset A_n = G$$

such that A_{i+1}/A_i is abelian.
    3. G is solvable.

PROOF. Statement 1 implies 2: This is trivial since we know that $G^{(k)}/G^{(k+1)} = G^{(k)}/(G^{(k)})'$ is abelian. Hence by deleting superfluous terms in the chain

$$G \supset G^{(1)} \supset \cdots \supset G^{(h-1)} \supset G^{(h)} = 1,$$

we obtain a subnormal series with the desired property. (Note that if h is chosen to be the minimal positive integer such that $G^{(h)} = \{1\}$ then all the inclusions of the chain are proper.

Statement 2 implies 3: We prove this by induction on n. If $n = 1$ then $G = A_1/A_0$ is abelian and thus solvable. In general, A_{n-1} is solvable by the induction hypothesis and $G/A_{n-1} = A_n/A_{n-1}$ is abelian by assumption and so is solvable; hence by Theorem 12, G is solvable.

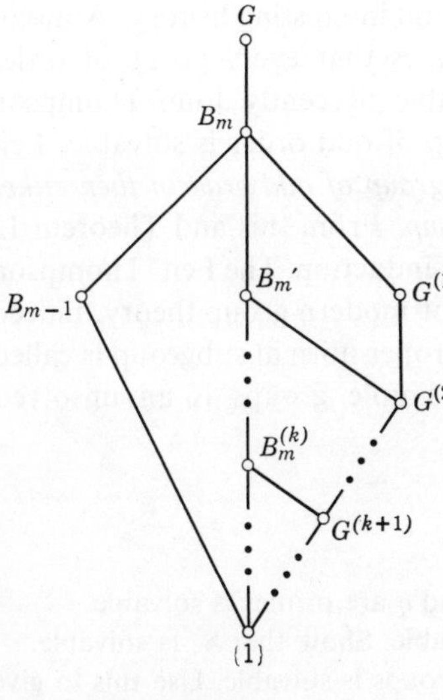

Statement 3 implies 1: Let $G = B_{m+1} \supset B_m \supset \cdots \supset B_0 = \{1\}$ be a composition series with $[B_{i+1} : B_i]$ a prime. In particular G/B_m is abelian and so $B_m \supseteq G'$ by Theorem 14; indeed we have that $B_m^{(k)} \supseteq G^{(k+1)}$ (see Figure 12). With these observations we may now easily prove that 3 implies 1 by induction on the length m of the given composition series. If $m = 1$ then G is abelian and $G^{(1)} = G' = \{1\}$. If $m > 1$, then by induction hypothesis we have $B_m^{(k)} = \{1\}$ for some k; hence $G^{(k+1)} = \{1\}$.

* * *

Figure 12

Conditions (1) or (2) are often given

as the definition of group solvability. (1) or (2) lend themselves to generalizations to infinite groups, whereas the insistence on prime indices in (3) restricts that notion to finite groups.

Up to now we have yet to see an example of a nonsolvable group. We give in the next theorem an important class of groups that are not solvable. For this theorem it will be convenient to recall some facts and notation about permutation groups. A quick review of Exercise 1.4 may be helpful. In particular recall that a 3-cycle is a permutation of order 3 which moves exactly 3 letters and fixes all others, for example, $(1, 2, 3) = \begin{pmatrix} 1\ 2\ 3\ 4 \dots n \\ 2\ 3\ 1\ 4 \dots n \end{pmatrix}$.

> **Theorem 16.** The full symmetric group S_n on n symbols is not solvable if $n \geq 5$.

PROOF. The theorem follows directly from the fact: If T is a subgroup of S_n ($n \geq 5$) containing all 3-cycles then T' contains all 3-cycles.

Thus if $T = S_n$ it follows that S_n' contains all 3-cycles, and by induction $S_n^{(k)}$ contains all 3-cycles. Thus $S_n^{(m)} = \{1\}$ is impossible and so S_n is not solvable.

To prove our stated assertion let $\pi = (a, b, c)$ be a 3-cycle in S_n. Since $n \geq 5$ we may select symbols d and e such that a, b, c, d and e are five distinct symbols. Since T contains all 3-cycles, T must contain $\rho = (a, b, d)$ and $\sigma = (a, c, e)$. Thus T' contains $\rho\sigma\rho^{-1}\sigma^{-1} = (a, b, d)(a, c, e)(a, d, b)(a, e, c) = (a, b, c)$, and so we conclude that T' contains every 3-cycle.

$$* \quad * \quad *$$

The theory of solvable groups has a long and interesting history. A major result obtained by Burnside (1852–1927) states that every group of order $n = p^a q^b$ where p and q are primes is solvable. Recently John Thompson and Walter Feit have shown that every group of odd order is solvable. Feit and Thompson in fact proved that *if G is a group of odd order n then either n is a prime or G has a proper normal subgroup*. From this and Theorem 12 the solvability theorem follows by an obvious induction. The Feit–Thompson result is one of the spectacular achievements of modern group theory, indeed of modern mathematics. A group without a proper normal subgroup is called a *simple* group. The determination of all simple groups is an unsolved problem.

EXERCISE 3

1. Prove that a group of order pq where p and q are primes is solvable.

2. Show that every group of order 12 is solvable. Show that S_4 is solvable.

3. Show that the direct product of solvable groups is solvable. Use this to give a new proof of Theorem 9.11.

4. Prove that an abelian group A is a homomorphic image of G if and only if A is a homomorphic image of G/G'.

5. Prove or disprove the converse of Lemma 5.

6. Let G be a p-group. Prove that if G/G' is cyclic then G is cyclic. (*Hint:* Recall problem 4 of Exercise 9.1.)

9.5. ABELIAN GROUPS

In this section we shall improve our description of abelian groups. We know that every finite abelian group is the direct product of its Sylow subgroups (Theorem 5.18). Here we shall prove that every finite abelian group A is the direct product of cyclic groups: $A = C_1 \times \cdots \times C_n$; where in fact $|C_i| \mid |C_{i+1}|$. The proof which we shall give for this theorem enables us to prove the theorem for any abelian group which can be generated by a finite subset of it. For many situations this proof is constructive; that is, the proof yields an algorithm for finding the cyclic subgroups C_i. The algorithm can be programmed for a digital computer. So that we can state our theorems in a classical form we shall introduce some terminology. In this section we shall write all groups additively.

If the reader wishes an elegant, short, but nonconstructive proof he should consult the article by R. Rado listed at the end of this chapter.

Definition. A group G is said to be *finitely generated* if there is a finite set S of elements in G such that $G = \langle S \rangle$.

Equivalently this says that every element $g \in G$ has the form $g = e_1 s_1 + \cdots + e_t s_t$ for some integer t, and where $s_i \in S$, and $e_i = \pm 1$. Clearly, every finite group is finitely generated.

If the group G is abelian, a set S is called a *basis* for G if S generates G and if whenever $n_1 s_1 + \cdots + n_k s_k = 0$ it follows that $n_i s_i = 0$. (We do not insist that $n_i = 0$ for that would be too restrictive.)

Example 5. If $\langle G, + \rangle$ is cyclic, say $G = \langle g \rangle$, then $\{g\}$ is a basis.

Example 6. If $\langle G, + \rangle$ is the four-group, $G = \{0, a, b, a + b\}$, then $\{a, b\}$, $\{a, a + b\}$, $\{b, a + b\}$ are bases.

Example 7. If $G = A \times B$ then a basis for G is given by the set union of a basis for A and a basis for B.

Example 8. If $G = \langle g \rangle$ is the cyclic group of order 6 then $\{g\}$ and $\{2g, 3g\}$ are bases.

Lemma 6. $\langle G, + \rangle$ is an abelian group with a basis $\{a_1, \ldots, a_k\}$ if and only if $G = \langle a_1 \rangle \times \cdots \times \langle a_k \rangle$.

PROOF. If $\{a_1, \ldots, a_k\}$ is a basis, it is easy to see that the conditions of Theorem 1.36 are satisfied since a "basis" implies both existence and uniqueness of a representation of the elements of G. Conversely, if G is a direct product of cyclic groups the existence and uniqueness of a representation of the elements of G is guaranteed.

$$* \quad * \quad *$$

In view of this lemma we may state the result, which we wish to prove as follows:

> **Basis Theorem for Abelian Groups.** Every finitely generated abelian group has a basis $\{g_1, \ldots, g_k\}$ such that
>
> 1. The orders of $g_1, \ldots, g_h$ ($h \le k$) are finite, and the order of g_i divides the order of g_{i+1}.
> 2. The orders of $g_{h+1}, \ldots, g_k$ are infinite.

To indicate those groups for which our proof is constructive we shall introduce the notion of a "finitely presented abelian group" and the concept of a "free abelian group."

Definition. Let $F_n = \langle w_1 \rangle \times \cdots \times \langle w_n \rangle$ where $\langle w_i \rangle \cong \langle I, + \rangle$ is an infinite cyclic group. A group F is called a free abelian group on n generators if $F \cong F_n$.

> ***Theorem 17.*** Let A be an abelian group generated by n elements, $a_1, \ldots, a_n$. The mapping φ defined by $\varphi(e_1 w_1, \ldots, e_n w_n) = e_1 a_1 + \cdots + e_n a_n$ is a homomorphism of F_n onto A.

PROOF. We shall omit the details of this proof. It is easy since addition in F_n is done component-wise whereas addition in A is commutative. φ maps w_i into a_i; indeed once an image for each of the w_i is chosen, φ is determined. We shall call φ the natural homomorphism of $F_n \to A$.

$$* \quad * \quad *$$

Hereafter, instead of writing the elements of F_n as n-tuples, we shall write them additively, too: $e_1 w_1 + \cdots + e_n w_n$. A trivial remark is that $\{w_1, \ldots, w_n\}$ is a basis for F_n. We obtain the following corollary in an easy manner.

Corollary. If F is a free abelian group with a basis $\{y_1, \ldots, y_n\}$ and A is an abelian group generated by n elements $\{a_1, \ldots, a_n\}$ then the mapping $\psi(y_i) = a_i$, $i = 1, \ldots, n$ can be extended to a homomorphism of F onto A.

> ***Theorem 18.*** Every subgroup of a free abelian group F with n generators is finitely generated.

PROOF. Let F have a basis $\{x_1, \ldots, x_n\}$. Let K be a subgroup of F_n. We shall use a diagonal process to show the existence of a set of generators for K.

Let $T_1 = \{e_1 : \text{There exists } h \in K \text{ such that } h = e_1 x_1 + \cdots + e_n x_n\}$. Thus T_1 is the set of integers which appear as coefficients of x_1 in the elements of K. We have $0 \in T_1$ as $0 = 0x_1 + \cdots + 0x_n \in K$. Clearly, T_1 is an ideal of I and so $T_1 = \langle m_{11} \rangle$. Choose $g_1 \in K$ such that $g_1 = m_{11} x_1 + \cdots + m_{1n} x_n$. Now if $h \in K$ we have for a suitable integer a that $h - ag_1 = 0x_1 + d_2 x_2 + \cdots + d_n x_n$. Now let $T_2 = \{d_2 : \text{There exists } h \in K \text{ such that } h = 0x_1 + d_2 x_2 + \cdots + d_n x_n\}$. Again T_2 is an ideal of I and $T_2 = \langle m_{22} \rangle$. Select $g_2 \in K$ such that $g_2 = m_{22} x_2 + \cdots + m_{2n} x_n$.

In general, $T_i = \{f_i : \text{There exists } h \in K \text{ such that } h = f_i x_i + \cdots + f_n x_n\}$ is an ideal, $T_i = \langle m_{ii} \rangle$. Choose $g_i \in K$ such that $g_i = m_{ii} x_i + \cdots + m_{in} x_n$. We claim $g_1, \ldots, g_n$ generates K, for let $h = e_1 x_1 + \cdots + e_n x_n$. Then as we observed, $h - (e_1/m_{11})g_1 = f_2 x_2 + \cdots + f_n x_n = h_2 \in K$. Now $h_2 - (f_2/m_{22})g_2 = d_3 x_3 + \cdots + d_n x_n = h_3 \in K$. At this point we have $h = (e_1/m_{11})g_1 + h_2 = (e_1/m_{11})g_1 + (f_2/m_{22})g_2 + h_3$. Clearly by continuing this process we obtain an expression for h as an integral combination of $g_1, \ldots, g_n$.

$$* \quad * \quad *$$

Notice that this is not an algorithm we can use in a computer for we are not told how to find all the integers in the ideal T_1, and hence we do not have a constructive way to obtain m_{11} or g_1. Of course, if there were a constructive way to describe the elements in K then we could adjust our algorithm so that it would be constructive too. In fact our next theorem assumes that we are given a finite set of generators for K.

Theorem 19. Let F be a free abelian group with basis $\{x_1, \ldots, x_n\}$. Let K be a subgroup of F which is generated by a finite set $G = \{g_1, \ldots, g_m\}$. Then there is a basis $\{y_1, \ldots, y_n\}$ for F and integers $e_i \geq 0$ so that K is generated by $\{e_1 y_1, \ldots, e_n y_n\}$ and $e_i \mid e_{i+1}$ for $i = 1, \ldots, k-1$, and $e_j = 0$ if $k < j \leq n$. ($k = n$ is a possibility).

PROOF. We shall give an algorithm by which we make successive changes in the basis for F and in the generators of K until we obtain the form required by the theorem. Actually our proof will be an inductive proof of a somewhat different type from our inductions heretofore.

Let the generators of K be given: $g_i = \sum_j a_{ij} x_j$. We define an integer $M(G, X)$, depending on G and the basis $X = \{x_1, \ldots, x_n\}$, as follows: Let $M(G, X) = 0$ if all $a_{ij} = 0$; otherwise let $M(G, X) = \text{minimum } \{|a_{ij}| : a_{ij} \neq 0\}$. Our proof is by induction on the pairs $(n, M(G, X))$, which we order lexicographically. (Remember n is the number of elements in the basis of F.) If $n = 1$ then the theorem holds since in that case $g_i = a_i x$, and if $e = \text{GCD}(a_1, \ldots, a_m)$ we have that $K = \langle ex \rangle$. If $M(G, X) = 0$, then $K = \{0\}$ and so $e_1 = \cdots = e_n = 0$ are the appropriate integers.

A word about our proof and our induction. We shall show that if the theorem is true for all free abelian groups E with a basis $T = \{t_1, \ldots, t_k\}$ and all subgroups H of E with a finite set of generators S such that $(k, M(S, T))$ precedes (n, m) in the lexicographic ordering (that is, $k < n$ or $k = n$ and $M(S, T) < m$), then the theorem is true for F with basis X and a subgroup K with generators G such that $(n, m) = (n, M(G, X))$.

We shall do this by showing how, starting with the basis $X = \{x_1, \ldots, x_n\}$ for F and generators $G = \{g_1, \ldots, g_m\}$ for K, we may change the basis for F or the generators for K, or both, so that the induction hypothesis holds. This will be a constructive process; at each stage directions will be given as to how the reduction of the pair $(n, M(G, X))$ is to take place. In this way the algorithm resembles very much the euclidean algorithm. The flow chart on page 260 serves as a guide to the proof and as a plan for executing the algorithm.

Step 1. By reordering if necessary the basis elements and the generators of K we may assume that $M(G, X) = |a_{11}|$.

Step 2. For some i suppose that $a_{11} \nmid a_{i1}$. For ease of notation in the proof suppose that $i = 2$. We have $a_{21} = a_{11}q + r$ where $0 < r < |a_{11}|$. Let $h_2 = g_2 - qg_1$. Clearly $G' = \{g_1, h_2, g_3, \ldots, g_m\}$ generates K. However, $h_2 = \sum a_{2j}x_j - \sum qa_{1j}x_j = rx_1 + b_2x_2 + \cdots + b_nx_n$ and so $(n, M(G', X))$ precedes $(n, M(G, X))$. Thus the theorem holds by the induction hypothesis.

Step 3. For some j suppose that $a_{11} \nmid a_{1j}$. For ease of notation suppose that $j = 2$. Let $a_{12} = a_{11}q + r$ where $0 < r < |a_{11}|$. Let $z_1 = x_1 + qx_2$. Clearly $Z = \{z_1, x_2, \ldots, x_n\}$ is a basis for F. We may express the generators of K in terms of this basis as follows:

$$g_i = \sum a_{ij}x_j = a_{i1}(z_1 - qx_2) + a_{i2}x_2 + \sum_{j \geq 3} a_{ij}x_j$$

$$= a_{i1}z_1 + (a_{i2} - a_{i1}q)x_2 + \sum_{j \geq 3} a_{ij}x_j;$$

in particular $g_1 = a_{11}z_1 + rx_2 + \sum_{j \geq 3} a_{1j}x_j$. Thus for this set of generators G of K and basis Z for F we have that $(n, M(G, Z))$ precedes $(n, M(G, X))$ and so the theorem is proved from the induction hypothesis.

Step 4. Suppose that $a_{11} \mid a_{i1}$ and $a_{11} \mid a_{1j}$ for all i, j. For $i \geq 2$ let $c_i = a_{i1}/a_{11}$. If some $c_i \neq 0$ we make a change in the generators for K by defining, for $i \geq 2$, $h_i = g_i - c_ig_1$. Now K is generated by $\{g_1, h_2, \ldots, h_m\}$ and for $i \geq 2$, $h_i = (a_{i1} - c_ia_{11})x_1 + \sum_{j \geq 2} b_{ij}x_j = \sum_{j \geq 2} b_{ij}x_j$. That is, for $i \geq 2$, h_i belongs to the subgroup E with basis $\{x_2, \ldots, x_n\} = X'$.

For $j \geq 2$ let $d_j = a_{1j}/a_{11}$. If some $d_j \neq 0$ we make a change in the basis for F. Let $z_1 = x_1 + d_2x_2 + \cdots + d_nx_n$. $Y = \{z_1, x_2, \ldots, x_n\}$ is a basis for F, as we shall show. Certainly Y generates F whereas if $n_1z_1 + \sum n_jx_j = 0$ then $n_1x_1 + \sum (n_j + d_jn_1)x_j = 0$, and so $n_1 = 0$ and thus $n_j = 0$ for all j.

In terms of the basis Y, the generators for K become $G' = \{a_{11}z_1, h_2, \ldots, h_m\}$. In terms of this basis we have the hypotheses satisfied for the next step.

Step 5. Suppose that $a_{i1} = 0$ for all $i \geq 2$ and $a_{j1} = 0$ for all $j \geq 2$. $X = \{x_1, x_2, \ldots, x_n\}$ and K is generated by $G = \{g_1 \, (= a_{11}x_1), g_2, \ldots, g_n\}$ with $g_i = \sum_{j \geq 2} a_{ij}x_j$ if $i \geq 2$. If, for $i \geq 2$, $g_i = f_i x_i$ and if $f_i \mid f_{i+1}$ for $2 \leq i < n$ we go to the next step. If not we consider the subgroup E of F generated by the basis $X' = \{x_2, \ldots, x_n\}$ and its subgroup N generated by $H = \{h_2, \ldots, h_n\}$. E is a free abelian group with basis X'. Since $(n - 1, M(H, X'))$ precedes $(n, M(G, X))$ we may, by the induction hypothesis, find a basis $\{z_2, \ldots, z_n\}$ for E and integers $f_2, \ldots, f_n$ such that $N = \langle f_2 z_2, \ldots, f_n z_n \rangle$ where $f_i \mid f_{i+1}$ or $f_i = f_{i+1} = \cdots = f_n = 0$ for $i = 1, 2, \ldots$.

We claim that $Z = \{z_1 (= x_1), z_2, \ldots, z_n\}$ is a basis for F. Since $F = \langle x_1 \rangle \vee E$ and $E = \langle z_2, \ldots, z_n \rangle$ it is clear that Z generates F. Suppose that $\sum n_i z_i = 0$. We have that $z_1 = x_1$ and that for $i \geq 2$ we have $z_i = \sum_{j \geq 2} k_{ij}x_j$. Hence $\sum n_i z_i = n_1 x_1 + \sum_{j \geq 2} t_j x_j$ and so $n_1 = 0$. But then, since $\{z_2, \ldots, z_n\}$ is a basis for E, it follows that $n_i = 0$ if $i \geq 2$, and so we have shown that Z is a basis for F. Clearly $K = \langle a_{11}z_1 \rangle \vee N$ and so K is generated by $\{a_{11}z_1, f_2 z_2, \ldots, f_n z_n\}$. Moreover $f_i \mid f_{i+1}$ for $i \geq 2$. In terms of this basis we have the hypotheses satisfied for the next step.

Step 6. Suppose that K is generated by $G = \{a_{11}x_1, f_2 x_2, \ldots, f_n x_n\}$ and that $f_i \mid f_{i+1}$ for $i = 1, \ldots, k - 1$, and $f_j = 0$ if $k < j \leq n$. Our proof is complete if $a_{11} \mid f_2$. If not, let $f_2 = a_{11}q + r$ where $0 < r < |a_{11}|$. We have that $a_{11}x_1 + f_2 x_2 \in K$. Rewriting this element as $a_{11}(x_1 + qx_2) + rx_2$ suggests setting $w_1 = x_1 + qx_2$. Then $W = \{w_1, x_2, \ldots, x_n\}$ is a basis for F. Moreover, K, which was generated by $\{a_{11}x_1, f_2 x_2, \ldots, f_n x_n\}$ is now generated by $S = \{a_{11}x_1 + rx_2, f_2 x_2, \ldots, f_n x_n\}$. But $M(S, W) = r < |a_{11}|$ and so $(n, M(S, W))$ precedes $(n, M(G, X))$. By a final application of the induction hypothesis we are done!

$* \quad * \quad *$

Our algorithm is displayed on the next page as a flow chart. In the chart the hypotheses of each step are phrased as questions.

Example 9. Let F be the free abelian group with the basis $\{x_1, x_2\}$. Let K be the subgroup of F generated by $\{g_1 = 2x_1 + 4x_2, g_2 = 3x_2\}$. We shall find a basis for F and a set of generators for K by employing the algorithm of Theorem 19 and following the flow chart. The smallest nonzero coefficient is 2 and so Step 1 is unnecessary as are Steps 2 and 3. (In practice these steps give little difficulty. This example will show the sort of complexities introduced by Steps 4, 5, and 6.) We have $M(G, X) = a_{11} = 2$.

Step 4. $c_2 = 0$ and $d_2 = 2$. Thus $h_2 = g_2$, $z_1 = x_1 + 2x_2$. The basis for F becomes $Y = \{z_1, x_2\}$. The generating set $G' = \{2z_1, h_2\}$ where $h_2 = g_2 = 3x_2$. In terms of x_1 and x_2 we have $2z_1 = 2x_1 + 4x_2$.

Flow Chart for the Algorithm of Theorem 19

We assume that $X = \{x_1, \ldots, x_n\}$ is a basis for F, that $G = \{g_1, \ldots, g_m\}$ is a set of generators for the subgroup K of F, and that $g_i = \sum_j a_{ij}x_j$ for $1 \leq i \leq n$. $M(G, X)$ is the minimal nonzero $|a_{ij}|$.

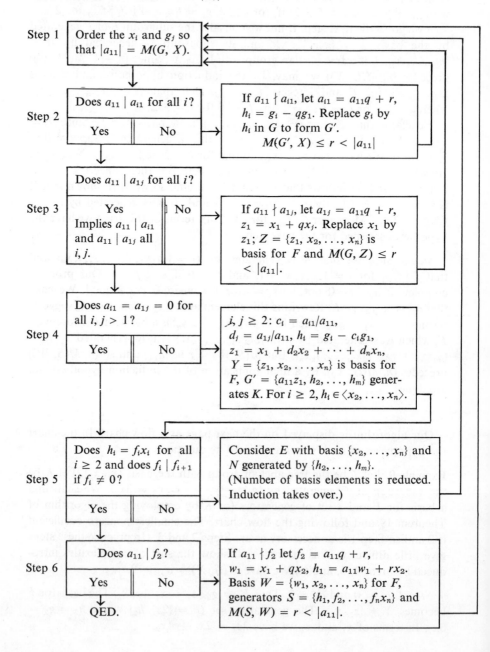

Step 5. The answer to the question is yes. However note that $E = \langle x_2 \rangle$ and N is the subgroup generated by $H = \{3x_2\}$ since $h_2 = 3x_2$. Since E and N satisfy the conditions of the theorem, we now have a basis $\{z_1, x_2\}$ for F and a set of generators $\{2z_1, 3x_2\}$ for K.

Step 6. The answer to the question is no. $2 \nmid 3$, so $f_2 = 3 = 2 \cdot 1 + 1$. We have $w_1 = z_1 + x_2 = (x_1 + 2x_2) + x_2 = x_1 + 3x_2$. Thus $W = \{w_1, x_2\}$ is a basis for F and K is generated by $S = \{2w_1 + x_2, 3x_2\}$. Here the minimal nonzero coefficient is 1 and by induction we return to Step 1.

Step 1. We reorder the basis elements in W by setting $\bar{x}_1 = x_2$ and $\bar{x}_2 = w_1$. To avoid confusion we shall place a bar over the new symbols. Thus $\{\bar{x}_1, \bar{x}_2\}$ is a basis for F and $\{\bar{g}_1, \bar{g}_2\}$ generates K where $\bar{g}_1 = \bar{x}_1 + 2\bar{x}_2$ and $\bar{g}_2 = 3\bar{x}_1$. Again Steps 2 and 3 give yes answers.

Step 4. Neither $\bar{a}_{21}$ nor $\bar{a}_{12}$ is zero. $\bar{c}_2 = 3, \bar{d}_2 = 2; \bar{h}_2 = \bar{g}_2 - 3\bar{g}_1 = -6\bar{x}_2$. The new basis for F becomes $\{\bar{z}_1, \bar{x}_2\}$ where $\bar{z}_1 = \bar{x}_1 + 2\bar{x}_2$ and in terms of this basis $\{\bar{z}_1, \bar{h}_2\}$ generates K. But now $\bar{h}_2 = -6\bar{x}_2$ so that $F = \langle \bar{z}_1, \bar{x}_2 \rangle$ and $K = \langle \bar{z}_1, -6\bar{x}_2 \rangle$. The answers in Steps 5 and 6 are now yes. Thus we have achieved the form claimed by the theorem. Tracing back to the original generators we see that $\bar{z}_1 = \bar{x}_1 + 2\bar{x}_2 = x_2 + 2w_1 = x_2 + 2(x_1 + 3x_2) = 2x_1 + 7x_2$ and $\bar{x}_2 = w_1 = x_1 + 3x_2$. Thus $F = \langle 2x_1 + 7x_2, x_1 + 3x_2 \rangle$ while $K = \langle 2x_1 + 7x_2, -6x_1 - 18x_2 \rangle$.

Corollary. If K is a subgroup of a free abelian group F with n generators then there is a basis $\{y_1, \ldots, y_n\}$ for F and integers $\{e_1, \ldots, e_n\}$ such that $K = \langle e_1 y_1, \ldots, e_n y_n \rangle$, and for each i, $e_i \mid e_{i+1}$ or $e_i = e_{i+1} = \cdots = e_n = 0$.

PROOF. By Theorem 17, K has a finite set of generators. Now the corollary follows directly.

* * *

Definition. An abelian group A is said to be *finitely presented* if there is given a finite sequence of generators $\{a_1, \ldots, a_n\}$ for A and a finite set of relations

$$\sum_{1 \le h \le n} e_{ih} a_h = 0; \qquad i = 1, 2, \ldots, m$$

holding in A such that there is a free abelian group F with basis $\{y_1, \ldots, y_n\}$ so that in the natural homomorphism $\varphi : F \to A$ such that $\varphi(y_i) = a_i$ the kernel K of φ is generated by $\{g_i = \sum_h e_{ih} y_h : i = 1, 2, \ldots, m\}$.

The set of relations occurring in a finite presentation of A is called a set of defining relations (DR) for A. Any finite abelian group A is finitely presented: A is a set of generators itself while $DR = \{a - (b + c) = 0: a = b + c$ in $A\}$.

Theorem 20. For every finitely generated abelian group there exists a finite presentation.

Our proof will actually show that if $\{a_1, \ldots, a_n\}$ generate the group, there is a finite presentation with $\{a_1, \ldots, a_n\}$ as the generators.

PROOF. Let A be an abelian group with n generators $\{a_1, \ldots, a_n\}$. Let $\varphi: F_n \to A$ with $\varphi(w_i) = a_i$ be the natural homomorphism. Let K be the kernel of φ. By Theorem 18, K has a finite set of generators $\{g_1 = \sum e_{ij}w_j \ (i = 1, 2, \ldots, n)\}$ and so A has a set of defining relations $\sum e_{ij}a_j = 0; 1 \leq i \leq n$.

$$* \quad * \quad *$$

Theorem 21. If A is a finitely presented abelian group then there is a presentation with generators $\{b_1, \ldots, b_n\}$ and $\mathrm{DR}\{e_ib_i = 0: i = 1, 2, \ldots, n\}$ such that $e_i \mid e_{i+1}$ for $i = 1, \ldots, h - 1$ and $e_{h+1} = \cdots = e_n = 0$. Moreover, given the finite presentation there is an algorithm for obtaining this particular presentation.

PROOF. Let F be the free abelian group with basis $\{x_1, \ldots, x_n\}$, and $\varphi: F \to A$. Let K be the kernel of φ. Since A is finitely presented, a finite set of generators for K is given. By the algorithm of Theorem 19 we can find a basis $\{y_1, \ldots, y_n\}$ for F so that $K = \langle e_1y_1, \ldots, e_ny_n \rangle$ with the appropriate divisibility properties. Let $\varphi(y_i) = b_i$. Now it follows from the corollary to Theorem 17 that $\{b_1, \ldots, b_n\}$ generates A and indeed A has the presentation; generators $\{b_1, \ldots, b_n\}$ and defining relations $\{e_ib_i = 0 : 1 \leq i \leq n\}$ and the corresponding divisibility conditions hold. Note that if $e_i = 0$, then $my_i \notin K$ for all integers m and so it follows that b_i has infinite order in A.

$$* \quad * \quad *$$

Theorem 22. The following conditions are equivalent for an abelian group.

1. A is the direct product of a finite number of cyclic groups.
2. A has a finite basis.
3. A has a finite presentation:
    Generators: $\{a_1, \ldots, a_n\}$
    Defining Relations: $\{e_ia_i = 0 : e_i \geq 0\}$

PROOF. Lemma 6 has established that 1 and 2 are equivalent. To show that 1 implies 3 we choose the a's to be the generators of the given cyclic groups and take e_i as the order of a_i or $e_i = 0$ if a_i is infinite. We have only to observe that in the free abelian group F_n if we let K be the subgroup generated by $\{e_1w_1, \ldots, e_nw_n\}$, that is, $K = \{f_1w_1 + \cdots + f_nw_n : e_i \mid f_i$ if $e_i \neq 0$ and $f_i = 0$ if $e_i = 0\}$, then $F_n/K = A$. We shall omit the details of this argument.

Now we show that 3 implies 2 by showing that $\{a_1, \ldots, a_n\}$ is a basis. Let $\{y_1, \ldots, y_n\}$ be the basis of the free abelian group F associated with the presentation, and $\theta: F \to A$ be the homomorphism with $\theta(y_i) = a_i$. Suppose $f_1a_1 + \cdots + f_na_n = 0$. Thus $z = f_1y_1 + \cdots + f_ny_n \in K$, and since $\{e_iy_i : 1 \leq i \leq n\}$ generates K we must have $z = m_1e_1y_1 + \cdots + m_ne_ny_n$, and since

$\{y_i : 1 \leq i \leq n\}$ is a basis for F we must have that $m_i e_i = f_i$ for all i; thus $f_i a_i = m_i(e_i a_i) = 0$ in A. In particular if $e_i \neq 0$ then e_i is the order of a_i and if $e_i = 0$ then a_i has infinite order.

* * *

An amalgamation of Theorems 21 and 22 yields the promised basis theorem: Theorem 21 gives a presentation of the correct form while the last paragraph of the proof of Theorem 22 shows the generating set to be a basis. The direct product form of this theorem (p. 255) is then implied by Theorem 22. As we have seen, if A is finitely presented there is an algorithm for determining the generators of the groups C_i in terms of the generators for A.

Example 10. Let A be the abelian group given by the finite presentation: generators, $\{a, b\}$, and DR, $\{2a + 4b = 0$ and $3b = 0\}$. We consider the free abelian group $F = \langle x_1, x_2 \rangle$ and its subgroup generated by $\{2x_1 + 4x_2, 3x_2\}$. As in Example 9 another basis for F is $\{\bar{z}_1, \bar{x}_2\}$ and in terms of this basis K is generated by $\{\bar{z}_1, -6\bar{x}_2\}$. It now follows, as in the proof of Theorem 21, that A has the presentation; generators $\{a_1, b_1\}$ and $DR(a_1 = 0$ and $-6b_1 = 0)$. Indeed, $a_1 = 2a + 7b$ while $b_1 = a + 3b$ as we found in Example 9. Clearly the generator a_1 is superfluous and we may replace b_1 by $c = -b_1$. Thus A is the cyclic group of order 6 whose generator is c.

Example 11. Let A be the abelian group given by the finite presentation: generators $\{a, b, c, d\}$ and $DR\{2a + 3b = 0, 4a = 0,$ and $5c + 11d = 0\}$. Find a basis for A with the appropriate divisibility conditions. We let F be a free abelian group with a set $X = \{w, x, y, z\}$ of generators and φ the homomorphism of F onto A such that $\varphi(w) = a$, $\varphi(x) = b$, $\varphi(y) = c$, and $\varphi(z) = d$. Then the kernel K is generated by $G = \{2w + 3x, 4w, 5y + 11z\}$. We shall use the algorithm of Theorem 19 to find a basis for F and generators for K. We see that $M(G, X) = 2$. We do not need to apply Step 1 nor Step 2 since $2 \mid 4$; however, $2 \nmid 3$ so we apply Step 3. $3 = 2 \cdot 1 + 1$ and we define $w_1 = w + x$. We have a basis $X_1 = \{w_1, x, y, z\}$ and a generating set for K, $G_1 = \{g_1 = 2w_1 + x, g_2 = 4w_1 - 4x, g_3 = 5y + 11z\}$. We have $M(G_1, X_1) = 1$. We may easily dispense with Step 1 (it was really a convenience for the proof), and since 1 divides every integer we go directly to Step 4. Let $g_1 = h_1 = 2w_1 + x$, $h_2 = 4w_1 - 4x + 4(2w_1 + x) = 12w_1$, and $h_3 = 5y + 11z$. Thus K is generated by $\{g_1, h_2, h_3\}$ and we set $x_1 = 2w_1 + x$. Thus $X_2 = \{w_1, x_1, y, z\}$ is a basis for F, and K is generated by $G_2 = \{x_1, 12w_1, 5y + 11z\}$. In addition, we have from the theorem that $F = \langle x_1 \rangle \times E$ where E has the basis $X_3 = \{w_1, y, z\}$ and $K = \langle x_1 \rangle \vee N$ where N is generated by $G_3 = \{12w_1, 5y + 11z\}$. Now we must apply induction to E and N. $M(G_3, X_3) = 5$. Now $5 \mid 0$ but $5 \nmid 11$, so we apply Step 3: $11 = 5 \cdot 2 + 1$. Let $y_1 = y + 2z$. Then $X_4 = \{w_1, y_1, z\}$ is a basis for E, and N is generated by $G_4 = \{12w_1, 5y_1 + z\}$, and so $M(G_4, X_4) = 1$. Now we apply Step 4. Replace z by $z_1 = 5y_1 + z$. $\{w_1, y_1, z_1\}$ is a basis for E, and N is generated by $\{12w_1, z_1\}$. After a reordering we are done! F has a basis by $\{x_1, z_1, w_1, y_1\}$, and K is generated by $\{x_1, z_1, 12w_1, 0y_1\}$. It now follows as in the proof of Theorem 21 that A has a presentation with generators $\{a_1, b_1, c_1, d_1\}$ and defining relations $\{a_1 = 0, b_1 = 0, 12c_1 = 0\}$. That is, $A = Z_1 \times Z_2$, where Z_1 is a cyclic group of order 12 and Z_2 is an infinite cyclic group. Indeed,

$$
\begin{aligned}
x_1 &= 2w_1 + x = 2w + 3x, & \text{hence } \varphi(x_1) &= 2a + 3b = a_1 = 0; \\
z_1 &= 5y_1 + z = 5y + 11x, & \text{hence } \varphi(z_1) &= 5c + 11d = b_1 = 0; \\
w_1 &= w + x, & \text{hence } \varphi(w_1) &= a + b = c_1 \text{ and } 12c_1 = 0; \\
y_1 &= y + 2z, & \text{hence } \varphi(y_1) &= c + 2d = d_1.
\end{aligned}
$$

Since no multiple of y_1 is in the kernel K, it follows that no multiple of d_1 is equal to 0 in A; that is, d_1 has infinite order. In summary, we have shown that A is generated by $\{a + b, c + 2d\}$ and $a + b$ has order 12 whereas $c + 2d$ has infinite order.

The question of the uniqueness of the decomposition of A as a direct product is somewhat more complicated. As we noted in Example 8, the cyclic group of order 6 is the direct product of a cyclic group of order 2 and one of order 3. Thus there is no hope to prove much about the uniqueness of the basis. However, if we insist on the divisibility conditions of Theorem 19, then we obtain (Theorem 24) a uniqueness result, not on the cyclic subgroups which form the direct product, but on their number and their orders.

For the proof of this uniqueness theorem we shall prove an interesting "cancellation law" for direct products of abelian groups. This theorem is due to the contemporary mathematician P. M. Cohn, and was first proved in 1955. This result was also obtained independently by E. A. Walker.

> **Theorem 23** (*P. M. Cohn*). If A and K are isomorphic abelian groups such that $A = G \times \langle b \rangle$ and $K = H \times \langle c \rangle$ where $\langle b \rangle \simeq \langle c \rangle$, then G and H are isomorphic.

PROOF. We treat three cases depending on the order of $\langle b \rangle$. In the first, $\langle b \rangle$ and $\langle c \rangle$ are infinite cyclic groups, in the second each has prime power order, p^n, and in the third each has composite order n, which is not a prime power. In the first two cases it is convenient to assume that $A = K$. We can do this without loss of generality because in any event, in the isomorphism of K onto A the subgroup H goes onto a subgroup H_1 and $\langle c \rangle$ goes onto a cyclic subgroup $\langle c_1 \rangle$. Clearly $H \cong H_1$ and $\langle c \rangle \cong \langle c_1 \rangle$ and $A = H_1 \times \langle c_1 \rangle$. If we can prove that $H_1 \cong G$ our proof will be complete, thus we assume $A = K$.

Case 1. $\langle b \rangle$ and $\langle c \rangle$ are infinite groups. By Theorem 8 we know that $(G \vee H)/H \cong G/(G \cap H)$ and that $A/H \supseteq (G \vee H)/H$ by Theorem 1.29.

(The relationships of the subgroups in this case are pictured in Figure 13.) Since $A/H \cong \langle c \rangle$ it follows that $G/(G \cap H)$ is either $\{0\}$ or an infinite cyclic group (Theorem 1.15). In the former case $G \cap H = G$. Similarly $H/(G \cap H)$

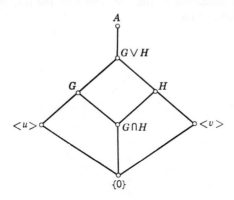

Figure 13

is either $\{0\}$ or an infinite cyclic group. If both are $\{0\}$ then $G = G \cap H = H$ and we are done. If, say, $G/G \cap H$ is an infinite cyclic group let $u \in G$ be such that $u + (G \cap H) = \bar{u}$ generates $G/G \cap H$. As $\bar{u}$ has infinite order it follows that $\langle u \rangle \cap (G \cap H) = \{0\}$ and $\langle u \rangle \vee (G \cap H) = G$. Hence $G = \langle u \rangle \times (G \cap H)$ (by Theorem 1.33), and so $A = (G \cap H) \times \langle u \rangle \times \langle b \rangle = H \times \langle c \rangle$. Since $G \cap H \subseteq H$ we have $A/(G \cap H) = \langle u \rangle \times \langle b \rangle = (H \times \langle c \rangle)/(G \cap H) \cong [H/(G \cap H)] \times \langle c \rangle$. It follows that $H/(G \cap H)$ is an infinite cyclic group since the alternative $H/(G \cap H) = \{0\}$ implies $\langle u \rangle \times \langle b \rangle \cong \langle c \rangle$, which is impossible. Now let $v \in H$ such that $\bar{v} = v + (G \cap H)$ generates $H/G \cap H$. As before, $\langle v \rangle \cap (G \cap H) = \{0\}$, and so $H = \langle v \rangle \times (G \cap H)$. Thus $G = \langle u \rangle \times (G \cap H)$, $H = \langle v \rangle \times (G \cap H)$, and since $\langle u \rangle \cong \langle v \rangle$ it follows that $G \cong H$.

Case 2. $\langle b \rangle$ and $\langle c \rangle$ have order p^n where p is a prime. We shall show first that there is an element $d \in A$ such that $\langle d \rangle$ has order p^n and $\langle d \rangle \cap H = \langle d \rangle \cap G = \{0\}$. If $\langle b \rangle \cap H = \{0\}$ or $\langle c \rangle \cap G = \{0\}$ then we may choose $d = b$ or c. Suppose then that $\langle b \rangle \cap H \neq \{0\} \neq \langle c \rangle \cap G$. We shall show that $d = b + c$ works. Now $\langle b \rangle \cap H$ is a subgroup of $\langle b \rangle$, a cyclic group of order p^n, and since p is a prime the subgroups of $\langle b \rangle$ form a chain, one subgroup for each $0 \leq k \leq n$ corresponding to the divisor p^k of p^n (Theorem 1.16). The condition $\{0\} \neq \langle b \rangle \cap H$ implies that the minimal nonzero subgroup $\langle p^{n-1}b \rangle$ is contained in $\langle b \rangle \cap H$; that is, that $p^{n-1}b \in H$. Similarly $p^{n-1}c \in G$. Now let $d = b + c$. Clearly $p^n(b + c) = 0$. However $p^{n-1}(b + c) \notin G$, since $p^{n-1}c \in G$ and if $p^{n-1}(b + c) \in G$ as well, then $p^{n-1}b \in G$, a contradiction of the assumption $A = G \times \langle b \rangle$. This implies of course that $p^{n-1}(b + c) \neq 0$ and so the order of $d = b + c$ is p^n. It also implies that

$\langle b + c \rangle \cap G = \{0\}$ since the minimal subgroup of $\langle b + c \rangle$ does not belong to G. In a similar fashion we have that $\langle b + c \rangle \cap H = \{0\}$. Thus we have established the key properties for the element $d = b + c$. (The relationships of the subgroups appearing in the remainder of the discussion of this case are pictured in Figure 14.)

Now $G_1 = G \vee \langle d \rangle = G \times \langle d \rangle$ and similarly $H_1 = H \vee \langle d \rangle = H \times \langle d \rangle$

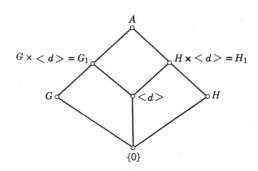

Figure 14

so that $(G \vee \langle d \rangle)/G = \langle (d) \rangle = (H \vee \langle d \rangle)/H$. In particular $[G_1 : G] = p^n$ and since $[A : G] = p^n$ and $A \supseteq G_1$, it follows that $A = G_1 = G \times \langle d \rangle$. Similarly $A = H \times \langle d \rangle$ and so $A/\langle d \rangle \simeq G \simeq H$.

Case 3. $\langle b \rangle$ and $\langle c \rangle$ have order m composite integer. Let $m = p_1^{n_1} \cdots p_k^{n_k}$ be the factorization of m as distinct prime powers. By combining Theorem 1.14 and Theorem 5.18 we know that $\langle b \rangle = \langle b_1 \rangle \times \cdots \times \langle b_k \rangle$ and $\langle c \rangle = \langle c_1 \rangle \times \cdots \times \langle c_k \rangle$ where $|\langle b_i \rangle| = |\langle c_i \rangle| = p_i^{n_i}$. By k applications of Case 2 we obtain $G \simeq H$.

$$* \quad * \quad *$$

Theorem 24 (*Unicity Theorem for Abelian Group Decomposition.*) Let A and $\overline{A}$ be isomorphic, finitely generated abelian groups. Let

$$A = \langle b_1 \rangle \times \cdots \times \langle b_h \rangle \times \langle b_{h+1} \rangle \times \cdots \times \langle b_n \rangle$$

and

$$\overline{A} = \langle c_1 \rangle \times \cdots \times \langle c_k \rangle \times \langle c_{k+1} \rangle \times \cdots \times \langle c_m \rangle$$

where $|\langle b_{i-1} \rangle|$ is finite and divides $|\langle b_i \rangle|$ for $i = 2, \ldots, h$; $\langle b_j \rangle$ is infinite for $h + 1 \leq j \leq n$; similarly $\langle c_{r-1} \rangle$ divides $\langle c_r \rangle$ for $r = 2, \ldots, k$, whereas $\langle c_t \rangle$ are infinite for $k + 1 \leq t \leq m$. Under these conditions $n = m$ and $\langle b_i \rangle \simeq \langle c_i \rangle$ for all i.

PROOF. Let us assume that $n \leq m$. We proceed by induction on n. If $n = 1$ then A is cyclic and the result is immediate. From the divisibility properties it follows that the order of b_n and equally the order c_m are the highest orders of any elements in A and $\overline{A}$. Since $A \simeq \overline{A}$ it follows from this intrinsic property that $\langle b_n \rangle \cong \langle c_m \rangle$ because they must have the same order. Thus from Theorem 23

$$\langle b_1 \rangle \times \cdots \times \langle b_{n-1} \rangle \cong \langle c_1 \rangle \times \cdots \times \langle c_{m-1} \rangle,$$

and the uniqueness follows from the induction hypothesis.

*   *   *

One result of the basis theorem and the uniqueness theorem is that we may now determine up to isomorphism all finite abelian groups of order m. If $m = p_1^{n_1} \cdots \cdot p_k^{n_k}$ then we know that every abelian group A of order m is the direct product of its Sylow subgroups: $A = S_{p_1^{e_1}} \times \cdots \times S_{p_k^{e_k}}$. Clearly $A \cong \bar{A}$ if and only if $S_{p_i^{e_i}} \cong \bar{S}_{p_i^{e_i}}$ for all i. Thus it suffices to determine all abelian groups of prime power order. If A has order p^n we know from the basis theorem that $A = Z_1 \times \cdots \times Z_t$ where $Z_i = p^{e_i}$ and $1 \leq e_1 \leq \cdots \leq e_t$ and $\sum e_i = n$, and that this representation is unique. That is to say that A is uniquely determined by the integers $e_1, \ldots, e_t$, which are subject to the conditions $1 \leq e_1 \leq \cdots \leq e_t$ and $\sum e_i = n$. Thus there are just as many nonisomorphic abelian groups of order p^n as there are ways to express n as the sum of positive integers! As a corollary we have that this number has nothing whatever to do with the prime p.

Example 12. There are five nonisomorphic abelian groups of order p^4. There are five ways of expressing 4 as the sum of positive integers: $4 = 0 + 4 = 1 + 3 = 1 + 1 + 2 = 1 + 1 + 1 + 1 = 2 + 2$. Hence any abelian group of order p^4 is isomorphic to one of the following groups,

$$C_{p^4}, C_p \times C_{p^3}, C_p \times C_p \times C_{p^2}, C_p \times C_p \times C_p \times C_p, C_{p^2} \times C_{p^2}.$$

The function $\pi(n)$, which is defined as the number of ways of expressing n as the sum of positive integers, is of much interest in number theory and combinatorial analysis. $\pi(n)$ is called the partition function.

EXERCISE 4

1. Determine, up to isomorphism, all abelian groups of order 144.

2. Characterize those integers n such that the only abelian groups of order n are cyclic.

3. Let A be the abelian group finitely presented by

Generators: a, b, c, d, e.
DR: $a - 7b + 14d - 21e = 0$
$5a - 7b - 2c + 10d - 15e = 0$
$3a - 3b - 2c + 6d - 9e = 0$
$a - b + 2d - 3e = 0$.

Express A as the direct product of four cyclic groups.

4. Show that any subgroup of a free abelian group is a free abelian group.

5. Show that there is no abelian group G such that G has exactly three proper subgroups that are related as shown by Figure 15. Does such a group, abelian or not, exist?

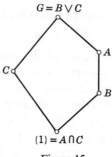

Figure 15

6. In the proof of Theorem 23, locate the steps which depend on the fact that A is abelian.

SUPPLEMENTARY READING

P. M. Cohn, The complement of a finitely generated direct summand of an abelian group, *Proceedings of the American Mathematical Society*, **7** (1956), 520–521.

W. Burnside, *Theory of Groups of Finite Order* (original edition published in 1911), New York: Dover (1955).

Marshall Hall, Jr., Generators and relations in groups—the Burnside problem, *Lectures on Modern Mathematics*, vol. 2 (edited by T. L. Saaty), New York: John Wiley & Sons (1964), 42–92.

Marshall Hall, Jr., *The Theory of Groups*, New York: Macmillan (1959).

R. Rado, A proof of the basis theorem for finitely generated abelian groups, *Journal of the London Mathematical Society*, **26** (1951), 74–75.

I. Niven and H. S. Zukerman, *An Introduction to the Theory of Numbers*, New York: John Wiley & Sons (1960).

E. A. Walker, Cancellation in direct sums of groups, *Proceedings of the American Mathematical Society*, **7** (1956), 898–902.

10 | Galois Theory

Galois Theory relates the subfield structure of an algebraic extension $E \supseteq F$ to the subgroup structure of the group $\mathcal{G}(E/F)$ of automorphisms of E which fix every element in F. As we shall see this theory is richest when we assume that E is the splitting field of a polynomial $f(x)$ in $F[x]$. Historically, it was in this connection that the concepts of "normal subgroup" and "solvable group" arose for they represented conditions on the group $\mathcal{G}(E/F)$ which were translatable into conditions on the equation $f(x) = 0$. We shall see how knowledge of the subgroups of $\mathcal{G}(E/F)$ gives knowledge of the subfields of E which contain F and indeed this information shall help us solve equations and to show us which equations cannot be solved "by radicals."

In this chapter we shall assume that all of our fields have characteristic zero. The primary result achieved by this assumption is that an irreducible polynomial over a field of characteristic zero has no multiple zeros (Corollary to Theorem 6.15). Other developments of Galois Theory apply to more general situations, but it is our intention to treat only this more easily handled situation. (In general a polynomial $f(x) \in F[x]$ is called *separable* if every irreducible factor $p(x)$ of $f(x)$ in $F[x]$ has simple zeros.) We shall also assume that all extensions considered in this chapter are finite, unless explicitly stated otherwise.

10.1. FUNDAMENTAL THEOREM OF GALOIS THEORY

The basic observation that starts us off into Galois Theory is the following simple but fundamental idea, which sets up a correspondence between fields K, where $E \supseteq K \supseteq F$, and subgroups of $\mathcal{G} = \mathcal{G}(E/F)$. For such a field K we define $\mathcal{S}(K) = \{\sigma : \sigma \in \mathcal{G} \text{ and } \sigma(a) = a \text{ for all } a \in K\}$. Clearly $\mathcal{S}(K)$ is a subgroup of $\mathcal{G}$. Note that $\mathcal{G} = \mathcal{S}(F)$. Similarly if $\mathcal{H}$ is a subgroup of $\mathcal{G}$, the set $I(\mathcal{H}) = \{a : \sigma(a) = a \text{ for all } \sigma \in \mathcal{H}\}$ is a subfield of E and $E \supseteq I(\mathcal{H}) \supseteq F$. $\mathcal{S}(K)$ is called the *group fixing* K while $I(\mathcal{H})$ is called the *fixed field* of $\mathcal{H}$.

The first examples we consider are not too promising, the first because it is rather trivial, the second because little information is given by $\mathscr{G}$. But we shall look at them anyway.

Example 1. Suppose that $[E:F] = 2$. Thus $E = F(a)$ where $a^2 + ba + c = 0$ for some $b, c \in F$ and $p(x) = x^2 + bx + c$ is irreducible in $F[x]$. Since $p(x)$ splits over E, $p(x) = (x - a)(x - a')$ and since $F(a) \cong F(a')$, by the corollary to Theorem 8.4, there is an automorphism σ of $F(a)$ such that $\sigma(a) = a'$. From Theorem 8.6 we know that $|\mathscr{G}| = |\mathscr{G}(E/F)| \leq 2$ so it must be that $\mathscr{G} = \{\iota, \sigma\}$. Now if $E \supseteq K \supseteq F$ then $K = E$ or $K = F$. If $K = E$ then $\mathscr{S}(K) = \{\iota\}$ while if $K = F$ then $\mathscr{S}(K) = \mathscr{G}$. Conversely, if $\mathscr{H} = \mathscr{G}$ then $I(\mathscr{G}) = F$ while $I(\{\iota\}) = E$. The relations between K and $\mathscr{H}$ are pictured in Figure 1.

Example 2. Let $F = Ra$, $f(x) = x^3 - 2$ and let $E = F(\sqrt[3]{2})$ where $\sqrt[3]{2}$ denotes the real zero of $x^3 - 2$. We argue that $\mathscr{G}(E/F) = \{\iota\}$ as follows. Any automorphism of E must map $\sqrt[3]{2}$ into another zero of $x^3 - 2$ but the other zeros are complex, and thus not in E. Therefore, every automorphism of E must map $\sqrt[3]{2}$ into itself and so the only automorphism of E is ι, the identity. Now $[E:Ra] = 3$ and so $E \supseteq K \supseteq F$ implies that $E = K$ or $K = F$. However, $\mathscr{S}(K) = \{\iota\}$ is the only possibility, and conversely $I(\{\iota\}) = E$ (see Figure 2).

Briefly, Galois theory tells us when the mapping $K \to \mathscr{S}(K)$ is a 1–1 correspondence between subfields K such that $E \supseteq K \supseteq F$ and subgroups of $\mathscr{G}$. When it is, its inverse is given by the correspondence $\mathscr{H} \to I(\mathscr{H})$. Note that if $K \supseteq H$ then $\mathscr{S}(K) \subseteq \mathscr{S}(H)$, and if $\mathscr{U} \subseteq \mathscr{V}$ then $I(\mathscr{U}) \supseteq I(\mathscr{V})$. We also have $I(\mathscr{S}(K)) \supseteq K$ and $\mathscr{S}(I(\mathscr{H})) \supseteq \mathscr{H}$. These relations are easily proved and are borne out by our examples. Figure 3 shows diagrams of the mappings. The red line emphasizes the reversed ordering.

Let E be a finite extension of F. We begin by reviewing what we already know about the group $\mathscr{G} = \mathscr{G}(E/F)$ of automorphisms of E which fix every element of F.

1. Since $[E:F]$ is finite, and F has characteristic 0 we know that $E = F(w)$ for some $w \in E$ (Corollary to Theorem 8.29).

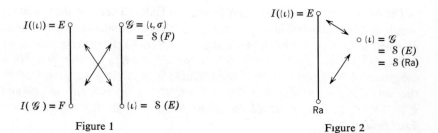

Figure 1   Figure 2

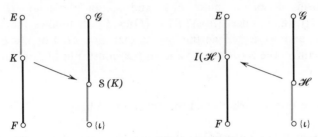

Figure 3

2. For every $\sigma \in \mathscr{G}$ and every $a \in E$, a and $\sigma(a)$ are conjugate over F; that is, they are zeros of the same irreducible polynomial $q(x)$ in $F[x]$. This is because $\sigma \in \mathscr{G}$ means that σ fixes each element of F, so that $0 = q(a)$ implies $0 = \sigma(q(a)) = q(\sigma(a))$ (Theorem 8.6).

3. $|\mathscr{G}(E/F)| \leq [E:F]$. If w is a zero of the irreducible polynomial $p(x) \in F[x]$ and if $E = F(w)$ is a *splitting* field of $p(x)$ then $|\mathscr{G}(E/F)| = [E:F] = \deg p(x)$ (Theorem 8.18).

The last result suggests that extensions of F, which are splitting fields for the irreducible polynomial of which a primitive element is a zero, are going to be interesting. They are! The next theorem tells us that we may dispense with some of the modifying clauses in the preceding sentence. On the face of it, this theorem is a truly remarkable and surprising result.

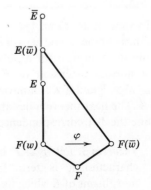

Figure 4

Theorem 1. Let E be a splitting field for $f(x) \in F[x]$. Let $p(x)$ be an irreducible polynomial in $F[x]$. If $p(x)$ has one zero in E then $p(x)$ splits in E.

PROOF. Let $w \in E$ be a zero of $p(x)$. Under the hypothesis it suffices to show that $p(x)$ has all its zeros in E. By assumption $E \supseteq F(w) \supseteq F$. Let $\bar{E}$ be a splitting field of $p(x)$ over E and let $\bar{w}$ be another zero of $p(x)$. (See Figure 4.) We shall prove that $\bar{E} = E$. We know that $F(w) \cong F(\bar{w})$ by an isomorphism φ. Now from Lemma 8.1 $E = F(a_1, \ldots, a_n)$ where $a_1, \ldots, a_n$ are the distinct zeros of $f(x)$. Clearly $E = F(w, a_1, \ldots, a_n)$. Now consider $E(\bar{w})$. We claim that $E(\bar{w})$ is a splitting field for $f(x)$ over $F(\bar{w})$. Certainly $f(x)$ splits in $E(\bar{w})$. Suppose that $f(x)$ splits in H where $E(\bar{w}) \supseteq H \supseteq F(\bar{w})$. Then $\{a_1, \ldots, a_n\} \subseteq H$ and so $H \supseteq F(\bar{w}, a_1, \ldots, a_n) = E(\bar{w})$. Thus $H = E(\bar{w})$. But by Theorem 8.5, we may extend φ to an isomorphism Φ of E onto $E(\bar{w})$ and so, in particular, $[E:F(w)] = [E(\bar{w}):F(\bar{w})]$; and since $[F(w):F] = [F(\bar{w}):F]$ it follows that $[E:F] = [E(\bar{w}):F]$, and as $E \subseteq E(\bar{w})$ this means that $E = E(\bar{w})$ or $\bar{w} \in E$. Thus E must contain all the zeros of $p(x)$ and so $p(x)$ must split in E. (Thus $E = \bar{E}$.)

* * *

In view of our remark (3) and this theorem we have

> **Theorem 2.** Let E be a finite extension of F, a field of characteristic 0. If E is the splitting field of a polynomial $f(x) \in F[x]$ then $|\mathscr{G}(E/F)| = [E:F]$.

PROOF. E is a simple extension of F; say $E = F(w)$. w is a zero of an irreducible polynomial $p(x) \in F[x]$ which, by Theorem 1, splits in E, and thus E is the splitting field for $p(x)$. Thus $|\mathscr{G}(E/F)| = [E:F]$.

* * *

Field extensions $E \supseteq F$, which are splitting fields of polynomials $f(x) \in F[x]$, have many desirable properties as we shall see. First we introduce a definition as an economy of communication.

Definition. A finite extension $E \supseteq F$ is called a *normal* extension of F if, whenever an irreducible polynomial $p(x) \in F[x]$ has one zero in E, $p(x)$ splits in $E[x]$.

In view of Theorem 1 it is but a trivial exercise in terminology to see that if F has characteristic zero then E is a normal extension of F if and only if E is the splitting field for a polynomial $f \in F[x]$. In this new terminology, if E is a normal extension of F then $|\mathscr{G}(E/F)| = [E:F]$. A final remark: if $E \supseteq K \supseteq F$ and if E is a normal extension of F, then E is a normal extension of K. The next theorem lies at the heart of Galois Theory, for it enables us to define the 1–1 correspondence we have promised.

> **Theorem 3.** Let $E \supseteq F$ be a finite extension of a field F whose characteristic is zero. Let $\mathscr{G} = \mathscr{G}(E/F)$ be the group of automorphisms of E which fix every element of F. E is a normal extension of F if and only if F is the fixed field of $\mathscr{G}(E/F)$; that is,
>
> $$F = \{a : \sigma(a) = a \quad \text{for all } \sigma \in \mathscr{G}\}.$$

PROOF. Let us suppose that E is a normal extension of F. We have $E = F(w)$, $|\mathscr{G}| = [E:F] = n$. Consider $K = \{a : \sigma(a) = a$ for all $\sigma \in \mathscr{G}\}$. By definition $E \supseteq K \supseteq F$ and so $E = K(w)$. Let $p(x)$ be an irreducible polynomial in $F[x]$ of which w is a zero. It will suffice to show that $p(x)$ is irreducible over K, for then $[E:F] = [E:K]$ and so from $K \supseteq F$ we can conclude $K = F$. Let $g(x)$ be the irreducible factor of $p(x)$ in $K[x]$ of which w is a zero. If $\bar{w}$ is another zero of $p(x)$ we know (corollary of Theorem 8.4) there is an automorphism $\varphi \in \mathcal{G}$ such that $\sigma(w) = \bar{w}$. But since $\sigma(a) = a$ for all $a \in K$ it must follow that $0 = \sigma(0) = \sigma(g(w)) = g(\sigma(w)) = g(\bar{w})$. Thus all n distinct zeros of $p(x)$ are zeros of $g(x)$ and so $g(x)$ must have degree $\geq n$. But $g(x) \mid p(x)$ and thus $g(x)$ must be an associate of $p(x)$ in $K[x]$ and hence it follows that $p(x)$ too must be irreducible in $K[x]$.

Conversely, suppose that $F = \{a : \sigma(a) = a,$ all $\sigma \in \mathcal{G}\}$. Since $[E:F]$ is finite and F has characteristic zero we know that $E = F(w)$, for some $w \in E$. We shall exhibit a polynomial in $F[x]$ of which w is a zero and for which E is a splitting field. From this it follows from Theorem 1 that E is normal over F. Let $\iota = \sigma_1, \sigma_2, \ldots, \sigma_n$ be the automorphisms in $\mathcal{G}$. Consider $g(x) = (x - \sigma_1(w))(x - \sigma_2(w))\ldots(x - \sigma_n(w))$. Clearly $g(x)$ splits in $E[x]$ and $g(w) = 0$, but we must show that $g(x)$ has coefficients in F. We argue as follows: We note that every automorphism $\sigma \in \mathcal{G}$ induces a natural automorphism σ of $E[x]$. We claim that if $f(x) \in E[x]$, then $\sigma(f(x)) = f(x)$ for all $\sigma \in \mathcal{G}$ if and only if $f(x) \in F[x]$. Let $f(x) = \sum a_i x^i$. $\sigma(f) = \sum \sigma(a_i)x^i$. Thus $f = \sigma(f)$ for all $\sigma \in \mathcal{G}$ if and only if $\sigma(a_j) = a_j$ for all σ and for all j, whereas by hypothesis $\sigma(a_j) = a_j$ for all σ if and only if $a_j \in F$. Now with this in mind we simply observe that in the automorphism σ of $E[x]$ we have $\sigma(g(x)) = (x - \sigma\sigma_1(w))\ldots(x - \sigma\sigma_n(w))$ for all $\sigma \in \mathcal{G}$, and since $\mathcal{G}$ is a *group* of automorphisms, we have that $\sigma(g(x)) = g(x)$ for all $\sigma \in \mathcal{G}$. Hence $g(x) \in F[x]$. Now $g(x)$ can split in no subfield $E \supset H \supseteq F$, since $E = F(w)$ and if $w \in H$ then $H \supseteq F(w) = E$. Thus E is a splitting for $g(x) \in F[x]$.

$$* \quad * \quad *$$

Lemma 1. Let E be a normal extension of F. Let $E \supseteq K \supseteq F$. If a subgroup S of $\mathcal{G}(E/F)$ has K as its fixed field then $\mathcal{G}(E/K) = S$.

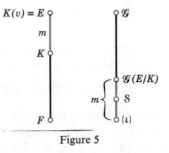

Figure 5

PROOF. By definition we have $S \subseteq \mathcal{G}(E/K)$. Since E is normal over K we have that $|\mathcal{G}(E/K)| = [E:K] = m$. Let $E = K(v)$ (see Figure 5). If $S = \{\iota = \sigma_1, \sigma_2, \ldots, \sigma_s\}(s \leq m)$, then the polynomial $h(x) = (x - \sigma_1(v))\ldots(x - \sigma_s(v))$ has coefficients in K since K is the fixed field of S; thus v satisfies a polynomial in $K[x]$ of degree $s \leq m$. Hence $m = [E:K] \leq s \leq m$. Thus $s = m$ and so $S = \mathcal{G}(E/K)$.

$$* \quad * \quad *$$

Theorem 4 (*Fundamental Theorem of Galois Theory*). Let E be a normal extension of F, a field of characteristic zero.

    1. The mapping $K \rightarrow \mathcal{G}(E/K)$ is a 1–1 mapping of the fields $\{K : E \supseteq K \supseteq F\}$ onto the subgroups of $\mathcal{G}(E/F)$.

2. If $E \supseteq K \supseteq F$ then $[E:K] = |\mathscr{G}(E/K)|$ and $[K:F] = [\mathscr{G}(E/F) : \mathscr{G}(E/K)]$.

3. $E \supseteq H \supset K \supseteq F$ if and only if $\{\iota\} \subseteq \mathscr{G}(E/H) \subset \mathscr{G}(E/K) \subseteq \mathscr{G}(E/F)$.

4. K is a normal extension of F if and only if $\mathscr{G}(E/K)$ is a normal subgroup of $\mathscr{G}(E/F)$, in which case $\mathscr{G}(K/F) \cong \mathscr{G}(E/F)/\mathscr{G}(E/K)$.

First let us make a diagram (Figure 6) of what the theorem tell us. Because of 3, the inclusions are reversed in the correspondence $K \rightarrow \mathscr{G}(E/K)$.

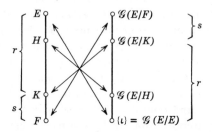

Figure 6

PROOF. The mapping Γ defined by $\Gamma(K) = \mathscr{G}(E/K)$ is 1–1 because by Theorem 3, K is the fixed field of $\mathscr{G}(E/K)$. Thus if $\mathscr{G}(E/K) = \mathscr{G}(E/H) = \mathcal{S}$ we have that $H = K$ equals the fixed field of $\mathcal{S} = \{a : \sigma(a) = a, \text{ all } \sigma \in \mathcal{S}\}$. To show that Γ is onto let $\mathcal{S}$ be a subgroup of $\mathscr{G}(E/K)$. Define $K = I(\mathcal{S}) = \{a : \sigma(a) = a, \text{ all } \sigma \in \mathcal{S}\}$. The fixed field of $\mathcal{S}$ is K, by definition, hence by Lemma 1 we must have that $\mathcal{S} = \mathscr{G}(E/K) = \Gamma(K)$. Thus 1 holds.

Property 2 follows directly from Theorem 2. Since $|\mathscr{G}(E/K)| = [E:K]$, the second equality comes by cancellation in

$$|\mathscr{G}(E/F)| = [\mathscr{G}(E/F : \mathscr{G}(E/K)] \cdot |\mathscr{G}(E/K)| = [E:F] = [E:K] \cdot [K:F].$$

Property 3 now follows from 2 and the observation already made that if $E \supseteq H \supset K \supseteq F$ then $\mathscr{G}(E/H) \subseteq \mathscr{G}(E/K)$. Thus strict containment follows from $[E:H] > [E:K]$. The converse is proved similarly since H and K are, respectively, the fixed fields of $\mathscr{G}(E/H)$ and $\mathscr{G}(E/K)$.

The proof of 4 is a little more difficult. Part 1: Suppose that K is a normal extension of F. Now let $\tau \in \mathscr{G}(E/K)$ and $\sigma \in \mathscr{G}(E/F)$. We are to show that $\sigma^{-1}\tau\sigma \in \mathscr{G}(E/K)$. To do this, in view of the 1–1 correspondence Γ given above it suffices to show that for all $k \in K$, we have $\sigma^{-1}\tau\sigma(k) = k$, or that $\tau\sigma(k) = \sigma(k)$, for all $k \in K$, and for all $\sigma \in \mathscr{G}(E/F)$. To show $\tau\sigma(k) = \sigma(k)$ it suffices to show that $\sigma(k) \in K$. But this is the case, because in any event k and $\sigma(k)$ are conjugate over F and hence zeros of the same irreducible polynomial $q(x)$ in $F[x]$. $q(x)$ has a zero, namely k, in K and as K is normal over F it follows that K must therefore contain all the zeros of $q(x)$, in particular $\sigma(k) \in K$.

Part 2: Conversely, suppose that $\mathscr{G}(E/K)$ is a normal subgroup of $\mathscr{G}(E/F)$. We shall show that the fixed field of $\mathscr{G}(K/F)$ is F. To do this we first prove that if $\sigma \in \mathscr{G}(E/F)$ then for all $k \in K$, we have $\sigma(k) \in K$. To do this, let $\tau \in \mathscr{G}(E/K)$. Then $\sigma^{-1}\tau\sigma \in \mathscr{G}(E/K)$ and so $\sigma^{-1}\tau\sigma(k) = k$ since K is fixed by $\mathscr{G}(E/K)$. Thus $\tau(\sigma(k)) = \sigma(k)$, and so $\sigma(k)$ is fixed by all of $\mathscr{G}(E/K)$ and so belongs to the fixed field of $\mathscr{G}(E/K)$, which is K. Thus $\sigma(k) \in K$. This means that every automorphism $\sigma \in \mathscr{G}(E/F)$ fixes K as a set and so the restriction of σ to K is a mapping σ' of K onto K, which is of course an automorphism. Now to complete the proof we prove that the fixed field of $\mathscr{G}(K/F)$ is F. Let $f \in K$ and suppose $\sigma^*(f) = f$ for all $\sigma^* \in \mathscr{G}(K/F)$. Then, in particular, $\sigma'(f) = f$ for all $\sigma \in \mathscr{G}(E/F)$ and so it follows that $\sigma(f) = f$ for all $\sigma \in \mathscr{G}(E/F)$ since $\sigma(f) = \sigma'(f)$. Hence f belongs to the fixed field of $\mathscr{G}(E/F)$, which is F.

This part of the proof suggests that if σ' denotes the restriction of σ to K, then the function $R : \mathscr{G}(E/F) \to \mathscr{G}(K/F)$ given by $R(\sigma) = \sigma'$ might be a group homomorphism. We prove this by verifying (i) $R(\sigma\tau) = R(\sigma)R(\tau)$, (ii) R is an onto map, and (iii) the kernel of R is $\mathscr{G}(E/K)$. The proof of (i) is easy because the restriction of a function does not change the ordered pairs which constitute the function, thus since $\sigma\tau(k) = \sigma(\tau(k))$ it follows that if $k \in K$ then $(\sigma\tau)'(k) = \sigma\tau(k) = \sigma(\tau(k)) = \sigma(\tau'(k)) = \sigma'(\tau'(k)) = \sigma'\tau'(k)$. The proof of (iii) is easy because if $\sigma \in \mathscr{G}(E/F)$ is the identity automorphism when restricted to K this means that $\sigma \in \mathscr{G}(E/K)$ by definition.

To prove (ii) we show that every automorphism in $\mathscr{G}(K/F)$ arises as the restriction of an automorphism in $\mathscr{G}(E/F)$ to K. To do this it suffices to show that every automorphism σ^* can be extended to an automorphism σ in $\mathscr{G}(E/F)$. This is so since E is the splitting field of a polynomial in K, and every automorphism of K (fixing the elements of F) can be extended to an automorphism of E (fixing the elements of F) by Theorem 8.5. Thus our proof of the fundamental theorem of Galois Theory is complete. We shall often refer to this theorem as simply FTGT.

* * *

The extensions $E \supseteq F$ we have been considering have been splitting fields of polynomials, $f(x) \in F[x]$, indeed even splitting fields of irreducible polynomials in $F[x]$ so that we could utilize the fact that $E = F(w)$ where w was a zero of an irreducible polynomial in $F[x]$. This facilitated our theoretical work for the automorphism group $\mathscr{G}(E/F)$ was most easily handled in terms of w. However, suppose that we are given $f(x) \in F[x]$ and suppose that E is a splitting field for $f(x)$. Now what is $\mathscr{G}(E/F)$? It may be rather awkward to have to find a primitive element and the irreducible polynomial it satisfies. We should like, rather, to describe $\mathscr{G}(E/F)$, as much as possible, in terms of the zeros of $f(x)$. Certainly it would be nice if we did not have to find a primitive element. Let us suppose that $f(x)$ has the set $\{a_1, \ldots, a_n\}$ as its set of distinct zeros. Now we know that $E = F(a_1, \ldots, a_n)$ and that we can form an ascending chain of field extensions $F \subseteq F(a_1) \subseteq F(a_1, a_2) \subseteq \cdots \subseteq F(a_1, \ldots, a_n) = E$ as shown in Figure 7. Moreover $[E : F] \leq n!$ since we can

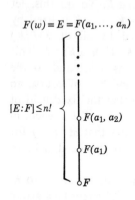

$F(w) = E = F(a_1, \ldots, a_n)$

$[E:F] \leq n!$

$F(a_1, a_2)$

$F(a_1)$

F

split off at least the linear factor $(x - a_i)$ in going from $F(a_1, \ldots, a_{i-1})$ to $F(a_1, \ldots, a_i)$, and the first extension from F to $F(a_1)$ must have degree $\leq n$. (Why?) Now we also know that any automorphism $\sigma \in \mathscr{G}(E/F)$ must send each zero a_i into another zero a_j. Thus any $\sigma \in \mathscr{G}(E/F)$ permutes the set $\{a_1, \ldots, a_n\}$. Since $E = F(a_1, \ldots, a_n)$ it is also clear that this permutation determines the automorphism σ. Hence $\mathscr{G}(E/F)$ may be thought of as a set of permutations on $\{a_1, \ldots, a_n\}$. We can strengthen this observation as in the following theorem.

Figure 7

Theorem 5. Let $E \supseteq F$ be the splitting field of a polynomial $f(x) \in F[x]$. The group $\mathscr{G} = \mathscr{G}(E/F)$ of automorphisms of E over F is isomorphic to a group of permutations on the zeros of $F(x)$.

PROOF. Let $\{a_1, \ldots, a_n\}$ be the distinct zeros of $f(x)$. We define a function Φ from $\mathscr{G}$ into the full symmetric group S_n of all permutations on $\{a_1, \ldots, a_n\}$ as follows:

$$\Phi(\sigma) = \Phi_\sigma = \begin{pmatrix} a_1, \ldots, a_n \\ \sigma(a_1), \ldots, \sigma(a_n) \end{pmatrix}; \qquad \text{briefly } \Phi_\sigma(a_i) = \sigma(a_i).$$

Since σ is 1–1 and $\sigma(a_i)$ is a zero of $f(x)$, it is clear that Φ_σ is a permutation. Φ is 1–1, since if $\sigma(a_i) = \tau(a_i)$ for all i, then $\sigma = \tau$ since $E = F(a_1, \ldots, a_n)$. Finally $\Phi(\sigma\tau) = \Phi(\sigma)\Phi(\tau)$ since $\Phi_{\sigma\tau}(a_i) = \sigma\tau(a_i) = \sigma(\tau(a_i)) = \sigma(\Phi_\tau(a_i)) = \Phi_\sigma(\Phi_\tau(a_i)) = \Phi_\sigma\Phi_\tau(a_i)$.

* * *

Corollary. Let E be the splitting field of a polynomial $f(x) \in F[x]$ of degree n. Then $[E : F] = |\mathscr{G}|$ and $|\mathscr{G}| \,\big|\, n!$.

PROOF. E is a normal extension of F and so by Theorem 2, $[E : F] = |\mathscr{G}|$. Now $\mathscr{G}$ is isomorphic to a subgroup of S_n, which has order $n!$ and so by Lagrange's Theorem $|\mathscr{G}| \,\big|\, n!$.

If $f(x)$ has degree n and is irreducible we can say a little more, because then $[F(a_1) : F] = n$ and so $n \mid [E : F]$.

* * *

Terminology

When we refer to the "group of the polynomial $f(x)$" or the "group of the equation $f(x) = 0$" we shall mean the group $\mathscr{G}(E/F)$ where E is a splitting field of $f(x)$ over F, it being understood that $f(x) \in F[x]$. Since all splitting fields over F are isomorphic, the group of $f(x)$ is uniquely determined. When E is normal over F, as it is in this case, we shall call the group $\mathscr{G}(E/F)$ the Galois group of $f(x)$. We shall often denote an element of the Galois group of a polynomial by the permutation on $(1, \ldots, n)$ corresponding to the permutation it induces on the roots $\{a_1, \ldots, a_n\}$ of $f(x)$. In effect this replaces a_i by i for ease of notation. We say the extension E over F, the polynomial $f(x)$, and the equation $f(x) = 0$ are cyclic, abelian, or solvable, as the group $\mathscr{G}(E/F)$ is cyclic, abelian, or solvable.

It is high time to consider some examples. In all three examples to follow we shall let $F = \text{Ra}$. We use the notation of $I(\mathcal{S})$ for the fixed field of a subgroup $\mathcal{S} \subseteq \mathscr{G}(E/\text{Ra})$.

Example 3. $f(x) = x^4 - 5x^2 + 6$. We discover that $f(x) = (x^2 - 2)(x^2 - 3)$. We have $\text{Ra} \subset \text{Ra}(\sqrt{2}) \subseteq \text{Ra}(\sqrt{2}, \sqrt{3}) = E$. We argue that the last containment is proper by showing that $x^2 - 3$ is irreducible over $\text{Ra}(\sqrt{2})$—which is the case because if $x^2 - 3$ had a zero, $a + b\sqrt{2}$, in $\text{Ra}(\sqrt{2})$ then $(a^2+2b^2) + 2ab\sqrt{2} = 3$—and hence that $\sqrt{2}$ or $\sqrt{3}$ is rational, a contradiction. Thus

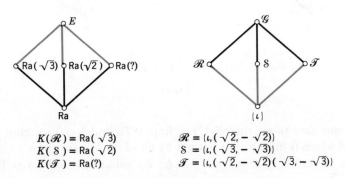

$$K(\mathscr{R}) = \text{Ra}(\sqrt{3}) \qquad \mathscr{R} = \{\iota, (\sqrt{2}, -\sqrt{2})\}$$
$$K(\mathcal{S}) = \text{Ra}(\sqrt{2}) \qquad \mathcal{S} = \{\iota, (\sqrt{3}, -\sqrt{3})\}$$
$$K(\mathscr{T}) = \text{Ra}(?) \qquad \mathscr{T} = \{\iota, (\sqrt{2}, -\sqrt{2})(\sqrt{3}, -\sqrt{3})\}$$

Figure 8

$[E : \text{Ra}] = 4$ and so $|\mathscr{G}| = 4$. There are two possibilities for $\mathscr{G}$: either it is cyclic or it is the four-group. $\mathscr{G}$ cannot be cyclic for then it would have only one proper subgroup, and hence by FTGT, E would have only one proper subfield properly larger than Ra; but of course E has $\text{Ra}(\sqrt{2})$ and $\text{Ra}(\sqrt{3})$ as subfields.

The subfield and subgroup diagrams are shown in Figure 8. Again we use a red line to emphasize the reversed ordering. Find the missing field!

Example 4. $f(x) = x^3 - 2$. $f(x)$ is irreducible in Ra$[x]$; its roots are $a_1 = \sqrt[3]{2}$, $a_2 = \zeta\sqrt[3]{2} = \zeta a_1$, and $a_3 = \zeta^2\sqrt[3]{2} = \zeta^2 a_1$ where ζ is a primitive cube root of unity. Since Ra(a_1) is real we know that $E \neq$ Ra(a_1); hence $[E : \text{Ra}] = 3! = 6$. Thus the group $\mathscr{G}$ is either cyclic or S_3. Since $\mathscr{G}$ is isomorphic to a subgroup of S_n it cannot be cyclic of order 6. Also since the fields Ra(a_i) are all distinct and of degree 3 over Ra, $\mathscr{G}$ must have subgroups $\mathscr{N}_i$ $(i = 1, 2, 3)$ each of index 3 in $\mathscr{G}$; hence $\mathscr{G}$ cannot be cyclic. Thus the subfield–subgroup diagrams must look like Figure 9. The red line denotes the normal extension and the normal subgroup, whichever is appropriate.

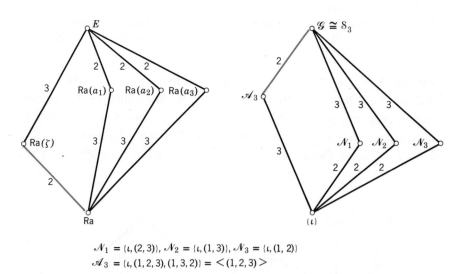

$$\mathscr{N}_1 = \{\iota, (2, 3)\}, \; \mathscr{N}_2 = \{\iota, (1, 3)\}, \; \mathscr{N}_3 = \{\iota, (1, 2)\}$$
$$\mathscr{A}_3 = \{\iota, (1, 2, 3), (1, 3, 2)\} = \langle(1, 2, 3)\rangle$$

Figure 9

It is not hard to see that $I(\mathscr{N}_i) = \text{Ra}(a_i)$. To find $I(\mathscr{A}_3)$ we must find an element which is fixed by $\mathscr{A}_3$ but not by all of S_3. We are given a clue as to "where to look" since we see that $\zeta \in E$; indeed $\zeta = a_2/a_1$ and Ra$(\zeta) = \text{Ra}(\sqrt{-3})$ has degree 2 over Ra. So it must be the case that Ra$(\zeta) = I(\mathscr{A}_3)$, and indeed if $\sigma = (1, 2, 3)$ then we see that $\sigma(\zeta) = \sigma(a_2/a_1) = a_3/a_2 = \zeta$; hence ζ is fixed by $\mathscr{A}_3$ but ζ is not fixed by $\tau = (2, 3)$ as $\tau(\zeta) = \tau(a_2/a_1) = a_3/a_1 = \zeta^2$. Note that $\tau(\zeta) = \zeta^2 \in I(\mathscr{A}_3)$ since that is a normal extension of Ra, thus our theory tells us that τ affects an automorphism of $I(\mathscr{A}_3)$; that is, $\tau(\zeta) \in I(\mathscr{A}_3)$.

We shall have to invent a more general argument to handle the solution of cubic equations in general, but such a general method hardly seems warranted here.

Example 5. $f(x) = x^4 + 1$. We recognize this as the cyclotomic polynomial $\Phi_8(x)$ whose roots are the primitive eighth roots of unity; $\pm\sqrt{i}$ and $\pm\sqrt{-i}$. For specificity we let $\zeta = (1 + i)/\sqrt{2}$. We can prove that $\Phi_8(x)$ is irreducible by the trick of considering $\Phi_8(x + 1) = (x + 1)^4 + 1 = x^4 + 4x^3 + 6x^2 + 4x + 2$, which is irreducible by Eisenstein's criteria and so it must be the case that $\Phi_8(x)$ is irreducible also. (Why?) Since $\mathrm{Ra}(\zeta)$ contains all of the eighth roots of unity $E = \mathrm{Ra}(\zeta)$ and $[E:F] = 4$. Now we can determine $\mathscr{G}$ explicitly because we are in the happy circumstance of having a primitive element for E, and one which satisfies a particularly nice equation. We know there is an automorphism taking ζ into any other primitive eighth root of unity ζ^k, where $(k, n) = 1$ since such a root of unity is another zero of $\Phi_8(x)$. Now $\{1, 3, 5, 7\}$ is the set of integers less than or equal to 8 and relative prime to 8, hence there are automorphisms ρ, σ, τ defined by $\rho(\zeta) = \zeta^3$, $\sigma(\zeta) = \zeta^5 = -\zeta$, and $\tau(\zeta) = \zeta^7 = \zeta^{-1}$. It is interesting to make a brief table.

	ρ	σ	τ
$\zeta \rightarrow$	ζ^3	$-\zeta = \zeta^5$	$\zeta^{-1} = \zeta^7$
$\zeta^2 \rightarrow$	$-\zeta^2$	ζ^2	$\zeta^{-2} = \zeta^6$
$\zeta^3 \rightarrow$	ζ	$-\zeta^3$	$\zeta^{-3} = \zeta^5$
$-1 = \zeta^4 \rightarrow$	-1	-1	-1

Therefore,

$$\rho = (\zeta, \zeta^3)(\zeta^5, \zeta^7). \qquad \text{Let } \mathscr{R} = \langle\rho\rangle.$$
$$\sigma = (\zeta, -\zeta)(\zeta^3, \zeta^7). \qquad \text{Let } \mathcal{S} = \langle\sigma\rangle.$$
$$\tau = (\zeta, \zeta^{-1})(\zeta^3, \zeta^{-3}). \qquad \text{Let } \mathscr{T} = \langle\tau\rangle.$$

Thus $\mathscr{G}$ is again the four group, but note that its action on the zeros of $x^4 + 1$ is quite different from its action on the zeros of $(x^2 - 2)(x^2 - 3)$.

We see that $I(\mathscr{R}) = \mathrm{Ra}(\zeta + \zeta^3)$ and $I(\mathscr{T}) = \mathrm{Ra}(\zeta + \zeta^{-1})$ since, for example, $\zeta + \zeta^3$ is left fixed by ρ. We argue that $\zeta + \zeta^3 \notin \mathrm{Ra}$ since $\sigma(\zeta + \zeta^3) = -\zeta - \zeta^3 \neq \zeta + \zeta^3$. The trick of the addition $\zeta + \sigma(\zeta)$ backfires on us in attempting to find $I(\mathcal{S})$, since $\zeta + \sigma(\zeta) = \zeta - \zeta = 0 \in \mathrm{Ra}$. We shall have to look elsewhere for the primitive element of $I(\mathcal{S})$. We see by the table that $\sigma(\zeta^2) = \zeta^2$, and we note that $\zeta^2 = i$, so we have $I(\mathcal{S}) = \mathrm{Ra}(\zeta^2) = \mathrm{Ra}(i)$.

EXERCISE 1

1. Prove that if E is a normal extension over F, and $\mathcal{S}$ and $\mathscr{T}$ are subgroups of $\mathscr{G}(E/F)$, then

$$I(\mathcal{S} \cap \mathscr{T}) = I(\mathcal{S}) \vee I(\mathscr{T})$$
$$I(\mathcal{S} \vee \mathscr{T}) = I(\mathcal{S}) \cap I(\mathscr{T})$$

where $I(\mathscr{R})$ denotes the fixed field of a subgroup $\mathscr{R} \subseteq \mathscr{G}(E/F)$.

2. Under the notations introduced prior to Theorem 1 prove that

$$S(I(S(K))) = S(K) \quad \text{for all } K \text{ such that } E \supseteq K \supseteq F$$

and

$$I(S(I(\mathscr{H}))) = I(\mathscr{H}) \quad \text{for all } \mathscr{H} \subseteq \mathscr{G}(E/F).$$

(No assumption of normality is needed.)

3. Find the Galois group G of $x^3 - x - 1$ over the rational numbers, Ra. Determine all subgroups of G and find all corresponding subfields of the splitting field. Let a, b, c denote the zeros of $x^3 - x - 1$, and let $d = (a - b)(a - c)(b - c)$. Describe Ra($d$).

4. Find the Galois groups of the following polynomials over Ra.

   (i) $(x^2 - 3x + 1)^2(x^3 - 2)$
   (ii) $x^4 + x^3 + x^2 + x + 1$
   (iii) $x^4 - x^2 + 1$.

5. Find the Galois group of the polynomial $x^6 - 2$ considered over Ra($\sqrt{-3}$). Find all the fields between Ra($\sqrt{-3}$) and the splitting field of $x^6 - 2$ over Ra($\sqrt{-3}$).

6. Let $D \supseteq E \supseteq F$ where E is an algebraic extension of F. Let $w \in D$ be algebraic over E. Exhibit a polynomial in $F[x]$ for which w is a zero. [*Hint:* Let w be a zero of $g(x) = \sum_{0 \le i \le n} a_i x^i \in E[x]$ and let a_i be a zero of $f_i(x) \in F[x]$. Consider the splitting field H of $\prod f_i(x)$ over $F(a_0, \ldots, a_n)$ and the group $\mathscr{G}(H/F)$.]

7. Show that the Galois group of $(x^2 - 2)(x^3 - 3)$ over Ra is isomorphic to $S_3 \times C_2$. Find all the subfields of its splitting over Ra.

10.2. CYCLOTOMIC FIELDS AND CYCLIC EXTENSIONS

The ease with which we determined the Galois group of $\Phi_8(x)$ suggests that we should be able to say something definitive about the equation of a cyclotomic polynomial in general. We can, and this information plays an important role in the problem of solving equations by radicals.

Theorem 6. Let F be a field of characteristic zero. Let $Z \supseteq F$ be a splitting field of $x^n - 1$. The group $\mathscr{G} = \mathscr{G}(Z/F)$ is abelian.

PROOF. Since Z is a splitting field of $x^n - 1$, Z contains a primitive nth root of unity which we shall call ζ. Moreover since the other nth roots of unity are powers of ζ it follows that $Z = F(\zeta)$. Now let $\sigma \in \mathscr{G}(Z/F)$. What can we say about $\sigma(\zeta)$? Recall that the nth roots of unity form a multiplicative group and so it must be that σ effects an automorphism of this group. Thus $\sigma(\zeta)$ must be another generator of this group, that is, another primitive nth root of unity, ζ^{k_σ}. We, of course, cannot claim that any mapping of ζ into any other primitive nth root of unity can be extended to an automorphism in $\mathscr{G}(Z/F)$ since, among other things, we have no information about F—indeed $F = Z$ is a possibility. However, we claim that there is a group isomorphism of $\mathscr{G}$ onto a subgroup of the multiplicative group of units in the ring $I/\langle n \rangle$. We must recall at this point that these units are the congruence classes $\bar{h}$ where $1 \leq h \leq n$ and $(h, n) = 1$. It is in these cases that we can solve the congruence $hu \equiv 1 \pmod{n}$, and so $\bar{h}\bar{u} = \bar{1}$ in $I/\langle n \rangle$. Define $t(\sigma) = \bar{k}_\sigma$. Now t is a function since σ is a function, and as we noted $(k_\sigma, n) = 1$ so that $\bar{k}_\sigma$ is a unit in $I/\langle n \rangle$. To prove the homomorphism property we first note that if $\sigma(\zeta) = \zeta^{k_\sigma}$ then $\sigma(\zeta^m) = (\zeta^{k_\sigma})^m = \zeta^{mk_\sigma}$. Thus $(\tau\sigma)(\zeta) = \tau(\sigma(\zeta)) = \tau(\zeta^{k_\sigma}) = \zeta^{k_\sigma k_\tau}$. Hence $t(\tau\sigma) = t(\tau)t(\sigma)$. Finally, t is 1–1 as if $k_\sigma \equiv k_\tau \pmod{n}$ then $\zeta^{k_\sigma} = \zeta^{k_\tau}$, and so $\sigma = \tau$ since the image of ζ determines the entire automorphism of Z.

* * *

The mapping t is in fact an isomorphism of $\mathscr{G}$ onto the units of $I/\langle n \rangle$ if and only if $\Phi_n(x)$ is irreducible over F. This is so because then and only then is $F(\zeta) \cong F(\zeta^k)$ if $(k, n) = 1$. We include the next result without proof.

$\mathscr{G}(Z/\text{Ra})$ *is isomorphic to the multiplicative group of units in* $I/\langle n \rangle$ *and it is cyclic if* $n = 2, 4, p^e,$ *or* $2p^e$ *where* p *is an odd prime.*

We cannot prove this in all generality for two reasons. We have not proved that $\Phi_n(x)$ is irreducible over Ra, and we have not proved that the multiplicative group of units in $I/\langle n \rangle$ is cyclic if and only if $n = 2, 4, p^e,$ or $2p^e$ where p is an odd prime. This last result is a standard theorem in elementary number theory and is proved in the references listed at the end of this chapter.

We can, however, prove all of this when $n = p$—a prime. For then we have proved that $\Phi_p(x)$ is irreducible and we do know that $I/\langle p \rangle$ is the Galois field $GF(p)$ whose nonzero elements form a cyclic group.

Our next lemma we insert here for future reference.

Lemma 2. If $\epsilon^n = 1$ then $\sum_{i=0}^{n-1} \epsilon^i = 0$ unless $\epsilon = 1$.

PROOF. We simply sum the geometric progression:

$$\text{If } \epsilon \neq 1 \text{ then } \sum_{i=0}^{n-1} \epsilon^i = \frac{\epsilon^n - 1}{\epsilon - 1}.$$

* * *

We conclude this section with the three fundamental theorems about cyclic extensions.

Theorem 7. If F contains the nth roots of unity and if E is a splitting field of $x^n - a$ $(a \in F)$ over F, then E is a cyclic extension of F.

PROOF. We shall assume $a \neq 0$. Let ζ be a primitive nth root of unity $\zeta \in F$, by hypothesis. Let w be one zero of $x^n - a$ in E. Clearly, $w, \zeta w, \ldots, \zeta^{n-1}w$ are n distinct zeros of $x^n - a$ and hence comprise all the zeros of $x^n - a$. If $\sigma \in \mathscr{G}(E/F)$ then we must have $\sigma(w) = \zeta^{k_\sigma}w$. We claim that $t(\sigma) = \zeta^{k_\sigma}$ is an isomorphism of $\mathcal{G}$ onto a subgroup of C—the cyclic group of the nth roots of unity. From this it will follow easily that $\mathcal{G}$ is cyclic since all subgroups of a cyclic group are cyclic. First we verify that $t(\tau\sigma) = t(\tau)t(\sigma)$. Let $\tau(w) = \zeta^{k_\tau}w$. Thus $\tau\sigma(w) = \tau(\zeta^{k_\sigma}w) = \zeta^{k_\sigma}\tau(w) = \zeta^{k_\sigma k_\tau}$ since $\zeta^{k_\sigma} \in F$ and so is fixed by all elements of $\mathcal{G}$. Thus $t(\tau\sigma) = t(\tau)t(\sigma)$. Now if $t(\tau) = t(\sigma)$, then $\zeta^{k_\sigma} = \zeta^{k_\tau}$, and so $\sigma = \tau$; that is, t is 1–1.

* * *

Theorem 8. If $x^n - a$ $(0 \neq a \in F)$ splits in $E \supseteq F$ then E contains a primitive nth root of unity.

PROOF. $x^n - a$ has n distinct zeros $\{w_1, \ldots, w_n\}$ in E. (Why?) If we let $\zeta_i = w_1/w_i$ then $\zeta_i^n = (w_1)^n/(w_i)^n = a/a = 1$. Moreover, if $i \neq j$ then $\zeta_i \neq \zeta_j$ and so $\zeta_1, \ldots, \zeta_n$ are distinct nth roots of unity, one of which must be primitive!

* * *

Theorem 9. If E is a normal cyclic extension of F and if F contains the nth roots of unity where $n = [E:F]$, then E is a splitting field of a polynomial $(x^n - a_1)\ldots(x^n - a_r)$ where the $a_i \in F$. If $n = p$, a prime, then E is the splitting field of $x^p - a$ which is irreducible over F.

PROOF. We may assume that $E = F(w)$ and we suppose that $\mathcal{G}(E/F) = \langle\sigma\rangle$ where $\sigma^n = \iota$. For the purpose of this proof we introduce the *Lagrange resolvent*. The idea behind this device is the need to produce some element from E whose nth power lies in F. We must take advantage of the fact that $\mathcal{G}$ is cyclic and that F contains the nth roots of unity. The Lagrange resolvent makes use of both these facts. Let ϵ be an nth root of unity and let $a \in E$. The Lagrange resolvent of ϵ and a we denote by $\lambda(\epsilon, a)$ and define it by

$$\lambda(\epsilon, a) = a + \epsilon\cdot\sigma(a) + \epsilon^2\cdot\sigma^2(a) + \cdots + \epsilon^{n-1}\cdot\sigma^{n-1}(a).$$

For brevity we write $\lambda = \lambda(\epsilon, a)$.

A remarkably nice thing happens when we determine $\sigma(\lambda)$. Since $\sigma(\epsilon^i\cdot\sigma^i(a)) = \epsilon^i\cdot\sigma^{i+1}(a)$ it follows that

$$\sigma(\lambda) = \epsilon^{n-1}a + \sigma(a) + \epsilon\cdot\sigma^2(a) + \cdots + \epsilon^{n-2}\cdot\sigma^{n-1}(a)$$
$$= \epsilon^{n-1}\lambda, \quad \text{or}$$
$$\epsilon\cdot\sigma(\lambda) = \lambda.$$

Thus, unless $\lambda = 0$, we obtain $\epsilon = \lambda/\sigma(\lambda)$, and the force of this is that by starting with λ we obtain an nth root of unity, unless $\lambda = 0$. Moreover $1 = \epsilon^n = \lambda^n/(\sigma(\lambda))^n = \lambda^n/\sigma(\lambda^n)$, that is, $\lambda^n = \sigma(\lambda^n)$ and so $\lambda^n \in F$—thus $\lambda \in E$ and $\lambda^n \in F$. (This, of course, is true even if $\lambda = 0$.)

Now we consider the particular Lagrange resolvent $\lambda(\zeta^k, w)$ where ζ is a primitive nth root of unity and $E = F(w)$. For brevity we shall denote this by v_k. We have shown that $v_k{}^n \in F$.

$$v_1 = w + \zeta\sigma(w) + \cdots + \zeta^{n-1}\sigma^{n-1}(w)$$

$$v_2 = w + \zeta^2\sigma(w) + \cdots + \zeta^{2(n-1)}\sigma^{n-1}(w)$$

$$\vdots$$

$$v_n = w + \quad \sigma(w) + \cdots + \quad \sigma^{n-1}(w).$$

The second remarkable feature of the Lagrange resolvent occurs when we add these resolvents together. It is convenient to add the "columns" together and so we interchange the order of summation as follows:

$$\sum_{k=1}^{n} v_k = \sum_{k=1}^{n}\left(\sum_{i=0}^{n-1}\zeta^{ki}\sigma^i(w)\right) = \sum_{i=0}^{n-1}\left(\sum_{k=1}^{n}(\zeta^i)^k\right)\sigma^i(w) = nw.$$

The last equality holds by virtue of Lemma 2. In particular for some v_k we have $v_k \neq 0$; moreover this addition shows that $w \in F(v_1, \ldots, v_n) \subseteq E$, and so $F(v_1, \ldots, v_n) = E$. But since, for each i, $v_i{}^n \in F$ we have that v_i is a zero of $(x^n - v_i{}^n)$, and thus E is the splitting field of $\prod (x^n - v_i{}^n)$.

Now if $n = p$, a prime, then each ζ^k is a primitive pth root of unity. Now let $v = v_k \neq 0$; thus the conjugates of v are $\{v, \zeta v, \ldots, \zeta^{p-1}v\}$, which are all distinct. Hence they are all of the zeros of $x^p - v^p$. Since v has p distinct conjugates, it must be that $x^p - v^p$ is irreducible in $F[x]$ and so E is the splitting field of $x^p - v^p$.

* * *

10.3.   SOLUTION OF EQUATIONS BY RADICALS

The first great theorem of high school algebra is the quadratic formula: The roots of $x^2 + bx + c = 0$ are $(-b \pm \sqrt{b^2 - 4c})/2$. With this formula, into which we can simply substitute b and c, requiring only that the characteristic of the field to which they belong not equal 2, we can solve all of our quadratic factoring problems. In a similar but more complicated fashion, there are solutions for a cubic equation $x^3 + ax^2 + bx + c = 0$. One root is given in the form

$$\frac{1}{3}\left[\sqrt[3]{-\frac{27}{2}q + \frac{3}{2}\sqrt{-3\Delta}} + \sqrt[3]{-\frac{27}{2}q - \frac{3}{2}\sqrt{-3\Delta}}\right]$$

where $\Delta = \sqrt{-(27q^2 + 4p^3)}$ and $p = b - a^2/3$ and $q = c + (2a^3 - 9ab)/27$. Some care must be exercised about which of the multiple cube roots and square roots are chosen. It is important to note that the solution is given as a combination of square roots and cube roots, and does not depend on the field F to which a, b and c belong, except that char $F \neq 2$ or 3.

To say that we have given a solution of $x^3 + ax^2 + bx + c = 0$ in radicals really means that we have found a sequence of extensions $F = F_0 \subseteq F_1$

$\subseteq F_2 \subseteq \cdots \subseteq F_n$ where F_{i+1} is constructed from F_i by adjoining a zero of an especially simple kind of polynomial; one of the form $x^m - a_m$ where $a_m \in F_i$ and the last field F_n contains a splitting field of the cubic. We have $F \subseteq F(\Delta) \subseteq F(\Delta, \sqrt{-3}) \subseteq F(\Delta, \sqrt{-3}, u) \subseteq F(\Delta, \sqrt{-3}, u, v) = E$ where u is a zero of $x^3 - (-\frac{27}{2}q + \frac{3}{2}\sqrt{-3\Delta})$ and v is a zero of $x^3 - (-\frac{27}{2}q - \frac{3}{2}\sqrt{-3\Delta})$.

Similar, although more complicated, expressions can be obtained for solutions of a quartic equation. They do not depend on the field F, although of course we are assuming that char $F = 0$. The techniques for the quartic are not essentially more difficult, certainly they require no more "theory" than we have at our disposal, but shall not do the computations here. The interesting fact is that this process stops at degree 5. There is no general formula which gives a solution for the zeros of a fifth degree polynomial in terms of radicals.

Now we shall formally define what is meant by a "solution in radicals."

Definition. Let $f(x) \in F[x]$ with $\deg(f(x)) \geq 1$. The equation $f(x) = 0$ is solvable by radicals if a splitting field E for $f(x)$ over F is a subfield of an extension $K \supseteq F$ for which there is a chain of subfields

$$(T) \qquad\qquad F = F_0 \subseteq F_1 \subseteq \cdots \subseteq F_r = K$$

such that $F_{i+1} = F_i(w_i)$ where $w_i^{n_i} \in F_i$. (That is, w_i is a zero of $x^{n_i} - w_i^{n_i} \in F_i[x]$.) It is customary to call a chain (T) a *root tower* for K over F. It is important to note that we do not require the root tower to end at E, rather that E be a subfield of the top of a root tower (see Figure 10).

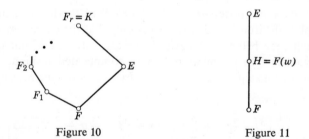

Figure 10   Figure 11

Thus, given $f(x) \in F[x]$, if a root tower exists we know that a zero θ can be expressed in the form $\theta = t(w_1, \ldots, w_r)$ where each $w_j \in F_{j+1}$ and is the zero of the equation $x^{n_j} - w_j^{n_j} \in F_j[x]$, and $t(x_1, \ldots, x_n) \in F[x_1, \ldots, x_n]$. The elements $w_j = \sqrt[n_j]{w_j^{n_j}}$ are "radicals" and $t(w_1, \ldots, w_r)$ is a rational expression for a root of $f(x) = 0$ in terms of these radicals.

The next lemma gives us a useful result. Note that just as not every normal subgroup of a normal subgroup of a group G is a normal subgroup of G, not every normal extension E of a normal extension H of F is a normal extension of F. However in one important case this transitivity holds true.

Lemma 3. Let $H \supseteq F$ be a normal extension of F. Let $g(x) \in F[x]$. If E is the splitting field of $g(x)$ over H then E is a normal extension of F.

PROOF. Let $H = F(w)$ where w is a zero of an irreducible polynomial $h(x) \in F[x]$ (see Figure 11). We know that H is the splitting field of $h(x)$ over F. Consider $f(x) = g(x)h(x) \in F[x]$. We claim that E is the splitting field of $f(x)$ over F and hence is a normal extension of F. We clearly have that $f(x)$ splits in E. If $f(x)$ splits in N where $F \subseteq N \subseteq E$, then $w \in N$ and hence $H \subseteq N$. Thus N is a field over H in which $g(x)$ splits; but this means that $E \supseteq N$. Thus $E = N$.

* * *

The main theorem of this section is the following celebrated one.

Theorem 10. (*Galois*). Let $f(x) \in F[x]$, where F is a field of characteristic zero. A necessary and sufficient condition that an equation $f(x) = 0$ is solvable by radicals is that its Galois group is solvable.

PROOF OF THE NECESSITY. Throughout this proof E shall denote a splitting field of $f(x)$ over F. The crux of the necessity proof is to show that under the assumption of a root tower for F there is a field K', $K' \supseteq E \supseteq F$, which is a normal extension of F, such that $\mathcal{G}(K'/F)$ is solvable. Then, as E is normal over F, it follows from FTGT that $\mathcal{G}(E/F) \cong \mathcal{G}(K'/F)/\mathcal{G}(K'/E)$ is a homomorphic image of a solvable group and hence is itself solvable.

In the following lemma we prove the essential special case of the necessity. The relationships required by the hypothesis are pictured in Figure 12.

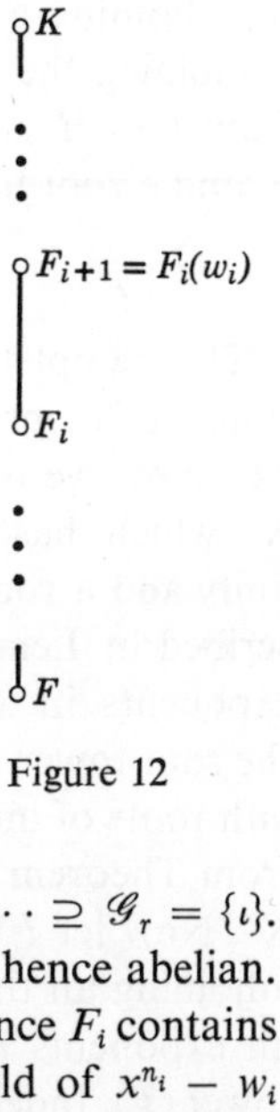

Lemma 4. Let $F = F_0 \subseteq F_1 \subseteq \cdots \subseteq F_r = K$ be a root tower where $F_{i+1} = F_i(w_i)$ and $w_i^{n_i} \in F_i$. If K is a normal extension of F and if F contains all the n_ith roots of unity for all i, then $\mathcal{G}(K/F)$ is solvable.

Figure 12

PROOF. Let $\mathcal{G}_i = \mathcal{G}(K/F_i)$. Consider the chain $\mathcal{G}_0 \supseteq \mathcal{G}_1 \supseteq \cdots \supseteq \mathcal{G}_r = \{\iota\}$. We claim that $\mathcal{G}_{i+1}$ is normal in $\mathcal{G}_i$ and that $\mathcal{G}_i/\mathcal{G}_{i+1}$ is cyclic, hence abelian. From Theorem 9.15 it then follows that $\mathcal{G}_0 = \mathcal{G}$ is solvable. Since F_i contains the n_ith roots of unity it follows that F_{i+1} is a splitting field of $x^{n_i} - w_i$ over F_i and so, by Theorem 7, $\mathcal{G}(F_{i+1}/F_i)$ is cyclic. However, by the FTGT, since F_{i+1} is a normal extension of F_i, we have $\mathcal{G}(F_{i+1}/F_i) \cong \mathcal{G}(K/F_i)/\mathcal{G}(K/F_{i+1}) = \mathcal{G}_i/\mathcal{G}_{i+1}$.

* * *

We reduce the proof of the necessity essentially to this lemma. We construct a field K' such that $K' \supseteq E$ and find a subfield $F^* \subseteq K'$ such that K' and F^* satisfy the hypothesis of Lemma 4 and such that F^* is a normal abelian extension of F. This reduction is in two stages. First we shall prove that if $F = F_0 \subseteq F_1 \subseteq \cdots \subseteq F_r = K$, $(K \supseteq E \supseteq F)$ is a root tower over F, then we can build a root tower

$$F = F_0' \subseteq F_1' \subseteq \cdots \subseteq F_s' = K'$$

such that $K' \supseteq K \supseteq E \supseteq F$ where K' is a *normal* extension of F. We proceed to define a sequence of extensions $F = H_0 \subseteq H_1 \subseteq \cdots \subseteq H_r$ where H_i is a normal extension over F, $H_i \supseteq F_i$ and there is a root tower from F to H_i. We shall then simply choose $K' = H_r$. We define $H_0 = F$ and proceed by induction. Let us suppose that H_i has been constructed. Let $\mathscr{H}_i = \mathscr{G}(H_i/F) = \{\iota = \sigma_1, \sigma_2, \ldots, \sigma_{s_i}\}$. We are assuming that $F_{i+1} = F_i(w_i)$ where $w_i^{n_i} \in F_i$. Consider the polynomial $g(x) = \prod_{j=1}^{s_i} (x^{n_i} - \sigma_j(w_i^{n_i}))$. Now $g(x) \in F[x]$ because it is fixed under all automorphisms $\sigma_k \in \mathscr{H}_i$, and H_i is a normal extension of F. Moreover w_i is a zero of $g(x)$. Let H_{i+1} be the splitting field of $g(x)$ over H_i. H_{i+1} is a normal extension of F by Lemma 3 (see Figure 13). $w_i \in H_{i+1}$ and $F_i \subseteq H_i \subseteq H_{i+1}$; hence $F_{i+1} = F_i(w_i) \subseteq H_{i+1}$. Moreover $H_i = H_{i1} \subseteq H_{i2} \subseteq \cdots \subseteq H_{ir_i} = H_{i+1}$, where $H_{i(j_k+1)}$ is obtained from H_{ij_k} by adjoining a zero of $(x^{n_i} - \sigma_j(w_i))_i^{n_i}$, is a root tower from H_i to H_{i+1}. By combining the root tower from F to H_i with this one we obtain a root tower from F to H_{i+1}. Hence we eventually obtain $H_r = K'$, a normal extension of F, and a root tower (T) from F to K'.

$$(T) \qquad\qquad F = F_0' \subseteq F_1' \subseteq \cdots \subseteq F_s' = K'.$$

This completes stage 1. (All constructions in this proof are shown in Figure 14.) Now we must find a subfield $F^* \subseteq K'$ which has the necessary roots of unity and a root tower of the kind prescribed in Lemma 4. If m is one of the exponents in $x^m - a_m$ associated with the root tower (T), then K' contains all mth roots of unity. This follows directly from Theorem 8 since $x^m - a_m$ splits in K'. Now let F^* be obtained from F by adjoining all the mth roots of unity for all exponents m occurring in the root tower (T). Indeed $K' \supseteq F^* = F(\zeta)$ where ζ is a primitive Mth root of unity and the exponents M is the least common multiple of all associated with the root tower (T). By Theorem 6 we know that F^* is a normal abelian extension of F. Of course K' is a normal extension of F^*.

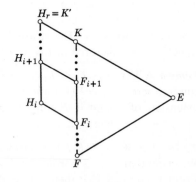

Figure 13

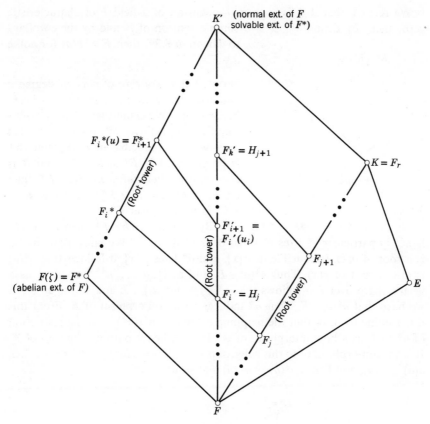

Figure 14

Finally as illustrated in Figure 14 then let $F_0{}^* = F^*$ and $F_{i+1}^* = F_i{}^*(u_i)$ if $F'_{i+1} = F_i(u_i)$. We have $F \subseteq F_0{}^* \subseteq F_1{}^* \subseteq \cdots \subseteq F_s{}^* = K'$. Clearly $F^* \subseteq F_1{}^* \subseteq \cdots \subseteq K'$ is a root tower for K' over F^* and so by Lemma 4 we have that $\mathscr{G}(K'/F^*)$ is solvable. By Theorem 9.11 we know that the abelian group $\mathscr{G}(F^*/F)$ is solvable and by FTGT $\mathscr{G}(F^*/F) \cong \mathscr{G}(K'/F)/\mathscr{G}(K'/F^*)$. Thus $\mathscr{G}(K'/F)$ has a solvable normal subgroup $\mathscr{G}(K'/F^*)$ whose factor group $\mathscr{G}(F^*/F)$ is solvable. Hence by Theorem 9.12, $\mathscr{G}(K'/F)$ is solvable. Finally, then, as we anticipated, $\mathscr{G}(E/F)$ is solvable.

$$* \quad * \quad *$$

Before giving a proof of the sufficiency we require still one more lemma. Figure 15 pictures the fields mentioned in the hypothesis.

Lemma 5. Let E be a normal extension of F (char $F = 0$). Let F^* be an extension of F. If $E = F(a)$ then $F^*(a) = E^*$ is a normal extension of F^* and $\mathscr{G}(E^*/F^*)$ is isomorphic to a subgroup of $\mathscr{G}(E/F)$.

We remark that if E is a normal extension of a field F of characteristic zero, then, by definition, E is a finite extension of F, and by the corollary to Theorem 8.29, then $E = F(a)$ for some $a \in E$.

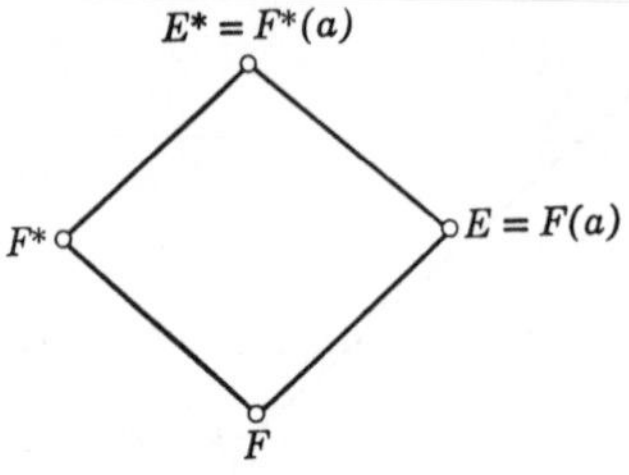

$E^* = F^*(a)$

PROOF. Let a be a zero of $p(x)$, of degree n and irreducible in $F[x]$. $p(x)$ splits in E, hence in E^*. We claim that E^* is the splitting field of $p(x)$ over F^*. (Of course, $p(x)$ may well be reducible in $F^*[x]$, but this is immaterial.) If $E^* \supseteq K \supseteq F^*$ and K is the splitting field of $p(x)$ over F^* then $a \in K$, and as $K \supseteq F^*$ we have $K \supseteq F^*(a) = E^*$. Thus $K = E^*$ and so E^* is normal over F^*.

F^* ... $E = F(a)$

F

Figure 15

Now consider $\sigma^* \in \mathscr{G}^* = \mathscr{G}(E^*/F^*)$. By definition, if $b \in F^*$, then $\sigma^*(b) = b$; hence in particular σ^* fixes F. What does σ^* do to E? We know that since a is a root of $p(x)$, irreducible in $F[x]$, and σ^* fixes $F[x]$, it follows that $\sigma^*(a)$ is also a root of $p(x)$. Thus $\sigma^*(a) \in E$, and as $\{1, a, \ldots, a^{n-1}\}$ spans E as a vector space over F it follows that $\sigma^*(a^i) = [\sigma^*(a)]^i \in E$ and so for all $e \in E$ we have that $\sigma^*(e) \in E$. Thus σ^* induces an automorphism of E. From this it is routine to show that the mapping r defined by $r(\sigma^*) = \sigma$, the restriction of σ^* to E, is a homomorphism of $\mathscr{G}^*$ into $\mathscr{G}$, hence onto a subgroup of $\mathscr{G}$. It is an isomorphism onto this subgroup since, if $\sigma = r(\sigma^*) = r(\tau^*) = \tau$, then $\sigma(a) = \tau(a)$, and hence $\sigma^*(a) = \tau^*(a)$ and so $\sigma^* = \tau^*$.

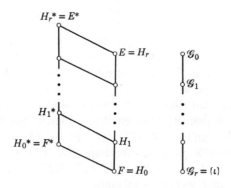

Figure 16

PROOF OF SUFFICIENCY. Let $f(x) \in F[x]$ have a solvable group. Let E be a splitting field over F for $f(x)$. We wish to embed E in a root tower. The construction is pictured in Figure 16.

Let $\mathscr{G}(E/F) = \mathscr{G} = \mathscr{G}_0 \supset \mathscr{G}_1 \supset \cdots \supset \mathscr{G}_r = \{\iota\}$ be a composition series for $\mathscr{G}$ in which every index $[\mathscr{G}_i : \mathscr{G}_{i+1}]$ is a prime p_i, and hence $\mathscr{G}_i/\mathscr{G}_{i+1}$ is a cyclic group of prime order. **By FTGT** there is a corresponding chain of subfields

$$F = H_0 \subset H_1 \subset \cdots \subset H_r = E$$

such that H_{i+1} is a normal extension of H_i. Moreover $\mathscr{G}(H_{i+1}/H_i)$ is cyclic since its order is a prime p_i.

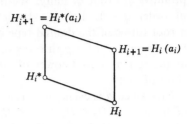

We begin our root tower by adjoining a splitting field for $x^m - 1$ where $m = [E:F] = |\mathscr{G}(E/F)|$. Call this field F^*. Now, since for every i, $p_i \mid m$ we have that F^* contains all the p_ith roots of unity. Let $H_{i+1} = H_i(a_i)$. We form

Figure 17

$H_0^* = F^*$, and for all i, $H_{i+1}^* = H_i^*(a_i)$. We claim that

$$F \subseteq F^* = H_0^* \subseteq H_1^* \subseteq \cdots \subseteq H_r^* = E^*$$

is a root tower. First $F^* \supseteq F$ is an extension of the appropriate kind. Next it follows from Lemma 5 that each H_{i+1}^* is a normal extension of H_i^* (see Figure 17) and that $\mathscr{G}_i^* = \mathscr{G}(H_{i+1}^*/H_i^*)$ is isomorphic to a subgroup of $\mathscr{G}_i = \mathscr{G}(H_{i+1}/H_i)$, and hence is cyclic. (Indeed, $\mathscr{G}_i^* = \{\iota\}$ or $\mathscr{G}_i^* \cong \mathscr{G}_i$.) Now from Theorem 9, since $[H_{i+1}^* : H_i^*] = 1$ or p_i and F^* contains a p_ith root of unity, it follows that $H_{i+1}^* = H_i^*(c_i)$ where $c_i^{p_i} \in H_i^*$. Thus we have proved our claim and the sufficiency is established.

* * *

The adjunction of the mth roots of unity was a quick way of obtaining the necessary roots of unity; however, although the spliting field of $x^m - 1$ does qualify as a root tower, it does not tell us how to express the roots of unity in terms of radicals with exponents less than m. Repeated application of the next theorem permits the replacement of F^* by a root tower in which each field extension has the form $T_{i+1} = T_i(a)$ where $x^p - a^p$ is an irreducible polynomial over T_i and p is a prime. The top of the tower will contain all the qth roots of unity for all primes q dividing m, although not necessarily all the mth roots of unity.

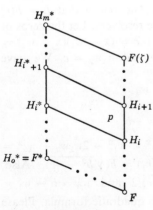

Figure 18

Theorem 11. Let q be a prime. The qth roots of unity belong to a root tower over F, $F = F_0 \subset F_1 \subset \cdots \subset F_r$, such that $F_{i+1} = F_i(a_i)$, and $x^{p_i} - a_i^{p_i}$ is irreducible in $F_i[x]$.

PROOF. The proof is by induction on q. We note that if $q = 1$ or 2 the primitive qth roots of unity (1 and -1 respectively) belong to F. Let ζ be a primitive qth root of unity. We do know that $\mathcal{G} = \mathcal{G}(F(\zeta)/F)$ is cyclic and of order $q - 1$. Let $q - 1 = p_1^{e_1} \ldots p_r^{e_r}$. By induction we may construct a root tower of the desired type of a primitive p_1th root of unity and over that a root tower for p_2th roots of unity, and so on, until we have a field F^* at the top of a root tower of the desired type which contains all the p_ith roots of unity.

Now since $\mathcal{G}$ is cyclic there is a composition series for $\mathcal{G}$ and hence a chain of fields $F = H_0 \subset H_1 \subset \cdots \subset H_m = F(\zeta)$ with $[H_{i+1} : H_i] = p_{ij}$, a prime, and $H_{i+1} = H_i(a_i)$ (see Figure 18). Thus if we define $H_0^* = F^*$ and $H_{i+1}^* = H_i^*(a_i)$ then since H^*_i contains a p_{ij}th root of unity and $\mathcal{G}(H_{i+1}^*/H_i^*)$ is, by Lemma 5, either the identity or cyclic of prime order, it follows from Theorem 9 that $H_0^* \subseteq \cdots \subseteq H_m^*$ is a root tower of F^* containing $F(\zeta)$ of the desired type. Thus, together with the root tower to F^* given by the induction hypothesis, we have a root tower for the prime q and so our proof is complete.

* * *

10.4. EQUATIONS OF 2nd AND 3rd DEGREE

As an illustration of this theory let us examine the familiar quadratic equation $x^2 + bx + c$, which we shall assume irreducible over F. (Since we know what the answer should be we can expect to gain an appreciation of this sophisticated theory.) We know the splitting field is $E = F(w)$ and that $[E : F] = 2$ so that E must be a cyclic extension, $\mathcal{G} = \langle \sigma \rangle$; $\sigma^2 = \iota$. Since the 2nd roots of unity belong to F we are told by Theorem 9 that $E = F(v)$ where $v^2 \in F$. How do we find v? By the Lagrange resolvent. Let the zeros of $x^2 + bx + c$ be w_1 and w_2. We have $x^2 + bx + c = (x - w_1)(x - w_2) = x^2 - (w_1 + w_2)x + w_1 w_2$. Thus $w_1 + w_2 = -b$ and $w_1 w_2 = c$. We have $\sigma(w_1) = w_2$. Thus

$$v_1 = \lambda(-1, w_1) = w_1 - w_2$$

and

$$v_2 = \lambda(1, w_1) = w_1 + w_2 = -b.$$

We know that $v_1^2 \in F$ and we calculate $v_1^2 = w_1^2 - 2w_1 w_2 + w_2^2 = (w_1 + w_2)^2 - 4w_1 w_2 = b^2 - 4c$. Thus $E = F(v_1) = F(\sqrt{b^2 - 4c})$. Also, $v_1 + v_2 = 2w_1$ and so $w_1 = (-b - \sqrt{b^2 - 4c})/2$ and $w_2 = b - w_1 = (-b + \sqrt{b^2 - 4c})/2$ as it should, confirming the quadratic formula. Please recall that the quadratic formula is usually derived by completing the square—this is a good trick in itself and it is certainly a preferable treatment for high school students!

We say that $w = (-b \pm \sqrt{b^2 - 4c})/2$ is a formula for the roots of

$x^2 + bx + c = 0$ since we have used no special properties for b and c, except that they came from a field whose characteristic was not 2. Thus we have, in effect, been considering b and c as indeterminates, and regarding $x^2 + bx + c$ as a polynomial in $F(b, c)[x]$. Recall that $F(b, c)$ denotes the quotient field of $F[b, c]$. Our work has thus taken place in a splitting field over $F(b, c)$. In this sense, $w = (-b \pm \sqrt{b^2 - 4c})/2$ is a *formula*.

Let us now consider the cubic equation $f(x) = x^3 + ax^2 + bx + c = 0$. To simplify matters slightly we shall replace this polynomial with $f(x - a/3) = x^3 + px + q$ where $p = b - a^2/3$ and $q = c + (2a^3 - 9ab)/27$. We shall assume that $x^3 + px + q$ is irreducible in $F[x]$, just to avoid trivialities. Let the zeros of $x^3 + px + q$ be w_1, w_2, w_3; we have

$$\begin{aligned} x^3 + px + q &= (x - w_1)(x - w_2)(x - w_3) \\ &= x^3 - (w_1 + w_2 + w_3)x^2 + (w_1w_2 + w_1w_3 + w_2w_3)x - w_1w_2w_3. \end{aligned}$$

Thus $\sum w_i = 0$, $\sum w_iw_j = p$, and $w_1w_2w_3 = -q$. If E is a splitting field of $x^3 + px + q$ over F, $E = F(w_1, w_2, w_3)$, then $[E:F] = 3$ or 6 and so $\mathscr{G} = \mathscr{G}(E/F)$ is isomorphic to a subgroup of $\mathcal{S}_3$; hence $\mathscr{G} \cong \mathcal{S}_3$ or $\mathscr{G} = \mathscr{A}_3 = \{\iota, (1, 2, 3), (1, 3, 2)\}$. In any event $\mathscr{G}$ has a subgroup $\mathscr{A}$ isomorphic to $\mathscr{A}_3$ which is a normal subgroup of $\mathscr{G}$. Since $\mathscr{A}$ is a normal subgroup of $\mathscr{G}$ there is a subfield K, $E \supset K \supseteq F$ such that K is a normal extension (see Figure 19). To find u such that $K = F(u)$ we seek an element of E which is left fixed by $\mathscr{A} = \{\iota, (w_1, w_2, w_3), (w_1, w_3, w_2)\}$, but not necessarily by all of $\mathscr{G}$. One such element is

$$\begin{aligned} \Delta = (w_1 - w_2)(w_1 - w_3)(w_2 - w_3) &= \prod_{i<j} (w_i - w_j) \\ &= w_1^2w_2 + w_2^2w_3 + w_1w_3^2 - w_1w_2^2 - w_2w_3^2 - w_1^2w_3. \end{aligned}$$

We have simply introduced this "out of the blue' and we can give no justification now, except to show that it works! Note that for any permutation σ of $\{w_1, w_2, w_3\}$ we have that $\sigma(\Delta) = \pm\Delta$ and so $\sigma(\Delta^2) = \Delta^2$. Thus it must be that $\Delta^2 \in F$. Δ^2 is called the *discriminant* of a cubic whose zeros are $\{w_1, w_2, w_3\}$. Check to see that if $\sigma \in \mathscr{A}$ then $\sigma(\Delta) = \Delta$, whereas if σ is any other permutation of $\{w_1, w_2, w_3\}$ then $\sigma(\Delta) = -\Delta$. To evaluate Δ we should naturally evaluate Δ^2. To do this we shall use one other trick. We have $f(x) = \prod (x - w_i)$, hence its derivative $f'(x) = \sum_{i<j} (x - w_i)(x - w_j)$, and so

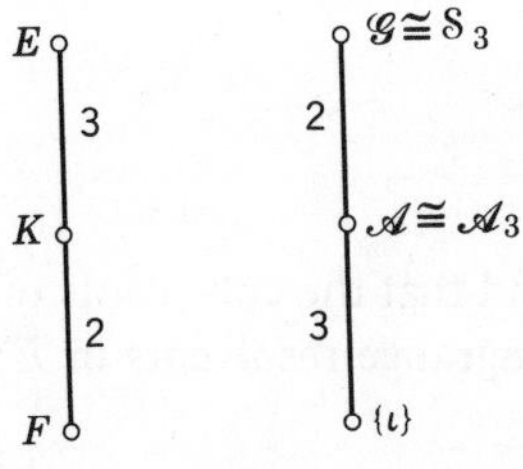

Figure 19

$$\begin{aligned} \Delta^2 = -f'(w_1)f'(w_2)f'(w_3) &= -(3w_1^2 + p)(3w_2^2 + p)(3w_3^2 + p) \\ &= -[27w_1^2w_2^2w_3^2 + 9p(w_1^2w_2^2 + w_1^2w_3^2 + w_2^2w_3^2) \\ &\qquad + 3p^2(w_1^2 + w_2^2 + w_3^2) + p^3]. \end{aligned}$$

The terms in this expression are clearly left invariant by every permutation of $\{w_1, w_2, w_3\}$ and hence are fixed by $\mathscr{G}$ and so belong to F. We shall show in the next section that we can always write such expressions as combinations of the coefficients of the cubic of which they are zeros. For now we shall do the calculations explicitly. We write, symbolically, $\sum w_1^2 w_2^2$ and $\sum w_1^2$ for these sums with the understanding that the terms that are to appear will make the expression invariant under S_3.

We have $w_1 w_2 w_3 = -q$ whereas $\sum w_1^2 = (\sum w_1)^2 - 2(\sum w_1 w_2) = -2p$; finally, $\sum w_1^2 w_2^2 = (\sum w_1 w_2)^2 - 2(\sum w_1^2 w_2 w_3) = p^2 - 2[(\sum w_1)(w_1 w_2 w_3)] = p^2$. Hence $\Delta^2 = -[27q^2 + 9p^3 - 6p^3 + p^3] = -(27q^2 + 4p^3)$. Thus $K = F(\Delta)$ is an extension of degree at most 2, and E is a cyclic extension over K. In particular if $\Delta \in F$ then $\mathscr{A} = \mathscr{G}$ and $[E : F] = 3$.

In any event we want to study the cyclic extension E over K. Let $\sigma = (w_1, w_2, w_3)$. To solve the equation $x^3 + px + q = 0$ by radicals, Theorem 10 tells us to adjoin to K the cube roots of unity $\zeta, \zeta^2, \zeta^3 = 1$; ζ is a zero of $x^2 + x + 1$ which we choose to be $\zeta = (-1 + \sqrt{3}i)/2$. Let $K^* = K(\zeta) = K(\sqrt{3}i)$. In general $K^* \neq K$, and this is certainly the case if $F = \text{Ra}$. Now Theorem 10 tells us to form the splitting field E^* of $x^3 + px + q$ over K^* (see Figure 20). We now know this a cyclic extension of degree 3

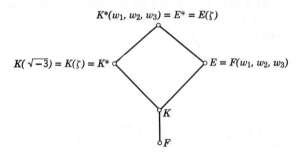

$$K^*(w_1, w_2, w_3) = E^* = E(\zeta)$$

$$K(\sqrt{-3}) = K(\zeta) = K^* \qquad E = F(w_1, w_2, w_3)$$

$$K$$

$$F$$

Figure 20

and that the cube roots of unity belong to K^*. Theorem 9 tells us to form the Lagrange resolvents in E^*.

$$v_1 = \lambda(1, w_1) = w_1 + w_2 + w_3 = 0$$

$$v_2 = \lambda(\zeta, w_1) = w_1 + \zeta w_2 + \zeta^2 w_3$$

$$v_3 = \lambda(\zeta^2, w_1) = w_1 + \zeta^2 w_2 + \zeta w_3$$

We know that v_2^3 and v_3^3 belong to K^* and that $w_1 = (v_1 + v_2 + v_3)/3 = (v_2 + v_3)/3$. Thus once we know v_2^3 and v_3^3 we shall have our formulas for the zeros of the cubic. Onward!

$$v_2{}^3 = (w_1 + \zeta w_2 + \zeta^2 w_3)^3$$

$$= w_1{}^3 + w_2{}^3 + w_3{}^3 + 3\zeta(w_1{}^2 w_2 + w_2{}^2 w_3 + w_1 w_3{}^2)$$

$$+ 3\zeta^2(w_1 w_2{}^2 + w_2 w_3{}^2 + w_1{}^2 w_3) + 6w_1 w_2 w_3$$

$$= \sum w_1{}^3 - \frac{3}{2} \sum (w_1{}^2 w_2 + w_1{}^2 w_3)$$

$$+ \frac{3}{2} \sqrt{3} i(w_1{}^2 w_2 + w_2{}^2 w_3 + w_1 w_3{}^2 - w_1 w_2{}^2 - w_2 w_3{}^2 - w_1{}^2 w_3)$$

$$+ 6w_1 w_2 w_3$$

$$= \sum w_1{}^3 - \frac{3}{2} \sum w_1{}^2(w_2 + w_3) + \frac{3}{2} \sqrt{3} i\Delta + 6w_1 w_2 w_3.$$

Now $\sum w_1{}^3 = (\sum w_1)^3 - 3 \sum w_1{}^2(w_2 + w_3) - 6w_1 w_2 w_3$ whereas

$$\sum w_1{}^2(w_2 + w_3) = \left(\sum w_1\right)\left(\sum w_1 w_2\right) - 3w_1 w_2 w_3.$$

Since $\sum w_1 = 0$ we have

$$v_2{}^3 = -\frac{9}{2} \sum w_1{}^2(w_2 + w_3) + \frac{3}{2} \sqrt{3} i\Delta$$

$$= \frac{27}{2} w_1 w_2 w_3 + \frac{3}{2} \sqrt{3} i\Delta = -\frac{27}{2} q + \frac{3}{2} \sqrt{3} i\Delta.$$

Similarly, by replacing ζ by ζ^2, we obtain

$$v_3{}^3 = -\frac{27}{2} q - \frac{3}{2} \sqrt{3} i\Delta.$$

Hence we may write

$$w_1 = \frac{1}{3} \left[\sqrt[3]{-\frac{27}{2} q + \frac{3}{2} \sqrt{3} i\Delta} + \sqrt[3]{-\frac{27}{2} q - \frac{3}{2} \sqrt{3} i\Delta} \right].$$

Similarly we obtain $(\zeta^2 v_2 + \zeta v_3)/3 = w_2$ and $(\zeta v_2 + \zeta^2 v_3)/3 = w_3$.

There is one hitch in these formulas: $\sqrt[3]{t}$ is a multiple-valued notation. Which cube roots of $v_2{}^3$ and $v_3{}^3$ are to be used? They have to be chosen so that $v_2 v_3 = (w_1 + \zeta w_2 + \zeta^2 w_3)(w_1 + \zeta^2 w_2 + \zeta w_3) = \sum w_1{}^2 + (\zeta + \zeta^2) \sum w_1 w_2 = \sum w_1{}^2 - \sum w_1 w_2 = (\sum w_1)^2 - 3 \sum w_1 w_2 = -3p$. (In general it is true that $\lambda(\zeta, w) \cdot \lambda(\zeta^{-1}, w) \in F$.)

As we have shown this is a necessary relation but it is also sufficient as we can verify by testing our solution $w_1 = (v_2 + v_3)/3$ subject to the condition $v_2 v_3 = -3p$.

$$w_1{}^3 + pw_1 + q = \frac{1}{27} (v_2{}^3 + 3v_2{}^2 v_3 + 3v_2 v_3{}^2 + v_3{}^3) + \frac{p}{3} (v_2 + v_3) + q$$

$$= \frac{1}{27} (v_2{}^3 + v_3{}^3) + q = -q + q = 0.$$

These formulas for w_1, w_2, w_3, v_2, v_3, and Δ, together with the relation $v_2 v_3 = -3p$ are called "Cardano's formulas" for the cubic.

It is interesting and important to note that in order to solve a cubic by radicals we may have to construct a field larger than the splitting field. Thus if $x^3 + ax^2 + bx + c \in \text{Ra}[x]$ has real irrational zeros, its splitting field is a subfield of the real numbers, but Cardano's formulas give the roots in terms of complex numbers which are not real.

With more effort, but essentially with the same kind of calculations, we can solve a quartic equation by radicals. We shall not give that solution here. It is based on the composition series in S_4:

$$S_4 \supset \mathscr{A}_4 \supset \mathscr{V}_4 \supset \{\iota, (12)(34)\} \supset \{\iota\}.$$

where $\mathscr{A}_4$ is the alternating group on 4 symbols of Problem 14 in Exercise 1.5 and $\mathscr{V}_4 = \{\iota, (12)(3, 4), (1, 3)(2, 4), (1, 4)(2, 3)\}$.

Since we have shown that S_5 is not solvable, to give an example of an equation not solvable by radicals we need only exhibit an equation whose group is S_5. One difficulty lies ahead—how can we calculate the Galois group of an equation? We shall not give a general procedure for doing this; however, we shall give one theorem about S_p and another theorem about rational polynomials which are of some help. In particular we shall be able to exhibit a polynomial in $\text{Ra}[x]$ whose group is S_5, and hence is not solvable by radicals.

Theorem 12. Let p be a prime. If G is a subgroup of the symmetric on p symbols, S_p, which contains a p-cycle and a transposition, then $G = S_p$.

PROOF. The theorem is trivial if $p = 2$ and it is easy to verify if $p = 3$. We give the proof for $p = 5$ and leave the generalization as an exercise. Let $\tau = (a, b)$ and let the 5-cycle be $\sigma = (u, v, w, x, y)$. Since $\{a, b\} \subseteq \{u, v, w, x, y\}$ there is a power of σ, call it ρ, such that $\rho = (a, b, c, d, e)$ where $\{a, b, c, d, e\} = \{u, v, w, x, y\}$. We shall show that $\langle \tau, \rho \rangle = S_5$. First we shall show that $\langle \tau, \rho \rangle$ contains all transpositions (s, t). We calculate:

$$\rho \tau \rho^{-1} = (a, b, c, d, e)(a, b)(a, e, d, c, b) = (b, c).$$
$$\rho^2 \tau \rho^{-2} = (a, c, e, b, d)(a, b)(a, d, b, e, c) = (c, d)$$
$$\rho^3 \tau \rho^{-3} = (a, d, b, e, c)(a, b)(a, c, e, b, d) = (d, e).$$

Now we have

$$(b, c)(a, b)(b, c) = (a, c)$$
$$(c, d)(a, c)(c, d) = (a, d)$$
$$(d, e)(a, d)(d, e) = (a, e)$$
$$(c, d)(b, c)(c, d) = (b, d)$$
$$(d, e)(b, d)(d, e) = (b, e)$$
$$(d, e)(c, d)(d, c) = (c, e).$$

From Problem 9 of Exercise 1.4 we know that every permutation is the product of disjoint cycles. Since any cycle is a product of transpositions, for example, $(1, 2, \ldots, n) = (1, n)(1, n - 1)\ldots(1, 3)(1, 2)$ (this was also proved in Problem 1 of Exercise 3.3), it follows that every cycle and every permutation in S_5 belongs to $\langle \tau, \sigma \rangle$.

        * * *

Theorem 13. Let p be a prime. If $f(x) \in \text{Ra}[x]$ is an irreducible polynomial of degree p which has exactly $(p - 2)$ real roots and two complex roots then the Galois group of $f(x)$ over Ra is S_p.

Fig. 21

PROOF. Let E be a splitting field of $f(x)$ over Ra contained in the complex numbers C (see Figure 21). Let $\mathscr{G} = \mathscr{G}(E/\text{Ra})$. We know that $p \mid [E : \text{Ra}] = |\mathscr{G}|$, hence $\mathscr{G}$, as a permutation group on the p roots $\{w_1, \ldots, w_p\}$, must contain an element of order p which must be a p-cycle. (Why?) Let w_1, w_2 be the complex roots; we know that w_2 is the complex conjugate of w_1. Next we claim that the automorphism τ of C, given by $\tau(a + bi) = a - bi$ which sends every complex number into its conjugate, when restricted to E is an automorphism of E. τ certainly sends w_1 into $w_2 = \bar{w}_1$, and τ fixes every real number. To establish our claim it suffices to show that if $a + bi \in E$ then $a - bi \in E$. If $a + bi \in E$, then $a + bi$ is a zero of a polynomial in Ra$[x]$ and hence $a - bi$ is a zero of the same polynomial which must also belong to E as E is a normal extension of Ra. Thus when τ is restricted to E it is a mapping from E into E and hence an automorphism of E. Finally $\tau^2 = \iota$. Now, as an automorphism of E, τ must be a transposition on $w_1, w_2, \ldots, w_n$. Indeed $\tau(w_1) = w_2$, $\tau(w_2) = w_1$ and for $2 < i$, $\tau(w_i) = w_i$ since these roots are real. Thus $\tau = (w_1, w_2)$. From the previous theorem it follows that $\mathscr{G} = S_p$.

        * * *

Example 6. The Galois group of $f(x) = x^5 - 10x^4 + 2x^3 - 24x^2 + 2$ over Ra is S_5, hence the equation $f(x) = 0$ is not solvable in radicals over Ra.

PROOF. $f(x)$ is irreducible in Ra$[x]$ by Eisenstein's criteria. $f'(x) = 5x^4 - 40x^3 + 6x^2 - 48x = x(5x^2 + 6)(x - 8)$ has real zeros $x = 0$ and $x = 8$ (see Figure 22). Hence $y = f(x)$ has exactly two critical points; moreover $f(0) = 2 > 0$ and $f(8) = 8^5 - 10 \cdot 8^4 + 2 \cdot 8^3 - 3 \cdot 8^3 + 2 < 0$, so that $f(x)$ has a local maximum at $x = 0$ and a local minimum at $x = 8$; thus $f(x)$ has three real roots w_3, w_4, w_5 where $w_3 < 0$, $0 < w_4 < 8$, and $8 < w_5$, and so $f(x)$ must have two complex roots. From Theorem 13 it then follows that the group of $f(x)$ is S_5.

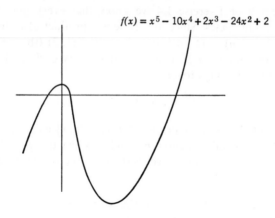

$$f(x) = x^5 - 10x^4 + 2x^3 - 24x^2 + 2$$

Figure 22

EXERCISE 2

1. Find the Galois group of $x^3 - 3x + 1$ over the rationals. Solve the equation in radicals.

2. Find the Galois group of $x^4 - 2$ over the rationals.

3. Give a general proof for Theorem 12.

4. Let E be a normal extension of K. Let G be the Galois group of E over K. Suppose that $G = H_1 \times H_2$. What can be said of the subfield structure of E? Illustrate your remarks with $E = \Gamma(\zeta)$, ζ a primitive 16th root of unity. Give sufficient conditions for the group of $f(x) = f_1(x)f_2(x) \in K[x]$ to be the direct product of the groups of $f_1(x)$ and of $f_2(x)$. Give examples in which your conditions *are* and *are not* satisfied.

5. Let K be a field of characteristic p, a prime. Show that if α is a root of $f(x) = x^p - x - c = 0$, then so are $\alpha + 1$, $\alpha + 2, \ldots, \alpha + (p - 1)$. What possible degree may the factors of $f(x)$ have in $K[x]$? What splitting fields are possible for $f(x)$? What Galois groups are possible for $f(x)$? Exhibit the automorphisms expl·citly.

6. Consider the equation $p(x) = x^4 - 2x^2 - 2 = 0$ over the rationals Ra.

(i) Show that $p(x)$ is irreducible over Ra.

(ii) Show that $p(x)$ has two real roots, u and v, and two complex roots, c and d.

(iii) Find the degrees:

$$[\text{Ra}(u) : \text{Ra}], \quad [\text{Ra}(u, v) : \text{Ra}], \quad [\text{Ra}(u, v, c, d) : \text{Ra}(u)].$$

(iv) In Ra(u) find the multiplicative inverse of $1 + u^3$.

(v) Do there exist automorphisms of Ra(u, v, c, d) such that

(1) $u \to u, v \to c$?   (2) $u \to u, c \to d$?
(3) $u \to v, c \to c$?   (4) $u \to c, c \to v$?

10.5. THE GENERAL POLYNOMIAL OF nth DEGREE

Our treatment of the quadratic and cubic equations was such that we obtained a "formula" for the roots of the equation. In effect we considered the coefficients as indeterminates. Thus if F is a field we may adjoin indeterminates $\{u_1, \ldots, u_n\}$ and consider $F[u_1, \ldots, u_n]$ and its quotient field $F(u_1, \ldots, u_n) = K$, and in $K[x]$ we may consider the polynomial

$$f(x) = x^n - u_1 x^{n-1} + u_2 x^{n-2} + \cdots + (-1)^n u_n.$$

This polynomial we call the *general polynomial* of nth degree over F. The reason for placing $(-1)^t$ before $u_t x^{n-t}$ is simply as a convenience, which we now describe.

Let E be a splitting field for $f(x)$ over K. In E we have $f(x) = \prod_{i=1}^n (x - v_i)$, and on multiplication we obtain

$$f(x) = x^n - (v_1 + \cdots + v_n)x^{n-1}$$
$$+ (v_1 v_2 + \cdots + v_1 v_n + v_2 v_3 + \cdots + v_{n-1}v_n)x^{n-2} + \cdots + (-1)^n(v_1 v_2 \ldots v_n).$$

Thus we must have

$$u_1 = v_1 + \cdots + v_n$$

$$u_2 = \sum_{i<j} v_i v_j = v_1 v_2 + v_1 v_3 + \cdots + v_1 v_n + v_2 v_3 + \cdots + \cdots + v_{n-1}v_n$$

$$\vdots$$

$$u_k = \sum_{i_1 < i_2 < \ldots i_k} v_{i_1} v_{i_2} \ldots v_{i_k}$$

$$\vdots$$

$$u_n = v_1 v_2 \ldots v_n.$$

The reason for adopting the convention of alternating the signs in the expression for $f(x)$ is now apparent, the signs are dictated by the expansion of $\prod (x - v_i)$.

We shall prove that the Galois group of $f(x)$ over K is the full symmetric group S_n. We begin by considering a situation which, while it may appear quite complicated, is really very straightforward.

Definition. Let F be a field and let $\{t_1, \ldots, t_n\}$ be a set of n distinct indeterminates over F. The elementary symmetric polynomials on $\{t_1, \ldots, t_n\}$ are the elements $s_1, \ldots, s_n$ of $F[t_1, \ldots, t_n]$ defined

$$s_1 = t_1 + \cdots + t_n = \sum_{i=1}^n t_i$$

$$s_2 = t_1 t_2 + \cdots + t_{n-1}t_n + \cdots + t_{n-1}t_n = \sum_{1 \le i < j \le n} t_i t_j$$

$$\vdots$$

$$s_k = \sum_{1 \le i_1 < i_2 < \ldots < i_k} t_{i_1} t_{i_2} \ldots t_{i_k}$$

$$\vdots$$

$$s_n = t_1 t_2 \ldots t_n$$

For brevity we shall write $s_k = \sum t_1 \ldots t_k$. The symbolic summation is meant to indicate a sum of all terms $t_{i_1} t_{i_2} \ldots t_{i_k}$ for all k-tuples $(i_1, i_2, \ldots, i_k)$ of positive integers from $\{1, 2, \ldots, n\}$ where $i_1 < i_2 < \cdots < i_k$.

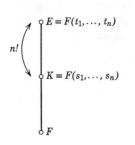

Figure 23

Theorem 14. Let F be a field and $\{t_1, \ldots, t_n\}$ be a set of n distinct indeterminates over F. Let $\{s_1, \ldots, s_n\}$ be the elementary symmetric polynomials on $\{t_1, t_2, \ldots, t_n\}$. If $E = F(t_1, \ldots, t_n)$ and $K = F(s_1, \ldots, s_n)$ then E is a normal extension of K such that $\mathscr{G}(E/K) = \mathcal{S}_n$ and $[E : K] = n!$.

PROOF. To show that E is normal over K we simply observe that E is the splitting field in $K[x]$ of the polynomial $f(x) = \prod_{i=1}^{n} (x - t_i) = x^n - s_1 x^{n-1} + \cdots + (-1)^n s_n$. From the corollary to Theorem 8.15 any permutation on $\{t_1, \ldots, t_n\}$ yields an automorphism of $F(t_1, \ldots, t_n)$ which clearly must fix each s_k and thus fixes K and so belongs to $\mathscr{G}(E/K)$. On the other hand $\mathscr{G}$ is isomorphic to a subgroup of $\mathcal{S}_n$, and hence it follows that $\mathscr{G} \cong \mathcal{S}_n$ and so $[E : K] = n!$ (see Figure 23).

For sake of completeness we add that if σ is a permutation on $\{t_1, \ldots, t_n\}$, say $\sigma(x_i) = x_{\sigma(i)}$, then the automorphism σ induces on $F[t_1, \ldots, t_n]$ is given by

$$\sigma(g) = \sigma\left(\sum a_{i_1 i_2 \cdots i_n} t_1^{i_1} t_2^{i_2} \cdots t_n^{i_n}\right) = \sum a_{i_1 i_2 \cdots i_n} t_{\sigma(1)}^{i_1} t_{\sigma(2)}^{i_2} \cdots t_{\sigma(n)}^{i_n}.$$

* * *

Definition. A function $r = g/h$ in $F(t_1, \ldots, t_n)$ is called a symmetric function, if for any $\sigma \in \mathcal{S}_n$ we have $\sigma(r) = \sigma(g)/\sigma(h) = r$.

Corollary. Any symmetric function $r(t_1, \ldots, t_n)$ can be expressed as a function $r_1(s_1, \ldots, s_n)$.

PROOF. If $r = r(t_1, \ldots, t_n)$ is a symmetric function then it is fixed by $\mathscr{G}(E/K)$ and hence $r \in K$, which is to say that $r = r_1(s_1, \ldots, s_n)$.

This corollary is an extremely useful result. In the next section we shall show that if $r(t_1, \ldots, t_n)$ is a symmetric polynomial with integer coefficients, then it may be written as a polynomial in $s_1, \ldots, s_n$ with integer coefficients. There our procedure will be constructive.

* * *

Theorem 15. The Galois group of the general polynomial of nth degree over F is $\mathcal{S}_n$.

PROOF. Let $u_1, \ldots, u_n$ be n distinct indeterminates over F. Let $f(x) = x_n - u_1 x^{n-1} + \cdots + (-1)^n u_n$. Let $K = F(u_1, \cdots, u_n)$ and let E be a splitting field of $f(x)$ over K. Let $v_1, \ldots, v_n$ be the n zeros of $f(x)$. $f(x) = \prod (x - v_i)$ and $u_k = \sum v_1 v_2 \ldots v_k$.

Let $\{t_1, \ldots, t_n\}$ be a set of n indeterminates over F. (It does not matter whether these are disjoint from the u_i's, but it may help if you think of them as being so.) Let $E^* = F(t_1, \ldots, t_n)$ and $K^* = F(s_1, \ldots, s_n)$ where $s_k = \sum t_1 \ldots t_k$ is the kth elementary symmetric function on $t_1, \ldots, t_n$ (see Figure 24). As in the preceding theorem, $\mathscr{G}(E^*/K^*) = \mathcal{S}_n$. We shall prove that there is an isomorphism $\Phi : K \to K^*$ from K onto K^* which sends u_i onto s_i and hence $f(x)$ onto $f^*(x) = x^n - s_1 x^{n-1} + \cdots + (-1)^n s_n$. We may then, by Theorem 8.5, extend Φ to an isomorphism θ of E onto E^*.

We obtain Φ by first defining a mapping φ from $F[u_1, \ldots, u_n]$ into $F(s_1, \ldots, s_n)$ by setting $\varphi(g(u_1, \ldots, u_n)) = g(s_1, \ldots, s_n)$. Since $F[u_1, \ldots, u_n]$ is a polynomial ring this mapping is clearly a ring homomorphism. Similarly

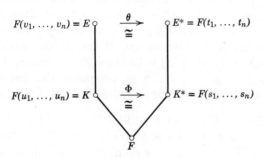

Figure 24

the mapping $\psi : F[t_1, \ldots, t_n] \to K[v_1, \ldots, v_n]$ given by $\psi(h(t_1, \ldots, t_n)) = h(v_1, \ldots, v_n)$ is a ring homomorphism. We now claim that φ is in fact 1–1. For if $g(s_1, \ldots, s_n) = 0$, that is, if $g(\sum t_1, \sum t_1 t_2, \ldots)$ is the zero polynomial, then $\psi(g(\sum t_1, \sum t_1 t_2, \ldots)) = g(\sum v_1, \sum v_1 v_2, \ldots) = g(u_1, \ldots, u_n) = 0$; thus $g(u_1, \ldots, u_n)$ must be the zero polynomial, and φ is 1–1. Now we can extend φ to an isomorphism Φ of the quotient field $F(u_1, \ldots, u_n)$ into $K^* = F(s_1, \ldots, s_n)$. Since $\{s_1, \ldots, s_n\}$ belongs to the range of Φ ($\Phi(u_i) = s_i$) it follows that Φ is onto and so K and K^* are isomorphic. Thus there is an isomorphism $\theta : E \to E^*$ which maps E onto E^* and which takes K onto K^*. Now it follows that if $\sigma \in \mathscr{G}(E^*/K^*)$ then $M(\sigma)$ defined by $M(\sigma)(a) = \theta^{-1}\sigma\theta(a)$ is an automorphism of E fixing K, and hence it belongs to $\mathscr{G}(E/K)$. It is easy to show that M is a group isomorphism from $\mathscr{G}(E^*/K^*)$ onto $\mathscr{G}(E/K)$. Thus it follows that $\mathscr{G}(E/K) \cong \mathcal{S}_n$.

* * *

Theorem 16 (*Abel and Ruffini*). The general polynomial of nth degree is not solvable by radicals if $n \geq 5$.

PROOF. The Galois group of the polynomial is $\mathcal{S}_n$ (Theorem 15). For $n \geq 5$ $\mathcal{S}_n$ is not a solvable group (Theorem 9.16). Hence by Theorem 10, the polynomial is not solvable by radicals.

10.6. THE DISCRIMINANT

The role played by Δ in solving the cubic $x^3 + px + q$ is but a special case of a more general phenomenon which we shall now describe.

Definition. Let $f(x) \in F[x]$ and suppose that $f(x)$ splits in $E \supseteq F$. Let $f(x) = \prod (x - w_i)$ in $E[x]$. The discriminant of $f(x)$ is Δ^2 where $\Delta = \prod_{i<j} (w_i - w_j)$.

If it is important to emphasize the polynomial we shall write $\Delta(f)$ for Δ. If $f(x)$ is the general polynomial of nth degree we shall write Δ_n for $\Delta(f)$.

Since Δ is in a splitting field of $f(x)$ and since all splitting fields are isomorphic, Δ is clearly determined "up to isomorphism"; indeed, as we shall prove shortly, $\Delta^2 \in F$ and so it is independent of the splitting extension. As we have observed, if $f(x) = x^2 - u_1 x + u_2$ is the general quadratic polynomial, then $\Delta_2 = w_1 - w_2$ and $(\Delta_2)^2 = w_1{}^2 - 2w_1 w_2 + w_2{}^2 = (w_1 + w_2)^2 - 4w_1 w_2 = u_1{}^2 - 4u_2$ is its discriminant. If $f(x)$ is the general cubic, then $x^3 - u_1 x^2 + u_2 x - u_3$, then $\Delta_3 = (w_1 - w_2)(w_1 - w_3)(w_2 - w_3)$. For the reduced cubic $x^3 + px + q$ we have computed the discriminant to be $\Delta^2 = -(27q^2 + 4p^3)$. Note that $\Delta(f) = 0$ if and only if f has a multiple zero.

> **Theorem 17.** Let E be a splitting field of $f(x) \in F[x]$. The discriminant Δ^2 of f belongs to F and so $[F(\Delta):F] = 1$ or 2 depending on whether $\sqrt{\Delta^2} = \Delta \in F$ or $\Delta \notin F$. If f is the general polynomial $f(x) = x^n - u_1 x^{n-1} + \cdots + (-1)^n u_n$ over F and $K = F(u_1, \ldots, u_n)$ then $[K(\Delta_n):K] = 2$.

PROOF. Let E be a splitting field of $f(x)$ over F. Just as we remarked in our discussion of the cubic any permutation σ on the zeros $\{w_1, \ldots, w_n\}$ of $f(x)$ takes Δ into $\pm\Delta$ and hence $\sigma(\Delta^2) = \Delta^2$. Thus Δ^2 belongs to the fixed field of all of $\mathscr{G}(E/F)$, which is of course just F itself. Thus Δ is a zero of $x^2 - \Delta^2 \in F[x]$. $x^2 - \Delta^2$ is either reducible, in this case $\Delta \in F$, or it is irreducible and in this case $\Delta \notin F$ and $[F(\Delta):F] = 2$.

Now let f be the general polynomial of degree n. Reverting to our notation in Theorem 15, let $K = F(u_1, \ldots, u_n)$, $f(x) = x^n - u_1 x^{n-1} + \cdots + (-1)^n u_n = \prod (x - v_i)$, and let $E = K(v_1, \ldots, v_n)$ be the splitting field of f over K. Thus $\Delta_n = \prod_{1 \le i < j \le n} (v_i - v_j) \in F(v_1, \ldots, v_n) = K(v_1, \ldots, v_n) = E$. We know that $\mathscr{G}(E/K) \cong S_n$ and that $\Delta_n \notin K$ since, for example, the permutation $\sigma = (v_1, v_2)$ sends Δ_n into $-\Delta_n$. To see this, note that the factor $(v_1 - v_2)$ is sent into $(v_2 - v_1) = -(v_1 - v_2)$, whereas all other factors $(v_i - v_j)$ are either fixed (this is the case that $2 < i < j$) or interchanged (in this case the factors $(v_1 - v_j)$ and $(v_2 - v_j)$ are interchanged). Hence it must be that $\Delta \notin K$ and so we have, by the first part that $[K(\Delta):K] = 2$.

In view of this theorem and the FTGT we can say something about the subgroup $\mathscr{G}(E/K(\Delta))$ of $\mathscr{G}(E/K) \cong S_n$. Since $[K(\Delta):K] = 2$ it follows that $[\mathscr{G}(E/K):\mathscr{G}(E/K(\Delta))] = 2$.

Thus $\mathcal{G}(E/K(\Delta_n))$ is a subgroup of index 2 in $\mathcal{G}(E/K) \cong S_n$ and hence is a normal subgroup of $\mathcal{G}(E/K)$. Thus $K(\Delta_n)$ is a normal extension of K. (This, of course, follows from the fact that it is of degree 2 over K without the FTGT.)

The subgroup of S_n to which $(E/K(\Delta_n))$ is isomorphic is called the alternating group $\mathcal{A}_n$. It is easy to see that any transposition $\tau = (v_i, v_j)$ sends Δ_n into $-\Delta_n$, and so we obtain another characterization of the alternating group as those permutations of $\{1, \ldots, n\}$, which can be expressed as the product of an even number of transpositions. These permutations, and only these, will fix Δ_n.

* * *

Corollary (*Role of the Discriminant*). Let $f(x) \in F[x]$ and have degree n. The group of $f(x)$ over F is a subgroup of the alternating group $\mathcal{A}_n$ if and only if $\Delta(f) \in F$.

PROOF. Let E be a splitting field of f over F. If $\Delta \in F$ then every permutation in $\mathcal{G}(E/F)$ must fix Δ. Since any permutation of S_n takes Δ into $\pm\Delta$ and $\mathcal{A}_n$ is, by definition, the set of those permutations which take Δ into Δ, it follows that each permutation in $\mathcal{G}(E/F)$ must belong to $\mathcal{A}_n$. Conversely, if $\Delta \notin F$, then some permutation $\sigma \in \mathcal{G}(E/F)$ must not fix Δ. Thus $\sigma(\Delta) = -\Delta$ and so $\sigma \notin \mathcal{A}_n$. Thus $\mathcal{G}(E/F) \nsubseteq \mathcal{A}_n$.

* * *

There is no need for Galois theory to define the alternating group $\mathcal{A}_n$. A standard development of determinants introduces the polynomial Δ_n as a polynomial in $I[t_1, \ldots, t_n]$ by defining

$$\Delta_n = \prod_{1 \leq i < j \leq n} (t_i - t_j).$$

Any permutation σ on $\{1, \ldots, n\}$ induces in the obvious way an automorphism of $I[t_1, \ldots, t_n]$. $\mathcal{A}_n$ is defined as those permutations on $\{1, \ldots, n\}$ which fix Δ_n in the induced automorphism of $I[t_1, \ldots, t_n]$. We observe that (i, j) takes Δ_n into $-\Delta_n$ and therefore that $\mathcal{A}_n$ consists of those permutations which can be written as an even number of transpositions. We should then prove directly that $[S_n : \mathcal{A}_n] = 2$.

We could of course have defined $\mathcal{A}_n$ as those permutations which can be expressed as the product of an even number of transpositions. But now we would have had to prove that a permutation cannot be written both as an even number of transpositions and as an odd number of transpositions. One way of doing this is to introduce Δ_n! For this reason $\pi \in \mathcal{A}_n$ is called an *even* permutation; $\pi \notin \mathcal{A}_n$ is called an *odd* permutation.

An interesting theorem, which we shall not prove, is that if $n \geq 5$ then $\mathcal{A}_n$ is a simple group. From this, of course, follows that $\mathcal{A}_n$ and hence S_n is not solvable.

10.7. SYMMETRIC POLYNOMIALS

> **Theorem 18.** Let $f(x_1, \ldots, x_n) \in I[x_1, \ldots, x_n]$ and let $s_1, \ldots, s_n$ be the elementary symmetric functions on $x_1, \ldots, x_n$. If $f(x_1, \ldots, x_n)$ is a symmetric function ($f \in \mathrm{Ra}(x_1, \ldots, x_n)$), then $f(x_1, \ldots, x_n)$ belongs to the subring $I[s_1, \ldots, s_n] \subseteq I[x_1, \ldots, x_n]$.

This theorem says that every symmetric polynomial with integer coefficients is a polynomial with *integer* coefficients in the elementary symmetric functions.

A typical term of $f(x_1, \ldots, x_n)$ is $ax_1^{e_1}x_2^{e_2}\ldots x_n^{e_n}$, where $a \in I$. We shall call the n-tuple $(e_1, \ldots, e_n)$ the degree vector of the term $ax_1^{e_1}\ldots x_n^{e_n}$. We shall order the degree vectors of the terms in f lexicographically. Specifically, $\vec{e} = (e_1, \ldots, e_n) \propto \vec{k} = (k_1, \ldots, k_n)$ if $\vec{e} = \vec{k}$, or if, for the least index at which $e_i \neq k_i$, it is the case that $e_i < k_i$. This is easily proved to be a well ordering of the degree vectors in $f(x_1, \ldots, x_n)$, indeed of all degree vectors in all polynomials in $F[x_1, \ldots, x_n]$.

Example 7. If $f(x_1, x_2, x_3) = x_1{}^2x_2x_3 + x_1x_2{}^2x_3 + x_1x_2x_3{}^2$, then the degree vectors are ordered as follows: $(1, 1, 2) \propto (1, 2, 1) \propto (2, 1, 1)$.

PROOF. We shall prove Theorem 18 by induction on the maximal degree vector (under $\propto$) in the polynomial $f(x_1, \ldots, x_n)$. If this maximal vector is $\vec{0}$, then f is a scalar polynomial and there is nothing to prove. We shall take as our induction hypothesis the validity of the theorem for all symmetric functions whose maximal degree vector is $\propto(e_1, e_2, \ldots, e_n)$. Now we suppose that in $f(x_1, \ldots, x_n)$ the term $ax_1^{e_1}x_2^{e_2}\ldots x_n^{e_n}$ ($a \in I$) has the maximal degree vector in F. We claim that $e_1 \geq e_2 \geq \cdots \geq e_n$. If this is not so, then there is clearly a permutation π of the indices so that $e_{\pi(1)} \geq e_{\pi(2)} \geq \cdots \geq e_{\pi(n)}$, and since f is a symmetric polynomial f must contain the term $ax_1^{e_{\pi(1)}}x_2^{e_{\pi(2)}}\ldots x_n^{e_{\pi(n)}}$ and $(e_1, e_2, \ldots, e_n) \propto (e_{\pi(1)}, e_{\pi(2)}, \ldots, e_{\pi(n)})$. This is so since $e_{\pi(1)} \geq e_1$, and if $e_{\pi(1)} = e_1, \ldots, e_{\pi(i)} = e_i$, then $e_{\pi(i+1)} \geq e_{i+1}$.

Now consider the product

$$as_1^{e_1 - e_2}s_2^{e_2 - e_3}\cdots s_{n-1}^{e_{n-1} - e_n}s_n^{e_n}$$

$$= a\left(\sum x_1\right)^{e_1 - e_2}\left(\sum x_1x_2\right)^{e_2 - e_3}\ldots\left(\sum x_1\ldots x_{n-1}\right)^{e_{n-1} - e_n}(x_1\ldots x_n)^{e_n}.$$

We wish to determine the term with the maximal degree vector. We obtain it by taking the term with as many factors equal to x_1 as possible, then with as many terms equal to x_2 as possible, and so on. Thus the term with the maximal degree vector is

$$ax_1^{e_1 - e_2}(x_1x_2)^{e_2 - e_3}\ldots(x_1x_2\ldots x_{n-1})^{e_{n-1} - e_n}(x_1\ldots x_n)^{e_n} = ax_1^{e_1}x_2^{e_2}\ldots x_n^{e_n}.$$

Hence in the function $f_1(x_1, \ldots, x_n)$, defined by

$$f_1(x_1, \ldots, x_n) = f(x_1, \ldots, x_n) - as_1^{e_1 - e_2}s_2^{e_2 - e_3}\ldots s_{n-1}^{e_{n-1} - e_n}s_n^{e_n},$$

the term with maximal degree vector must precede $(e_1, \ldots, e_n)$ in the lexicographic ordering. Since both $f(x_1, \ldots, x_n)$ and $as_1^{e_1-e_2}s_2^{e_2-e_3}\ldots s_n^{e_n}$ are symmetric and in $I[x_1, \ldots, x_n]$, it follows that f_1 is a symmetric polynomial in $I[x_1, \ldots, x_n]$. By induction, $f_1(x_1, \ldots, x_n) = g_1(s_1, \ldots, s_n) \in I[s_1, \ldots, s_n]$, and so $f = g_1 + as_1^{e_1-e_2}s_2^{e_2-e_3}\ldots s_n^{e_n} = g(s_1, \ldots, s_n) \in I[s_1, \ldots, s_n]$, as was to be proved.

* * *

Example 8. Let $f(x_1, x_2, x_3) = \sum x_1^4 x_2^2$. The maximal degree vector is $(4, 2, 0)$. Thus $f_1(x_1, x_2, x_3) = \sum x_1^4 x_2^2 - s_1^2 s_2^2 s_3^0$. Now $s_1^2 s_2^2 =$

$$(\sum x_1)^2 (\sum x_1 x_2)^2 = (\sum x_1^2 + 2 \sum x_1 x_2)(\sum x_1^2 x_2^2 + 2 \sum x_1^2 x_2 x_3)$$

$$= [(\sum x_1^2)(\sum x_1^2 x_2^2)] + [2(\sum x_1^2)(\sum x_1^2 x_2 x_3)] + [2(\sum x_1 x_2)(\sum x_1^2 x_2^2)]$$
$$+ [4(\sum x_1 x_2)(\sum x_1^2 x_2 x_3)]$$

$$= [\sum x_1^4 x_2^2 + 3 \sum x_1^2 x_2^2 x_3^2] + [2 \sum x_1^4 x_2 x_3 + 2 \sum x_1^3 x_2^2 x_3]$$
$$+ [2 \sum x_1^3 x_2^3 + 2 \sum x_1^3 x_2^2 x_3] + [4 \sum x_1^3 x_2^2 x_3 + 4 \cdot 3 \sum x_1^2 x_2^2 x_3^2].$$

Thus $f_1 = -\{2 \sum x_1^4 x_2 x_3 + 2 \sum x_1^3 x_2^3 + 8 \sum x_1^3 x_2^2 x_3 + 15 \sum x_1^2 x_2^2 x_3^2\}$. Now we must express each sum in f_1 as a polynomial in s_1, s_2, s_3. For example,

$$g = \sum x_1^3 x_2^2 x_3 = s_1 s_2 s_3 - g_1(x_1, x_2, x_3)$$

and

$$s_1 s_2 s_3 = (\sum x_1)(\sum x_1 x_2)(\sum x_1 x_2 x_3) = (\sum x_1^2 x_2 + 3 \sum x_1 x_2 x_3)(\sum x_1 x_2 x_3)$$

$$= \sum x_1^3 x_2^2 x_3 + 3 \sum x_1^2 x_2^2 x_3^2,$$

hence from one more step we get

$$g = s_1 s_2 s_3 - 3 s_3^2.$$

EXERCISE 3

1. Show that for every finite group G there is a field F and a polynomial $f(x) \in F[x]$ such that the Galois group of f over F is isomorphic with G.

2. Complete Example 8.

3. Let Δ^2 be the discriminant of $f(x)$ and let $f'(x)$ be its derivative. Let $f(x)$ have roots $w_1, \ldots, w_n$ with appropriate multiplicities. Find a relation between Δ^2 and $N = \Pi_i f'(w_i)$.

4. Let $u, v \in E$ be algebraic over F. Show that $u + v$ is algebraic over F by exhibiting a polynomial in $F[x]$ of which $u + v$ is a zero. [*Hint:* If $u = u_1, \ldots, u_n$ are the conjugates of u over F and if $v = v_1, \ldots, v_m$ are the conjugates of v over F, show that $\Pi_{i,j} (x - (u_i + v_j)) \in F[x]$.)

5. A complex number w is called an algebraic integer if w is the zero of a monic polynomial

$$x^n + a_1 x^{n-1} + \cdots + a_n$$

where $a_i \in I$. Show that the set of algebraic integers form a subring of C.

6. Let $x^3 + ax^2 + bx + c = 0$ have roots α, β, γ.

(i) Express a, b, and c in terms of α, β, γ.

(ii) Express the following as functions of a, b, c:

$$\alpha^2\beta^2\gamma^2$$
$$\alpha^2 + \beta^2 + \gamma^2$$
$$\alpha^2\beta^2 + \alpha^2\gamma^2 + \beta^2\gamma^2$$

7. If $\alpha, \beta, \gamma, \delta$ are the roots of the equation

$$x^4 + px^3 + qx^2 + rx + s = 0$$

find the value of $\sum (\alpha - \beta)^2(\gamma - \delta)^2$ in terms of the coefficients. What is the numerical value of this symmetric function when

$$\alpha = 1, \quad \beta = 2, \quad \gamma = 3, \quad \delta = 4?$$

8. Find an equation with integer coefficients such that its roots are the squares of the respective roots of the equation $x^3 + x^2 + 2x + 3 = 0$.

9. Prove that if $f(x_1, \ldots, x_n)$ is a symmetric polynomial with integral coefficients, then the polynomial with integral coefficients $g(s_{11}, \ldots, s_n)$ on the elementary symmetric functions such that $f(x_1, \ldots, x_n) = g(s_1, \ldots, s_n)$ is unique.

10. Which of the following equations can be solved in radicals over Ra?

(i) $x^5 - 38x^3 - 172x^2 - 312x - 206 = 0$.

(ii) $x^5 - x^4 - x^2 + 2x - 1 = 0$.

(iii) $x^5 - x^3 + x^2 - 2x - 2 = 0$.

SUPPLEMENTARY READING

E. Artin, Galois theory, *Notre Dame Mathematical Lectures*, no. 2, Notre Dame, Indiana (1946).

E. L. Gray, An alternate proof for the invariance of parity of a permutation written as a product of transpositions, *American Mathematical Monthly*, **70** (1963), 995.

N. Jacobson, *Lectures in Abstract Algebra*, vol. III, Princeton, New Jersey: Van Nostrand (1964).

W. J. LeVeque, *Topic in Number Theory*, vol. 1, Reading, Mass.: Addison-Wesley (1956).

B. L. van der Waerden, *Modern Algebra*, vol. 1 (translated by F. Blum), New York: Ungar (1948).

Answers

Exercise 1.1. Page 28

1. Let the vertices of a square be numbered as shown in Figure 1. Let J, R, S, T denote clockwise rotations of 0, 90, 180, 270 degrees respectively. Let A, B, C, D, be reflections about the lines so designated in Figure 1. The symmetries of the square

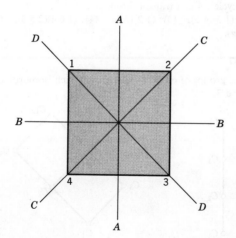

may then be denoted:

$$J = \begin{pmatrix} 1 & 2 & 3 & 4 \\ 1 & 2 & 3 & 4 \end{pmatrix} \quad R = \begin{pmatrix} 1 & 2 & 3 & 4 \\ 2 & 3 & 4 & 1 \end{pmatrix} \quad S = \begin{pmatrix} 1 & 2 & 3 & 4 \\ 3 & 4 & 1 & 2 \end{pmatrix} \quad T = \begin{pmatrix} 1 & 2 & 3 & 4 \\ 4 & 1 & 2 & 3 \end{pmatrix}$$

$$A = \begin{pmatrix} 1 & 2 & 3 & 4 \\ 2 & 1 & 4 & 3 \end{pmatrix} \quad B = \begin{pmatrix} 1 & 2 & 3 & 4 \\ 4 & 3 & 2 & 1 \end{pmatrix} \quad C = \begin{pmatrix} 1 & 2 & 3 & 4 \\ 3 & 2 & 1 & 4 \end{pmatrix} \quad D = \begin{pmatrix} 1 & 2 & 3 & 4 \\ 1 & 4 & 3 & 2 \end{pmatrix}$$

4. $\{f_1(x) = x, \quad f_2(x) = 1/x, \quad g_2(x) = 1/(1 - x), \quad g_3(x) = (x - 1)/x, \quad g_4(x) = 1 - x,$
$g_5(x) = x/(x - 1)\}$.

6. G4.

10. G2, G3.

11. $\{J, R, S\}$ and $\{J, A\}$.

Exercise 1.2. Page 34

1.

	J	R	S	A	B	C
J	J	R	S	A	B	C
R	R	S	J	C	A	B
S	S	J	R	B	C	A
A	A	B	C	J	R	S
B	B	C	A	S	J	R
C	C	A	B	R	S	J

	J	R	S	T	A	B	C	D
J	J	R	S	T	A	B	C	D
R	R	S	T	J	C	D	B	A
S	S	T	J	R	B	A	D	C
T	T	J	R	S	D	C	A	B
A	A	D	B	C	J	S	T	R
B	B	C	A	D	S	J	R	T
C	C	A	D	B	R	T	J	S
D	D	B	C	A	T	R	S	J

4. $\varepsilon = (2, 0)$, $(a, b)^* = (2 - b, -b)$.

5. Neither are group tables for $(ab)b \neq a(bb)$.

Exercise 1.3. Page 37

3. No. In the additive group of rationals for every a there is an x such that $x + x = a$. This is not so in the integers.

5. If $T = I$, then $\varphi(x) = x - 1$ maps S isomorphically onto T.

Exercise 1.4. Page 40

3. (1): $(1, 2, 3, 4)$,   (2): $(1, 4)(2, 3)$,   (3): $(1, 3, 2, 4)$,   (4): $(1, 3)$,   (5): $(2, 3, 4)$,   (6): $(1, 3)(2, 4)$,   (7): $(1), (2), (3), (4)$,   (8): $(1, 3, 4), (2, 5)$.

4. 1, 3, 4, 5, 7 are cycles. 4 is a transposition.

9. (1): $(2\ 3)$,   (2): $(1\ 3)(4\ 5)$,   (3): $(1\ 2)(3\ 4)$,   (4): $(1\ 6\ 4)(2\ 5\ 3)$,   (5): $(1\ 4\ 6\ 2)(3\ 8\ 7)$,   (6): $(a\ b)(c\ d)(f\ g)$.

Exercise 1.5. Page 57

1. There are 3 cyclic groups of order 4 and 4 groups each isomorphic to the four-group.

4. See Figures 2 and 3.

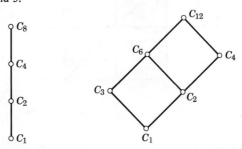

5. Consider any infinite cyclic group.

11. (ii) $|\mathscr{A}_4| = 12$.   (iii) $1 = a^3 = b^3 = c^3 = d^3 = r^2 = s^2 = t^2$.   (iv) $\{1, r, t, s\}$. (iv) $\{1, a, a^2\}$.

12. $\{1, a^2\}$ is the only subgroup listed.

13. A group of order 10 is either a cyclic group or a dihedral group.

Exercise 1.6. Page 67

3. $\{\iota, (12)(34), (13)(24), (14)(23)\}$ is the only normal subgroup of order 4 in $\mathcal{S}_4$.

4. (iv) is normal; (v) is not.

10. The order $\varphi(g)$ divides the order of g.

12. Let $D_n = \{r, a : r^n = 1, a^2 = 1, ar = r^{-1}a\}$. Every subgroup of $\langle r \rangle$ is normal. If

n is odd, these are the only ones; if n is even, then in addition $\langle a, r^2 \rangle$ and $\langle ar, r^2 \rangle$ are normal.

13. $(n + 1)!$ will do.

15. The cyclic group of order 5 is the commutator subgroup.

Exercise 1.7. Page 72

2. $C_2 \times C_2$ is the four-group, $C_2 \times C_3 \cong C_6$, $C_4 \times C_3 \cong C_{12}$.

3. $C_6 \times C_2 \cong V \times C_3$.

8. Consider $C_2 \times C_4 \times C_8 \times C_{16} \times \cdots$ and $C_4 \times C_8 \times C_{16} \times \cdots$.

9. See (8).

Exercise 2.1. Page 79

1. $(-4) + (-1) \neq -(4 - 1)$.

3. (i) is an integral domain, the others are not rings.

5. $D \times E$ is a commutative ring with identity.

7. There is no integral domain with 6 elements.

Exercise 2.2. Page 88

1. $D \cong D^*$ via $\varphi(a) = a - 1$.

5. (i) 4, (ii) 3 and 7, (iii) 2 and 3, (iv) 5.

9. The sum of the digits, with every second digit counted as negative, must be divisible by 11.

10. $\{\bar{0}\}$, $\{\bar{0}, \bar{3}\}$, $\{\bar{0}, \bar{2}, \bar{4}\}$, $\{\bar{0}, \bar{1}, \bar{2}, \bar{3}, \bar{4}, \bar{5}\}$.

Exercise 2.3. Page 92

2. The units of D_p are rational numbers of the form p^k, $k \in I$. The units of $\hat{D}_p$ are integers divisible by p and rational numbers of the form $1/b$ where p divides b.

6. Associativity of multiplication and the distributive law.

7. Associativity of multiplication, distributive law, additive inverse, no divisors of zero.

9. True only for $I/\langle 5 \rangle$.

10. $n = 6$: The units form a cyclic group of order 2.

$n = 7$: The units form a cyclic group of order 6.

$n = 8$: The units form a four-group.

Exercise 3.1. Page 97

1. An equivalence class is of the form $\{a, -a\}$.

2. Only if A is the empty set or a singleton set.

3. Cyclic groups of prime power order.

4. No. $A = \{\iota, (1\ 2)(3\ 4)\}$ is normal in $\{\iota, (1\ 2)(3\ 4), (1\ 3)(2\ 4), (1\ 4)(2\ 3)\}$ which is normal in S_4 but A is not normal in S_4.

Exercise 3.2. Page 99

4. Let a/b, c/d be in lowest terms $(0 = 0/1)$. A possible ordering is $a/b \ \tau \ c/d$ if $a < c$ or $a = c$ and $b \leq d$.

6. One possible ordering is $a \ \delta \ b$ if and only if $b \leq a$.

Exercise 3.3. Page 105

1. $m \leq n(n - 1)/2$.

6. $g(n, r) = r + a_{n+1}$, $A = R$, $f(1) = a = a_1$, $f(n) = \sum_{k=1}^{k=n} a_k$.

Exercise 3.4. Page 110

1. $104{,}976 = 3^8 2^4$, $857{,}375 = 5^3 19^3$, $97{,}344 = 2^6 3^2 13^2$.

2. \$1.00. Yes, whenever w_1 shows an odd number.

6. The order of p is n.

7. (iii): $[a/b] = q$.

8. 3 has exponent $33 + 11 + 3 + 1 = 48$; p has exponent $[n/p] + [n/p^2] + \cdots + [n/p^k]$ where $p^{k+1} > n$.

Exercise 4.1. Page 116

1. $\{a + b\sqrt{2}: a, b \in Ra\}$.

2. The field of quotients is isomorphic to Ra.

3. No; $(\sqrt{2} + \sqrt{3})^2$ is irrational.

Exercise 4.2. Page 119

1. $\{a + b\sqrt{2} + c\sqrt{3} + d\sqrt{6}: a, b, c, d \in Ra\}$ has Ra, $\{a + b\sqrt{2}: a, b \in Ra\}$, $\{a + c\sqrt{3}: a, c \in Ra\}$, and $\{a + d\sqrt{6}: a, d \in Ra\}$ as proper subfields.

2. $S = D_p$ is an example.

3. Disprove!

10. $\bar{3}^{13} = \bar{3}$.

13. $G/K \cong \{M_a: M_a(x) = ax\} \cong \langle F - \{0\}, \cdot \rangle$.

Exercise 4.4. Page 130

6. (i) closed disk; center at a and radius r.

(ii) The half plane containing a and determined by the perpendicular bisector of the line segment (a, b).

(iii) a circle containing a, or if $r = 0$, the point a.

(iv) ellipse.

7. (i) $z = re^{i\theta}$ where $r = \sqrt[n]{|c|}$ and $\theta = (1/n)$ argument $c + 2k\pi/n$.

(ii) $z = -a \pm (\sqrt{2}/2)[(\sqrt{u^2 + v^2} + u)^{1/2} + (\sqrt{u^2 + v^2} - u)^{1/2}i]$ where $a^2 - b = u + vi$ and $u, v \in Re$.

9. (i) $\varphi^{-1}(x) = a^{-1}(x - b)$.

(iii) $\varphi\theta\varphi^{-1}(x) = c(x - b) + ad + b$. A normal subgroup is $\{\varphi: \varphi(x) = cx, c \neq 0\}$.

13. $(-1)^{n+1}$.

Exercise 5.1. Page 137

3. $(6711, 831) = 3 = 66 \cdot 6711 - 533 \cdot 831$.

4. $\alpha = \beta \cdot 1 + (-2 - 2i)$.

5. $(3 + 4i, 7 - i) = 1$.

7. No.

11. Every GCD $(3/4, 7/2)$ is a unit.

12. $151,316 = 2^2 \cdot 11 \cdot 19 \cdot 181$.

Exercise 5.2. Page 142

2. $(4 + 11a)14 - (5 + 14a)11 = 1$. $c = 25$ is the least integer with one solution $c = 924 = 6 \cdot 11 \cdot 14$ is the greatest with five solutions.

3. $x \equiv 136 \bmod (6 \cdot 5 \cdot 77)$.

4. $(m, n) \mid (a - b)$.

5. Every member of D_3 is a solution!

Exercise 5.3. Page 146

5. If $n = p_1^2 \cdots p_k^2 p_{k+1} \cdots p_r$ is the prime factorization of n, then there are 2^k abelian groups of order n. Each has the form $C_d \times C_{n/d}$ where $p_{k+1} \cdots p_r \mid d$ and $d \mid n$. (C_h is a cyclic group of order h.)

Exercise 6.1. Page 154

2. All.
3. (i) -2, (ii) 0.

Exercise 6.2. Page 158

1. $x + 1$.
2. $f \equiv (1/2)(-x^2 - x + 1) \bmod (x^3 + 1)$.
3. $f \equiv x \bmod (x^2 + x + 1)$.
4. $x - 1$ has no inverse; $x^2 - 1$ is reducible.
5. Let F be a field and $f, g \in F[x]$. If $(f, g) = d$ and neither f nor g are associates of d then there exist $a, b \in F[x]$ such that $d = af + bg$ and $\deg(a) < \deg(g/d)$ and $\deg(b) < \deg(f/d)$.
7. $(1/4) \log (x + 1) - (1/4) \log (x - 1) - 1/[6(x - 1)] + (2/3\sqrt{3}) \arctan (2 + 1)/\sqrt{3}$.
10. An integral domain results.
11. No.
12. The "positive" polynomials are not well-ordered.

Exercise 6.3. Page 161

1. The elements are 0, 1, 2, i, $1 + i$, $2 + i$, $2i$, $1 + 2i$, $2 + 2i$, where $i^2 = -1 = 2$. A generator is $(1 + i)$.

Exercise 6.4. Page 166

1. If $a \neq b$, then $r = ([f(a) - f(b)]/(a - b))x + [af(b) - bf(a)]/(a - b)$. If $a = b$ then $r = f'(a)(x - a) + f(a)$.
2. $x^3 + 2x^2 + 2x + 1$ and $x^3 + x^2 + x + 1$ have one common root.
3. $x^4 - 2x^3 + 2x^2 - 2x + 1$ has multiple roots.
4. For some polynomial $g(x) \in F[x]$ it must be that $f(x) = g(x^p)$.

Exercise 6.5. Page 172

1. $x, x + 1, x^2 + x + 1, x^3 + x + 1, x^3 + x^2 + 1$.
2. It is not an automorphism.
4. If F is an integral domain, then $f(x) \rightarrow f(ax + b)$ is an automorphism if a is a unit of F.
5. Let f have degree n. Select $n + 1$ integers, $\{a_0, \ldots, a_n\}$. Tabulate the divisors d_{ij} of $f(a_i)$, $0 \leq i \leq n$. For an arbitrary set of divisors, $\{d_{ij} : 0 \leq i \leq n\}$, construct the polynomial, by the Lagrange interpolation formula, such that $g(a_i) = d_{ij}$. Test $g \mid f$. The polynomial f is irreducible if for every such g constructed, $g \nmid f$. Note that this need be done with at most $[n/2] + 1$ points since if f is reducible, it is divisible by a polynomial of degree $\leq [n/2]$.

Exercise 6.6. Page 175

2. $x^3 - y^3 = (x - y)(x^2 + xy + y^2)$.

Exercise 7.1. Page 179

2. q^n. $V_2(I_2) = \{(0, 0), (1, 0), (0, 1), (1, 1)\}$. The addition table is that of the four-group. $0 = (0, 0)$.
3. The nonzero elements form a cyclic group of order 3. $(1, 0)$ may serve as the identity. The addition table is that of Problem 2. The distributive law must be verified.
4. (a) and (d) have "yes" answers, the others "no" answers.

Exercise 7.2. Page 182

4. The vector v spans the space $\{av : a \in F\}$.

Exercise 7.3. Page 188

3. Any two of the three vectors given.
4. $V_3(F)$ has $7 \cdot 6 \cdot 4/3! = 28$ distinct bases. $V_n(F)$ has $(1/n!) \prod_{i=0}^{n-1} (2^n - 2^i)$ distinct bases.

5. (i)

x	$f(x)$
$(0, 0)$	0 1 0 1 0 1 0 1 0 1 0 1 0 1 0 1
$(1, 0)$	0 0 1 1 0 0 1 1 0 0 1 1 0 0 1 1
$(0, 1)$	0 0 0 0 1 1 1 1 0 0 0 0 1 1 1 1
$(1, 1)$	0 0 0 0 0 0 0 0 1 1 1 1 1 1 1 1

(ii) The dimension is q^n.

6. The dimension is 2. A basis is $\{e^x, e^{2x}\}$.

Exercise 7.4. Page 194

1. The inverse of a transformation of type E3 is $\mu(v) = \sum_{k \neq i,j} a_k u_k + a_i u_i + (-a_i + a_j)u_j$.
2. A basis for the kernel is $\{(3, 2, -1)\}$. A basis for the range is $\{(1, 0, 1, 0), (-1, 1, -1, 1)\}$.

Exercise 7.5. Page 198

1. A basis consists of any two of the given vectors except the pair $\{(4, 8, -5), (-8, -16, 10)\}$. $(5, 4, 3)$ does not belong to the subspace.
2. $\lambda(1, 0, 0) = (31/3, 4/3, 10)$; $\lambda(0, 1, 0) = (47/3, 20/3, 19)$;
   $\lambda(0, 0, 1) = (-10, +1, -10)$.
3. $k = 2$.
4. No solutions. Basis for kernel: $\{(2, 3, -1)\}$; range: $\{(1, 2, 2), (0, -2, -1)\}$.
6. The integers a, b, c must be such that $a + b = c - b$ and $3 \mid a + b$.

Exercise 8.1. Page 213

1. The elements are 0, 1, Θ, $\Theta + 1$, Θ^2, $\Theta^2 + 1$, $\Theta^2 + \Theta$, $\Theta^2 + \Theta + 1$, where $\Theta^3 + \Theta + 1 = 0$. A typical calculation gives $(\Theta^2 + \Theta)(\Theta^2 + \Theta + 1) = \Theta^2$. $x^3 + x + 1 = (x + \Theta)(x + \Theta^2)(x + \Theta^2 + \Theta)$.
2. $(1 + \Theta)^{-1} = (1 + 2\Theta + 2\Theta^2)/5$.
5. A sufficient condition is that $a \neq b$.

Exercise 8.2. Page 221

5. If $\mathrm{char}(F) = p$ then $ax^p - ax + 1$ is fixed by σ. Generalize!

Exercise 8.3. Page 227

2. If φ is the Euler φ-function then there are $\varphi(p^n - 1)/n$ of them.
3. The irreducible polynomials of degree 4 over $GF(2)$ are $x^4 + x^3 + x^2 + x + 1$, $x^4 + x^3 + 1$, and $x^4 + x + 1$. Also see Problem 6.
5. If α is a zero of $x^3 - x + 1$ and β is a zero of $x^3 - x - 1$, then there is an automorphism of $GF(3^3)$ taking α into $-\beta$.
6. Let $\Theta^4 = \Theta + 1$. The elements of order 15 are Θ, Θ^2, $\Theta^4 = \Theta + 1$, $\Theta^7 = \Theta^3 + \Theta + 1$, $\Theta^8 = \Theta^2 + 1$, $\Theta^{11} = \Theta^3 + \Theta^2 + \Theta$, $\Theta^{13} = \Theta^3 + \Theta^2 + 1$, and $\Theta^{14} = \Theta^3 + 1$. The elements of order 5 are Θ^3, $\Theta^6 = \Theta^3 + \Theta^2$, $\Theta^9 = \Theta^3 + \Theta$, and $\Theta^{12} = \Theta^3 + \Theta^2 + \Theta + 1$. The elements of order 3 are $\Theta^5 = \Theta^2 + \Theta$, and $\Theta^{10} = \Theta^2 + \Theta + 1$. $x^4 + x^2 + 1 = (x + \Theta^2 + \Theta)^2(x + \Theta^2 + \Theta + 1)^2$.

Exercise 8.4. Page 236

2. The set of primitive elements is $\{(ua + v)/(ra + s): u, v, r, s \in F \text{ and } us - rv \neq 0\}$.

Exercise 9.1. Page 242

6. The groups of order 8 are C_8, $C_4 \times C_2$, $C_2 \times$ ~~~~ C_2, Quaterions, and the dihedral group of order 8. The groups of order 9 are C_9 a~~ $C_3 \times C_3$.

7. There are 14 groups of order 16. For a full accoun~ see M. Hall, Jr., and J. K. Senior, *The Groups of Order* 2^n ($n \geq 6$), New York: Macmillan (1964).

Exercise 9.2. Page 247

2. There are 5 groups of order 18 and 20.

5. $S_q \cong C_q$ is normal. $S_p \cong C_p$ must be normal too. A necessary and sufficient condition is that $q \neq 1 + kp$.

6. Show that a group of order 30 must have a cyclic subgroup of order 15. There are four groups of order 30: C_{30}, $S_3 \times C_5$, $D_{10} \times C_3$, and D_{30}. (Here D_k denotes the dihedral group of order k.)

Exercise 9.3. Page 254

5. Disprove!

Exercise 9.4. Page 267

1. There are 10 abelian groups of order 144: $C_{16} \times C_9$, $C_{16} \times C_3 \times C_3$, $C_2 \times C_8 \times C_9$, $C_2 \times C_8 \times C_3 \times C_3$, $C_2 \times C_2 \times C_4 \times C_9$, $C_2 \times C_2 \times C_4 \times C_3 \times C_3$, $C_2 \times C_2 \times C_2 \times C_2 \times C_9$, $C_2 \times C_2 \times C_2 \times C_2 \times C_3 \times C_3$, $C_4 \times C_4 \times C_9$, $C_4 \times C_4 \times C_3 \times C_3$.

2. The integer n must not be divisible by a square other than 1.

3. $C_2 \times C_2 \times C_6 \times C_\infty$.

5. No.

Exercise 10.1. Page 279

3. $G \cong S_3$. $Ra(d) = Ra(\sqrt{-23})$.

4. (i) $S_3 \times C_2$, (ii) C_4, (iii) four-group.

5. C_6. $Ra(\sqrt{-3}, \sqrt[3]{2})$ and $Ra(\sqrt{-3}, \sqrt{2})$.

Exercise 10.2. Page 296

1. The Galois group is a cyclic group of order 3.

2. The dihedral group of order 8.

5. The possible degrees are 1 and p.

6. (iii) 4, 4, and 2.

   (iv) $(u^3 + 2u^2 - 4u - 5)/(-9)$.

   (v) No, Yes, Yes, and No.

Exercise 10.3. Page 303

2. $s_1^2 s_2^2 - 2s_3 s_1^2 + 4s_1 s_2 s_3 - 3s_3^2 - 2s_2^3$.

3. $N = (\Delta_n)^2 (-1)^{(n-1)n/2}$.

6. (ii) c^2, $a^2 - 2b$, and $b^2 - 2ac$.

7. $(2q - 6pr + 18s)$ and 26.

8. $x^3 + 3x^2 - 2x = 9$.

10. (ii) and (iii) only.

Special Symbols and Notation

I; the set of integers   1

$\mid$, $a \mid b$; a divides b 1

$\in$, $A \in B$; membership   4

$\notin$, $A \notin B$; non-membership   4

$=$, $A = B$; equality of sets   4

$\{a\}$; singleton set   5

$\varnothing$; empty set   5

$|A|$; cardinal number of elements in the set A   5

$\subseteq$, $A \subseteq B$; subset inclusion   5

$-$, $A - B$; set difference   6

$\cup$, $A \cup B$, $\bigcup A$; set union   6

$\cap$, $A \cap B$, $\bigcap A$; set intersection   6

(a, b); ordered pair   7

$\times$, $A \times B$; cartesian product   7

        direct product of groups A and B 68

$\mathscr{D}_T$; domain of relation T 8

$\mathscr{R}_T$; range of relation T 8

ι; iota, the identity function   11

$c_S(x)$; characteristic function   11

$f: A \to B$; function from A into B 12

$\binom{n}{k}$; combinatorial symbol   17

$\langle S, \circ \rangle$; Group with operation $\circ$ 25

a^{-1}; in a (multiplicative) group, the inverse of a 31

$\mathcal{S}_n$; symmetric group on n symbols   39

$\langle g \rangle$; cyclic group with generator g 42

        principal ideal with generator g 81

Sb, bS; cosets of subgroup S 50

$[G:S]$; index of subgroup S in group G 51

$\vee$, $A \vee B$; subgroup join   53

         subring join   78

         subspace join   182

$\langle S \rangle$; subgroup generated by subset S 54

$A \cdot B$; complex in a group   55

$\mathscr{A}_n$; alternating group on n symbols   58, 301

Z; center of group 59, 237

N_a; normalizer ($=$ centralizer) of element a in a group   234

N_S; normalizer of set S in a group   59, 238

G/K; factor (quotient) group   62

      factor (quotient) ring   83

$\langle R, +, \cdot \rangle$; ring   73

D_p; rational numbers a/b where $b = p^k$ 79

$\hat{D}_p$; rational numbers a/b where $p \nmid b$ 79

I_d; $I/\langle d \rangle$ 84

$\equiv$, $a \equiv b \pmod{K}$; congruence relation   85

$\sim$, $a \sim b$; in a ring, a is an associate of b 90

(b, c), $\text{GCD}(b, c)$; greatest common divisor   90, 108

$[b, c]$, $\text{LCM}(b, c)$; least common multiple   90, 108

$\langle D, +, \cdot, \leq \rangle$; ordered integral domain   95

E_+; set of positive elements   100

$|a|$; absolute value   96

φ; Euler phi function   111

$[r]$; greatest integer function   111

Q; field of quotients   113

Ra; field of rational numbers   116

$\text{char}(F)$; characteristic of F 118

$S(a_1, \ldots, a_n)$, $S(A)$; smallest subfield containing $S \cup A$ 118

Re; field of real numbers   124

C; field of complex numbers   125

i; the complex number $(0, 1)$, a zero of $x^2 + 1$ 126

$\bar{\alpha}$; complex conjugate of α 126

$|\alpha|$; modulus of complex number α 128

$\langle D, +, \cdot, v \rangle$; euclidean domain   133

G; the ring of gaussian integers   133

$R[x]$; the ring of polynomials with coefficients in R 151

x; indeterminate   152

f'; formal derivative of the polynomial f 164

UFD; unique factorization domain   166

$R(x)$; field of quotients of $R[x]$ 173

$V_n(F)$; vector space of n-tuples over F 178

$V_\infty(F)$; vector space of infinite sequences from F 178

$\dim(V)$; dimension of vector space V 186

$\mathscr{L}(V)$; full linear group   192

c, $a \, \underline{c} \, b$; a and b are conjugates in E over F 213

$[E : F]$; degree of field extension E over F 215

$\mathscr{G}(E/F)$; group of automorphisms of field extension E over F 219

$W_p(d)$; number of irreducible monic polynomials of degree d in $GF(p)[x]$ 225

μ; Möbius mu function   226

$\Phi_n(x)$; cyclotomic polynomial   231

$\underline{s}$, $D \, \underline{\underline{s}} \, E$; D and E are conjugate sets in G 238

p–SSG; a p Sylow subgroup   242

G'; derived (commutator) group of the group G 252

$S(K)$; group of automorphisms of $E \supseteq K$ fixing each element of K 269

$I(\mathscr{H})$; field of elements fixed by $\mathscr{H} \subseteq \mathscr{G}(E/F)$ 269

FTGT; fundamental theorem of Galois theory   275

$\lambda(\epsilon, a)$; Lagrange resolvant   282

Δ; discriminant   291, 300

$s_k = \sum t_1 \ldots t_k$; the kth elementary symmetric polynomial   298

Index

(**Bold-faced numerals** denote the page on which a definition occurs.)

Abel, N. H.   28, 299
Abelian group.   **28** 144, 255ff
  solvability of   249
  free abelian group   **256**
Abelian extension   **277**
Absolute value, in complex numbers   **128**
  in ordered integral domains   **96**
Abstract algebra   **20**ff, 132
Addition   1, 16
  in field of quotients   **114**
  of complex numbers   **125**
  of polynomials   **149**
  ring operation   **73**
Additive inverse   **77**
Adjunction of an indeterminate   **152**
Albert, A. A.   205, 236
Algebra, associative   **200**ff
  fundamental theorem of   127
  group   **203**
  linear   **205**
  quaternion   **201**
Algebraic, closure   **221**
  element   **214**
  extension   **214**, 218ff
  independence   **217**
  integer   **303**
Algebraically closed field   **219**
Algorithm, division, for integers   **106**
  euclidean   **135**
  for factoring a polynomial in $I[x]$ 172
  for obtaining a basis in an abelian group   260
  for polynomials   154, 156
Alternating group, $\mathscr{A}_4$ **58**, 249
  $\mathscr{A}_n$ **301**

Apostol, Tom M.   131
Argument of a complex number   **128**
Arithmetic   1, 106ff, 242
  fundamental theorem of   108
  in euclidean domains   138
Artin, E.   304
Associate elements in integral domains   **90**
Associative algebra   **200**
Associative operation   **14**, 21
Automorphism, fixed field of   **269**
  inner   **64**
  group of   68, 119
  of a field   119
  of a field E over F,   **119**
    as permutation group   276
  of a finite field   227
  of a group   **64**
  of a ring   **80**
Axiom of extensionality   **4**
Axioms, for a:
  division ring (skew field)   **73**
  group   **24**
  integral domain   **73**
  ordered integral domain   **95**, 100
  ring   **73**
  vector space   **177**, 184

Ball, R. W.   72
Basis, axiom for existence of   184
  for an abelian group   **255**
  for a vector space   **183**
  theorem for abelian groups   256ff
Bernays, P.   93, 111
Binary operation   **14**, 20
Binary relation   **7**

Bootstraps 39, 62
Buck, R. C. 106, 111
Burnside, W. 72, 254, 268
Burnside problem 145

Calculus 22, 158, 164, 295
Cancellation law, for direct products of
     abelian groups 264
  in groups 31, 35
  in integral domains 77
  in rings 77
Cardano's formulas (H. Cardano) 294
Cartesian product 7
Cauchy, A. L. 24
Cauchy's group theorem 72, 237
  for abelian groups 67
Cayley, A. 33, 203
Cayley table for a group 33
Center, of a group 59, 237
  of a p-group 239
  of S_n 242
Characteristic, of a field 118
  of a ring 120
  zero, field of 165, 269
Characteristic function 11
Chinese remainder theorem 141
Churchill, R. V. 131
Class equation for a group 234, 238, 243
Closed set under an operation 16
Coefficients of a polynomial 147, 149
Cohn, P. M. 264, 268
Combinatorics 16ff
Commutative group 28
Commutative operation 14, 21
Commutative ring 73
Commutator 68, 252
  subgroup 252, 253
Complex conjugate 126
Complex in a group 55, 238
Complex number 125, 159, 178, 214, 219
  argument of 128
  field as vector space 179
  modulus of 128
Composite number 2
Composition 13, 14
  of functions 15
  series 248,
Congruence, on a ring 85
  solution of, in euclidean domain 142
Conjugate elements, in a field 212
  in a group 59, 234
Conjugate sets, in a group 238
Conjugacy classes 234

Consistent set, of axioms 22
Continuous functions 181
Converse of Lagrange's theorem 72, 237
  for abelian groups 67
Coprime 138
Coordinate 186, 189
Coset 50
Cubic polynomial 149
  zeros of 283, 293
Curtis, C. W. 203, 205
Cycle (permutation) 41
Cyclic extensions 277, 280ff
Cyclic group 42, 111, 132, 255
  generator of 42
  infinite cyclic group 43
  of roots of unity 129, 230ff
  subgroups of 52, 53
Cyclotomic fields 280ff
Cyclotomic polynomial 231, 236

Definition, by induction 3, 102
Degree, of a field extension 215
  of a polynomial 149
Dependence 182ff
Dependent set, of vectors 182
Derivative, of a polynomial 164
Derived series 253
Derived subgroup 68, 252, 253
Diagram 6
Diamond theorem, for group
     homomorphism 243
Dickson, L. E. 203, 205
Difference ring 83
Dihedral groups 44
  of order 6 57
Dimension, of vector space 186ff, 191, 193
Direct product, of groups 68ff
Dirichlet, P. G. L. 18, 110
Discriminant, 300, 301
  of a cubic 291
Disjoint sets 6
Distributive laws 21, 73
Divisibility criterion 89
Division 1, 89, 132
  in an integral domain 89
  ordering of integers by 94
Division algorithm 106, 132
  for polynomials 154, 156
Division ring 73, 202, 233ff
Divisors, of zero 77, 91, 203, 204, 205
Domain, of a function 8, 10
  unique factorization 166
Dual space 194

Eisenstein's irreducibility criterion 171
Element **4**
Elementary symmetric polynomials **297**, 302
Elementary transformations 189
Empty set **5**
Endomorphism, of a group **65**
  of a ring **80**, 87
Equality **4**
Equation, class **234**
  of 2nd degree 290ff
  of 3rd degree 290ff
  solvable by radicals 269, **284**ff
Equivalence, class **9**
  relation **8**, 213
Eratosthenes 110
Erdos, P. 233, 236
Euclid 109
Euclidean algorithm 132ff, **135**
Euclidean domain **133**ff
Euler, L. 111
  φ-function **111**, 143, 230, 231
Even permutation **301**
Exponent, of a group **145**
Exponentiation 3, 16
Extension of a field **116**
  algebraic **214**, 218ff
  as a vector space 179
  degree of **215**
  finite **215**, 270
  normal **272**
  separable 269
  simple **228**ff
  transcendental **214**, 216ff
Extension of a:
  function **12**
  homomorphism 154
  isomorphism 210, 211, 216
Extension to a basis 186
Extensionality, axiom of **4**
External direct product **68**

Factor, group **62**
  ring **83**
  theorem 161
Factorization in $R[x]$ 166ff
Fefferman, S. 111, 120, 131, 236
Feit, W. 254
Fermat, Pierre de (1601–1665) 143
Fermat's little theorem 86
Field 22, **73**, 112ff
  algebraically closed **219**, 223
  automorphism 119

Field, automorphism of E over F **119**
  characteristic of **118**
  homomorphism 119
  of characteristic zero 118, 165, 229, 269ff
  of complex numbers 125–130, 159–161
  of quotients 112, **116**, 173
  of rational functions **173**
  of rational numbers **116**
  of real numbers 120-124
  splitting **208**, 271
Field extension **116**, 206ff
  abelian **277**
  algebraic **214**
  cyclic **277**
  degree of **215**
  finite **215**, 270
  simple **228**ff
  solvable **277**
  transcendental
Finite field 77, 84, 154, 158, 180, 187, 222ff
  existence and uniqueness of 223
  irreducible polynomials over $GF(p)$, 225
Finitely generated group **255**
Finitely presented abelian group **261**
  fundamental theorem of 262
Fixed element, under a permutation **39**
Fixed field, of a group **269**
Flow chart, for abelian group algorithm 260
Four-group **36**, 255
Four square theorem 203
Fraction 113
Fraenkel, A. A. 93, 111
Free abelian group **256**
Frobenius, G. 203
Full linear group **192**
Full symmetric group (*see* Symmetric group)
Function **10**, 22
  as element of a group 25
  as element of a ring 74
  as element of a vector space 178
  characteristic 11
  composition of **13**
  extension of **12**
  identity **11**
  into, onto **10**
  n-tuple 11
  one-to-one, 1-1 **13**
  restriction to a subset **12**
  sequence **11**
Fundamental theorem of:
  algebra 127
  arithmetic 108
  field theory 206

Fundamental theorem of:
　finitely generated abelian groups　256, 262
　Galois theory (FTGT)　273

Galois, E.　24, 223, 285
Galois fields　223
Galois group　277
　of general polynomial　298
Galois theory　269ff
Gauss, Karl Friedrich (1777–1855), lemma of
　169
Gaussian integers　133
Gelfond, A. D.　215
General polynomial of nth degree　297
Generator(s), for a cyclic group　42
　set of, for a group　54, 255
Gödel, K.　220
　numbering　220
Gray, E. L.　304
Greatest common divisor (GCD)　90
　in euclidean domain　132, 135
　in integers　108
　in polynomial ring $F[x]$　156
　in unique factorization domain　167
Greatest integer function　111
Group　23, 24–72, 130, 143–146, 203–205,
　224, 234, 237–268
　abelian　28
　alternating　58, 301
　automorphism of　64
　axioms　24
　center of　59, 237
　class equation　234
　conjugate elements in　234
　cyclic　42–44, 52, 67
　dihedral　44–47
　exponent of　145
　factor　62
　fixing a subfield　269
　full linear　192
　homomorphism　59–67, 243
　identity element　24
　identity subgroup　49
　inverse　24, 31
　of a polynomial　277
　of order 1　28
　of order 2　28
　of order 3　34
　of order 4　36
　of order 6　56
　of orders 8 and 9　242
　of order 10　58
　of order 12　246

Group, of order 15　245
　of orders 18, 20, 30　248
　of order p^2　242
　of permutations　37–42
　of prime order　13
　of units　92
　of units in $I/<n>$　280, 281
　of symmetries　27, 44
　quaternion　58
　quotient　59
　roots of unity　130, 230
　simple　254
　solvable　249ff

Hadamard, J.　110
Hall, Marshall, Jr.　72, 146, 268
Hall, Philip　242
Halmos, P. R.　19, 93, 111, 205
Hamilton, W. R.　203
Hardy, G. H.　109, 111
Henkin, L.　19
Herstein, I, N.　233, 236
Homomorphic image　60
Homomorphism, field　118-119
　group　59–68
　kernel of　60, 80
　ring　80–88
　vector space　189
Hopf, H.　203

Ideal　80
　in euclidean domain　134, 142
　in ring of integers　82–84
　intersection　81
　join　81
　maximal　91, 92
　principal　81, 134
　unit　81
　zero　81
Idempotent element　30
Identity element, in a group　24, 30
　in a ring　73, 77
Identity function　11
Image　12
　pre-image　12
Independence, algebraic　217
　linear　182
Independent set, of vectors　182
Indeterminate　152
Index, of a subgroup　51
Induction principle　2, 19, 101
　definition by　3, 102
　on m　2

Inductive hypothesis 2
  step 2
Infinite cyclic group 43
Integers 1, 20, 24, **100**, 132
  modulo n, $I/<n>$ 83–88, 142, 281
Integral domain **73**, 77, 89–92
  ordered **95**–98
Integral system **100**
Internal direct product **69**
Into function **10**
Inverse element in a group **24**
  unicity of 31
  mapping 13
Image 12
  pre-image 12
Irrationality of $\sqrt{2}$ 120
Irrational numbers 131, 214
Irreducible element in:
  euclidean domain 139
  integers 2, 108
  integral domain **90**
  polynomial ring **156**, 166–172, 225
  unique factorization domain 167
Isomorphism of two:
  groups **35**–37
  rings **80**
  integral systems 104

Jacobson, N. 92, 131, 205, 304
Join of:
  ideals **81**
  subgroups **53**
  subrings **78**
  subspaces **181**, 182

Kaczynski, T. J. 233, 236
Kernel of:
  group homomorphism **60**–63
  linear transformation 190
  ring homomorphism **80**
Kervaire, M. 203
Knuth, D. E. 236
Kronecker, L. 24, 206
Kuratowski, C. 7

Lagrange, J. L. 51
  group theorem of 51, 215, 239
    converse of 237
  interpolation theorem 162
  resolvent **282**
Landau, E. 120, 131
Lattice 132
Leading coefficient **149**

Leading term **149**
Least common multiple (LCM) **90**
  in euclidean domains 142
  in integral systems 107, 137
Least upper bound **121**, 124
Left inverse 13, 29, 31, 35
Lehmer, Emma 233, 236
Lemma of Gauss 169
LeVeque, W. J. 304
Lexicographic ordering **99**, 302
Linear:
  algebra 205
  equations, system of **194**–198
  functional **194**
  transformation **189**–194
    nullity of **196**
    null space of **190**
    range of **190**
    rank of **196**
  polynomial **149**
    irreducibility of 156

McCoy, N. H. 92
McKay, J. H. 72
Mapping 10, **11**, 24
  (*see also* Function, Permutation)
Maximal ideal **91**, 143
Maximal principle **184**
Member 4
Membership 4
Migotti, A. 233
Milnor, J. 203
Möbius, A. F. 226
  inversion formula 226, 232
  μ-function **226**, 232
Module 132
Modulus of complex number **128**
Monic polynomial **149**
Motzkin, T. 146
Mullin, R. C. 236
Multiple zeros **163**–166
Multiplication, as ring operation 73
  as group operation 31
  in field of quotients **113**
  of complex numbers **125**
  of polynomials **149**, 154

Natural homomorphism, group **63**
  ring **83**
Niven, I. 19, 92, 111, 131, 205, 268
Nonsingular linear transformation **189**
Normal chain **248**

Normal extension   272ff
  relation to normal subgroup   274
Normal subgroup   **61**, 64, 248, 269, 274
Normalizer in a group   59, **238**
Novikov, P. S.   146
n-tuple   **11**, 21, 178
Nullity of linear transformation   **196**
Nullring   **74**, 77
Null set   **5**
Number theory   19, **20**, 86, 87, 93–111, 225

Odd permutation   **301**
One-to-one, 1-1   **13**
Onto function   **10**
Operation   **14**
  binary   **14**
  n-ary   **16**
  set closed under   **16**
  ternary   **16**
  unary   **16**
Operators   **16**, 176
Orbits   **41**
Order, of a group   **33**
  of a group element   **49**
Ordered integral domain   **95**, 132
Ordered pair   **7**

Partial ordering   **94**
Partially ordered set   **94**
Pascal's triangle   18
Permutation   37–42, 106
  cycle   **41**
  even   **301**
  full symmetric group $\mathcal{S}_n$ **38**
  group of   38, 39
  odd   **301**
  orbits   **41**
  transposition   **41**
p-group   **239**
  center of   239
φ-function (Euler φ-function)   **111**, 143, 231
Pigeonhole principle   **18**
Point diagram   6
Polynomial   **149**, 147–175
  abelian   **277**
  cubic   **149**, 161, 283ff
  cyclic   **277**
  cyclotomic   **231**–233
  degree of   **149**
  division algorithm for   154
  euclidean algorithm for   155

Polynomial, function   **152**, 162
  GCD of   156, 157
  general, of nth degree   297
  group of   **277**
  in several variables   173, **174**, 175
  irreducible   **156**, 166–172, 207, 211, 219, 233
  irreducible over $GF(p)$ 224ff
  leading coefficient of   **149**
  leading term   **149**
  linear   **149**, 156
  monic   **149**
  over a field   154–158
  primitive   **168**
  quadratic   **149**, 161, 283
  quartic   **149**, 294
  quintic   **149**, 295, 299
  ring   150
  scalar   **149**
  solvable   **277**, 285
  splits   **208**
  symmetric   297, **298**, 302
  zeros of   **152**, 161–165
Pre-image   **12**
Prime element of integral domain   **90**
  co-prime   **138**
  integer   **2**, 108–111
Prime number theorem   109
Prime subfield   **117**, 118
Primitive element, mod p 281
  of a field extension   102, **228**, 272, 276
Primitive polynomial   **168**
Primitive root of unity   **129**, 130, **231**
Principal ideal   **81**
Proper subset   **6**
Proper subgroup   **49**
p-Sylow subgroup (p-SSG)   **242**
  isomorphism of   245

Quadratic polynomial   **149**, 161, 294
Quartic polynomial   **149**
  solvability of   294
Quaternion:
  algebra   **201**
  group   **58**
Quintic polynomial   **149**
  unsolvability of   299
Quotient:
  group   **62**
  ring   **83**
Quotients, field of   112, **113**–116

Radicals, solvability by **284**ff
Rado, R. 255, 268
Range, of a linear transformation **190**, 193
 of a relation **8**
Rank of a linear transformation **196**
Rational functions **173**
Rational numbers, field of **116**, 117
 polynomials over 166, 169, 170
Rational symmetric functions **298**
Real numbers, field of 120–**124**, 177, 178
Redheffer, R. M. 131
Reflection 26, 45, 76
Reflexive law **8**, 94
Relation 7–13
 antisymmetric **94**
 binary **7**
 equivalence **8**, 9, 50, 90, 212, 234
 reflexive **8**, 94
 symmetric **8**
 transitive **8**
Relative prime **138**
Remainder 2, **106**, 133, 154
 theorem 161
Representation theorem for: groups 39
 rings 87
 vector spaces 186
Residue class ring **83**
Restriction of functions **12**
Right inverse **24**
Ring 21, **73**–92
 automorphism 80, 86–87
 commutative **73**
 difference **83**
 division **73**
 endomorphism **80**
 euclidean 132, **133**–142
 factor **83**
 group 203, **204**
 homomorphism **80**
 integral domain **73**
 nullring **74**
 of integers 74, 86–87, **100**, 93–111
 of linear transformations **200**
 of polynomials **150**
 residue class **83**
 unique factorization (UFD) **166**
Rogers, K. 236
Root, of an equation **152**
 multiple **163**
 of unity **129**, 229ff
 solution for in radicals 283ff
 tower **284**

Rotations 26, 43, 45, 76
Row-reduced echelon form **196**, 197
Rudin, W. 146
Ruffini, P. 299

Samuel, P. 131, 146, 236
Scalar, **177**
 multiplication **177**
 polynomial **149**
Schreier, O. 205
Schneider, Th. 215
Separable polynomial **269**
Sequence **11**
 as element of a vector space 178
Set 4–7
 bounded from above **121**
 countable **220**
 disjoint **6**
 empty **5**
 intersection **6**
 mappings of 15
 partially ordered **94**
 totally ordered **94**
 union **6**
 well ordered **99**
Set-builder notation **5**
Set theory 4, 19, 93
Sieve method 110
Simple group **254**
Simple zero **163**
Singleton set **5**
Singular transformation **189**
Skew field **73**
Solution, congruence 141
 equations by radicals 283, **284**
 necessary and sufficient conditions for
 285
 equations of 2nd and 3rd degree 290ff
 space **196**
 to Exercises 306
Solvable group **249**ff, 269
Spanning set of vectors **181**
Sperner, E. 205
Splitting field **208**, 271
 existence of 209
 isomorphism of 211
 of $x^n - 1$ 280
 of $x^n - a$ 281, 282
Steinitz, E. 184
 replacement theorem 184
Stoll, R. R. 19, 111
Structure constants for an algebra **200**

Subfield **116**
  of finite field   223
  prime **117**
  proper **116**
Subgroup **48**–57
  commutator   68, **252**
  conjugate **238**
  coset of **50**
  derived   68, **252**
  generated by set **54**
  index **51**
  intersection **53**
  join **53**
  normal **61**
  of cyclic group   52, 53
  of index p in a p-group   241
  proper **49**
  p-Sylow (p-SSG) **242**
Subnormal chain **248**
Subring **78**
  intersection **78**
  join **78**
Suset **5**
  intersection **6**
  proper **6**
  restriction of function to **12**
  union **6**
Subspace **180**ff
  join **181**
Suppes, P.   93, 111
Sylow, L.   242
  subgroup **242**
  theorems   242ff
Symmetric group of permutations, $\mathcal{S}_n$
  38, 39, 40, 42, 49, 60, 249
  polynomial whose group is $\mathcal{S}_p$ 295
  $\mathcal{S}_4$ 294, 298
    solvability of   294
  unsolvability of $\mathcal{S}_n$ ($n \geqslant 5$)   254
Symmetric
  function **298**
  polynomial   302ff
  relation **8**
Symmetry of a:
  triangle   26
  regular n-gon   44
System of linear equations   194–198

Thompson, J.   254
Total ordering **94**
Totally ordered set **94**
Transcendental element **214**

Transcendental extension **214**, 216ff, 236
Transcendental real number   214
Transitive law **8**, **94**
  for algebraic field extensions   219
Transformation, linear **189**–193
Transposition **41**, 301
Triangle inequality   97, 130

Union of sets **6**
Unique factorization domain (UFD) **166**–172
Unique factorization theorem, for integers
  108
  for polynomials   156
  in euclidean domains   140
Unit **89**
  ideal **81**
  in euclidean domain   134
  in gaussian integers   133
  in integral systems   100

Vallee-Poussin, de la   110
van der Waerden, B. L.   120, 131, 146, 175,
  304
Vectors   25, 176, **177**
Vector space   22, 176, **177**–205
Venn diagram   6

Wahab, J. H.   175
Walker, E. A.   264, 268
Wedderburn, J. H. M.   76, 233
  theorem on finite division rings   234
Well ordered set   98, **99**
Well ordering   99
Wielandt, H.   242
Wiener, N.   7
Wilson's theorem   87
Witt, E.   233, 236
Wright, E. M.   111

Zariski, O.   131, 146, 236
Zassenhaus, H. J.   72
Zero **73**
  ideal **81**
  polynomial **149**
  vector **177**, 179
Zero divisor **77**
Zero, of a polynomial **152**
    multiple **163**–165
    simple **163**
Zukerman, H. S.   19, 92, 111, 205, 268